WITCHES,
AND THE
OCCULT

JOSH McDOWELL
AND
DON STEWART

POCKET GUIDES
Tyndale House Publishers, Inc.
Wheaton, Illinois

Unless otherwise indicated, Scripture quotations are from the *New American Standard Bible,* © The Lockman Foundation 1960, 1962, 1963, 1968, 1971, 1972, 1973, 1975, and are used by permission.

Demons, Witches, and the Occult is adapted from *Handbook of Today's Religions,* by Josh McDowell and Don Stewart, © 1983 by Campus Crusade for Christ, Inc., published by Here's Life Publishers, Inc.

First printing, October 1986
Library of Congress Catalog Card Number 86-50653
ISBN 0-8423-0541-6
© 1986 by Josh McDowell and Don Stewart
Printed in the United States of America

CONTENTS

Occult Phenomena

In this book we are attempting to expose the workings of Satan and the occultic realm by looking at what the Bible says about the subject. In doing this, it is our desire to give a balanced picture of the situation and to avoid sensationalism.

WHAT IS THE OCCULT?

The word "occult" comes from the Latin word "occultus" and it carries the idea of things hidden, secret, and mysterious. David Hoover, author of *How to Respond to the Occult* (St. Louis: Concordia Publishing House, 1977), lists three distinct characteristics of the occult:

1. The occult deals with things secret or hidden.
2. The occult deals with operations or events which seem to depend on human powers that go beyond the five senses.

3. The occult deals with the supernatural, the presence of angelic or demonic forces.

Under the designation occult we would class at least the following items: witchcraft, magic, palm reading, fortune-telling, ouija boards, tarot cards, satanism, spiritism, demons, and the use of crystal balls. To this list we could add much more.

> C. S. Lewis once commented, "There are two equal and opposite errors into which our race can fall about the devils. One is to disbelieve in their existence. The other is to believe, and to feel an unhealthy interest in them. They themselves are equally pleased by both errors and hail a materialist or a magician with the same delight" (C. S. Lewis, *The Screwtape Letters,* New York: Macmillan, 1961, preface).

A WORD OF WARNING
We realize that by informing people about the world of the occult, we will be exposing certain people to things and practices of which they have previously been ignorant. It is not our desire to stimulate one's curiosity in the realm of the occult to where it becomes an obsession. Seeing that mankind has a certain fascination about evil, it would be wise to take the advice of the Apostle Paul, "I want you to be wise in what is good

and innocent in what is evil" (Rom. 16:19).

Playing around with the world of the occult can lead to serious repercussions, both psychologically and spiritually. There is a difference between knowing intellectually that taking poison will kill you and actually taking the poison to experience what you already knew to be a fact. We need to be aware of the workings of the satanic realm but not to the point of unhealthy fascination, obsession, or involvement.

THE SUPERNATURAL DOES EXIST

We live in a day when people are looking for answers to life's basic questions, "What is the purpose of life?"; "Is there life after death?"; "Is there evidence for the existence of a supernatural God?"

According to the Bible there *is* a supernatural warfare going on: "For our struggle is not against flesh and blood, but against the rulers, against the powers, against the world forces of this darkness, against the spiritual forces of wickedness in the heavenly places" (Eph. 6:12).

This ongoing spiritual battle is between the kingdom of God and the kingdom of Satan. One purpose of Jesus Christ's coming to earth was given to us by the Apostle John, "The reason the Son of God appeared was to destroy the works of the devil" (1 John 3:8).

Although the Scriptures make it clear that the supernatural is real and that spiritual warfare is going on, there are those who would like to demythologize the accounts of the devil, demons, and demon possession. They contend that the supernatural references in the Bible are from a prescientific, superstitious worldview. However, if one takes the supernatural out of the Bible, all the meaning goes out with it. John Montgomery, dean of the Simon Greenleaf School of Law and leading contemporary theologian, comments:

> One of my theological professors used to state flatly that the demonic in the New Testament was to be regarded as symbolic (of evil, psychosis, disease, etc.), and he became quite agitated when I asked him whether we should also regard Jesus as symbolic (of the good, of mental and physical health, etc.) since in the narrative of Jesus' temptation in the wilderness a dialogue takes place between Jesus and the devil—both evidently regarded as having comparable reality or unreality! This points up the difficulty with demythologizing of the satanic in the New Testament: They are integrally bound up with the reality of Jesus and His entire message (John Warwick Montgomery, *Principalities and Powers,* Minneapolis: Bethany Fellowship, 1973, pp. 54, 55).

Those who would strip away the so-called myths from the Scripture are left with an empty gospel, devoid of any life-transforming power. In answer to such critics, we respond with the truth and rational claims of the whole gospel—including Satan's war against it and God's supernatural intervention and ultimate triumph. The world of the occult is real, and God's all-powerful Spirit is just as real!

OCCULTIC DECEPTION

Although we admit the reality of the supernatural, we must be careful not to place all unexplained phenomena into the supernatural category. There is much that goes on under the guise of the supernatural that is nothing but fakery. This pseudo-occult phenomenon has fooled many people into believing in its legitimacy.

In an excellent book entitled *The Fakers,* Danny Korem and Paul Meier expose much of this phenomenon that is taken to be supernatural. They explain the difference between what is real and what is actually deception:

> What is the difference between occult and pseudo-occult phenomena? Occult phenomena are phenomena of or relating to supernatural agencies, their effects, and knowledge of them. An example which many people consider a manifestation of occultic powers is demon possession. While the manifestation is visible, the force behind it is not. We can see the *effects* of a possession, but we cannot see the demon perpetrating the manifestation. Pseudo-occult phenomena are events which *appear* to be caused by secretive, supernatural powers and yet are brought about by physical or psychological means.
>
> One purpose of this book is to point out the difference between the occult and pseudo-

occult. There is a great danger in treating both on equal ground. One man who had reportedly performed the act of exorcism on several demon-possessed individuals tried his hand on a young teenager. The man strapped the young lady to a chair to prevent her from harming herself and proceeded with his ritual. It turned out that the girl was not demon-possessed but was schizophrenic and needed the help of a trained psychiatrist. The girl, obviously terrified by the trauma, was left in worse shape than when she first went to see the man in question (Danny Korem and Paul Meier, *The Fakers*, Grand Rapids, MI: Baker Book House, 1980, pp. 15, 16).

Needless to say, caution must be exercised before assuming some unexplained phenomenon is demonic. While not all Christian writers would place certain phenomena under the category of deception, as do Korem and Meier, the latter clearly demonstrate the need for restraint in attributing many unexplained phenomena to the occult.

THE OCCULT EXPLOSION

We live in a day when occult activity is rapidly increasing. Martin Ebon, former administrative secretary of the Parapsychology Foundation, and the author of *The Satan Trap* and *Dangers of the Occult*, gives his assessment of the upswing of interest in occult phenomena:

Occult practices and psychic phenomena are exercising a hold on millions of Americans today. . . .

Two mass stimuli have contributed to this trend. One is the drug cult, which causes an interest in such matters as a "non-drug high," to be sought in meditation and similar practices, as well as in confirmation of the drug-induced feeling that mind may control matter or events. Second, a series of highly popular motion pictures created successive waves of occult or pseudo-occult involvements. With *Rosemary's Baby*, which pictured the birth of a diabolic infant, came an upswing in witchcraft practices; with *The Exorcist*, demonic possession and exorcism were dramatized to a public of millions; other films and television shows have dealt with similar themes ("The Occult Temptation," by Martin Ebon, *The Humanist*, January/February, 1977).

It is evident that occult beliefs have now penetrated every web of our society. From the media to grocery stores, one cannot turn without encountering some type of occultic literature or influence. One can find horoscopes for weight loss and horoscopes for a better sex life.

WHY IS THERE SUCH AN INTEREST IN THE OCCULT?

With the alarming rate at which people are becoming involved in the occult, the inevitable question of "why" comes up: Why do people who live in this enlightened age with

Facts about the Growing Interest in the Occult

1. Women constitute a majority of the buyers of occult books, magazines, and charms.
2. A company called The American Astrological Association claims it has sold horoscopes to 339,660 individuals for $3.50-$9.95 each.
3. Some 86,000 women paid $8.40 each through the mail to purchase a genie-in-the-bottle good luck pendant.
4. A total of 208,302 people purchased the *Handbook of Supernatural Powers,* which gives directions for ancient spells and potions.
5. There are 16,842 members of the Circle of Mystic and Occult Arts Book Club of Prentice Hall Publishing.

all the marvelous scientific and technological advances become involved in occultic practices? We believe there are several factors that have contributed to the rise of occult popularity.

The secularization of Christianity. In recent years there has been a denial of the cardinal doctrines of the Christian faith from those occupying a position of leadership in the church. This leaves a greater spiritual vacuum in the world which invites people who have spiritual needs to go elsewhere to have them satisfied. Moreover, some of these church leaders who have forsaken the gospel have themselves become practitioners of the occult, causing a follow-the-leader mentality in many former churchgoers.

The classic example would be the Episcopal bishop, James Pike, who rejected the church's belief in the deity of Christ, His virgin birth, and other central truths. After the suicide death of his son, Pike began to consult mediums, including the famous Arthur Ford, in an attempt to contact the spirit of his dead son. Pike became a firm believer in life after death from his occultic involvement rather than from biblical doctrine and took many people with him into the dark world of the occult. When the church "waters down" the gospel of Christ, the door to occultic practice swings wide open.

Curiosity. There is a certain mystery about the occult that appeals to our curiosity. Many who get involved in occult practices do so by starting out with so-called "harmless" practices such as reading horoscopes or using a Ouija board. They afterward proceed into deeper involvement because of an increasing curiosity. Buzzard comments upon this fascination:

> Our age seems to have a deep fascination with evil, the bizarre, and the inexplicable. It thrives on horror and repulsion. What makes one faint or vomit or experience nightmares has a kind of magnetic charm. Mary Knoblauch summed up this fascination in commenting on *The Exorcist:* "Perhaps the most frightening thing about *The Exorcist* is that

thirst for and fascination with evil that lies buried in us all, surfacing with savage swiftness at the right incarnation." The moment of that incarnation seems to be upon us. What was buried has arisen and dances unashamedly in the streets (Lynn Buzzard, Introduction to *Demon Possession,* edited by John Warwick Montgomery, Minneapolis: Bethany Fellowship, 1976, pp. 17, 18).

Unfortunately, there is a price to pay for this curiosity about the occult. The occult is not something neutral that an individual can get in and out of without any adverse effects. In his book *Kingdom of Darkness,* F. W. Thomas relates a story of a man-and-wife journalistic team who desired to investigate the occult in London. They joined a satanic group to obtain firsthand information, but eventually withdrew because of the frightening things they observed. Their lives were never the same. They were troubled by many terrible experiences and incidents.

Thomas concluded, "Such was the experience of an unwise couple whose curiosity for black magic dragged them through untold anguish and despair. One cannot just pick up the dark bolts of magical fire and drop them at will without getting burned. There is always a price to pay for use of these forbidden powers, in this world as well as in the world to come" (F. W. Thomas, *Kingdom of Darkness,* cited by Clifford Wilson and John Weldon, *Occult Shock and Psychic Forces,* San Diego: Master Books, 1980, pp. 13, 14).

The occult offers reality. There is a reality in the occultic experience that attracts many people to it. All of us desire some sort of ultimate answer for life's basic questions, and the world of the occult gladly supplies answers. The astrologist will chart your future. The Ouija board promises you direction, and the medium talking to the spirit of your dead relative informs you that things are fine in the next world.

Since these occultic practices do reveal some amazing things, the practitioner is lulled into thinking that he has experienced ultimate reality and no longer needs to continue his search for truth. The spiritual vacuum is filled by means of a spiritual experience, not with God, but often from the very pit of hell.

THE BIBLE AND THE OCCULT
The Bible categorically denounces any and all occultic practices:

> When you enter the land which the Lord your God gives you, you shall not learn to imitate the detestable things of those nations. There shall not be found among you anyone who makes his son or his daughter pass through the fire, one who uses divination, one who practices witchcraft, or one who interprets omens, or a sorcerer, or one who casts a spell, or a medium, or a spiritualist, or one who calls upon the dead. For whoever does these things is detestable to the Lord; and because of these detestable things the Lord your God

will drive them out before you. You shall be blameless before the Lord your God. For those nations, which you shall dispossess, listen to those who practice witchcraft and to diviners, but as for you, the Lord your God has not allowed you to do so (Deut. 18:9-14).

In the same manner, the New Testament condemns such workings (Gal. 5:20). In the city of Ephesus many who were practicing in the occult became believers in Jesus Christ and renounced their occultic practices. "Many also of those who practiced magic brought their books together and began burning them in the sight of all . . ." (Acts 19:19).

Another encounter with the occult can be seen in Acts 13:6-12:

And when they had gone through the whole island as far as Paphos, they found a certain magician, a Jewish false prophet whose name was Bar-Jesus, who was with the proconsul, Sergius Paulus, a man of intelligence. This man summoned Barnabas and Saul and sought to hear the word of God. But Elymas the magician (for thus his name is translated) was opposing them, seeking to turn the proconsul away from the faith. But Saul, who was also known as Paul, filled with the Holy Spirit, fixed his gaze upon him, and said, "You who are full of all deceit and fraud, you son of the devil, you enemy of all righteousness, will you not cease to make crooked the straight ways of the Lord? And now, behold, the hand of the Lord is upon you, and you will be blind and not see the sun for a time." And immediately a mist and a darkness fell upon him, and he went about seeking those who would lead him by the hand. Then the proconsul believed when he saw what happened, being amazed at the teaching of the Lord.

The false prophet who called himself Bar-Jesus (Son of Jesus) was actually trying to keep the governor, Sergius Paulus, from becoming a believer, and the judgment of blindness on this man was immediate. Walter Martin makes some astute observations on the passage by listing five characteristics of those who oppose God:

1. They are in league with Satan and possess certain supernatural powers.
2. They are false prophets.
3. They seek to influence people politically and ecclesiastically, particularly those in positions of power (verses 6, 7).
4. They attempt to prevent those who are seeking to hear the Word of God from learning it by opposing those who preach it (verse 8).
5. They deliberately attempt to divert prospective converts from the faith (verse 8) as their ultimate goal (Walter Martin, *The Maze of Mormonism*, Santa Ana, CA: Vision House Publishers, Inc., 1977, pp. 216, 217).

Astrology

Two of the most crucial questions that haunt humanity are "Who am I?" and "What's going to happen in the future?" Many people lose sleep at night worrying about the future, wondering what will happen tomorrow. Astrology claims to have the solution to these basic questions. It offers daily horoscopes to predict individuals' futures. "What's your sign?" crops up in many casual conversations. The ancient occultic art of astrology has become very popular in our 20th-century culture.

WHAT IS ASTROLOGY?

Astrology is an ancient practice that assumes that the position of the stars and planets has a direct influence upon people and events. Supposedly, one's life pattern can be charted by determining the position of the stars and planets at the time of one's birth. The chart that attempts to accomplish this is known as a "horoscope." Rene Noorbergen explains how one's horoscope is charted:

> For every personal horoscope, the moment of birth is the essential starting point. This, coupled with the latitude and longitude of the individual's birthplace, provides the initial package for the usual astrological chart. While this is elementary, it is not complete; a factor known as "true local time" must also be considered. This "true" time is arrived at by adding or subtracting four minutes for each degree of longitude that your birthplace lies to the east or west of the center of your time zone of birth. Once this has been accomplished, the next step is to convert this "true" time into "sidereal" or star time. This is done with the aid of an ephemerus, a reference book showing the positions of the planets in relationship to the earth. . . .
>
> Once you have developed this data—these simple steps are no more difficult than solving a seventh-grade math problem—then you are ready to "chart" your horoscope. This means you align the "ascendant" with the nine-o'clock point on the inner circle of the horoscope, and from there you are prepared to "read" the various zodiacal "houses" that control your life and fortune (Rene Noorbergen, *The Soul Hustlers,* Grand Rapids, MI: Zondervan, 1976, pp. 176, 177).

HOW IS IT JUSTIFIED?
How astrologers justify their practice is explained by Michael Van Buskirk:

One's future can be forecast, allegedly, because astrology asserts the unity of all things. This is the belief that the Whole (or all of the universe put together) is in some way the same as the Part (or the individual component or man), or that the Part is a smaller reflection of the Whole (macrocosmic/microcosmic model). The position of the planets (the macro) influences and produces a corresponding reaction in man (the micro). This makes man a pawn in the cosmos with his life and actions pre-determined and unalterable (Michael Van Buskirk, *Astrology: Revival in the Cosmic Garden,* Costa Mesa, CA: Caris, 1976, p. 6).

Noorbergen concludes, "To believe in astrology, you must support the philosophy that you are either a 'born loser' or a 'born winner.' The stars, we are being told, do not merely forecast the course of our lives, but they also cause the events to take place. They both impel and compel . . ." (Rene Noorbergen, op. cit., pp. 178, 179).

THE PROBLEMS OF ASTROLOGY

The claims that astrologers have made have drawn severe criticism from the scientific community. In September 1975, 186 prominent American scientists, along with eighteen Nobel Prize winners, spoke out against "the pretentious claims of astrological charlatans," saying, among other things, that there is no scientific basis whatsoever for the assumption that the stars foretell events and influence lives. The following are some of the reasons the practice of astrology must be rejected as both unscientific and unbiblical.

The problem of authority. Astrologists are victims of their own system. They cannot have the objective authority necessary to explain our own world. If everything is predetermined in conjunction with the zodiac, then how can the astrologists get outside of that fatalism to accurately observe it?

What if the astrologists themselves are predetermined to explain everything by astrology? There is no way they can prove their system if they are pawns in that same system.

Conflicting systems. The problem of authority in astrology is graphically revealed when one realizes there are many systems of astrology that are diametrically opposed to each other. Astrologers in the West would not interpret a horoscope the same way a Chinese astrologer would.

Even in the West, there is no unanimity of interpretation among astrologers, seeing that some contend for eight zodiac signs rather than twelve, while others argue for fourteen or even twenty-four signs of the zodiac.

With these different systems employed by astrologers, an individual may go to two different astrologers and receive two totally opposed courses of behavior for the same day! This is not only a possibility, it is also a reality, for a simple comparison between astrological forecasts in daily newspapers will often reveal contradictions.

Earth-centered viewpoint. Astrology is based upon the premise that the planets revolve around the earth, known as the "geocentric theory." This theory was shown to be in error by Copernicus, who proved that the planets revolve around the sun, not the earth. This is known as the "heliocentric theory."

Since astrology is based upon the refuted geocentric theory, its reliability is destroyed. Since the basic assumption is false, all conclusions, even if feebly reinterpreted by today's knowledge and drawn from this assumption, are likewise false.

Missing planets. One of the major misconceptions that is the basis of astrology concerns the number of planets in our solar system. Most astrological charts are based upon the assumption that there are seven planets in our solar system (including the sun and the moon).

In ancient times, Uranus, Neptune, and Pluto were unobservable with the naked eye. Consequently, astrologers based their system upon the seven planets they believed revolved around the earth. Since that time, it has been proven that the sun, not the earth, is the center of the solar system and that three other planets exist in our solar system.

Twins. A constant source of embarrassment for astrologers is the birth of twins. Since they are born at exactly the same time and place, they should have the same destiny. Unfortunately, this is not the case, for experience shows us that two people who are born at the same time can live totally different lives. One may turn out to be very successful, while the other ends up a failure. The fact that twins do not live out the same lives shows another flaw in the theory.

Limited perspective. A serious problem with astrology is its limited perspective. Astrology was born in an area close to the equator and did not take into consideration those living in latitudes where the zodiac signs do not appear for the same periods of time.

As Michel Gauquelin points out, "Astrology, begun in latitudes relatively close to the equator, made no provisions for the possibility that no planet may be in sight (in the higher latitudes) for several weeks in a row" (Michel Gauquelin, *The Cosmic Clocks,* Chicago, IL: Henry Regnery Co., 1967, p. 78).

Since this is the case, one of the basic pillars of astrology now crumbles, as Van Buskirk points out, "Astrology can hardly be scientifically based on its own premise that the microcosm reflects the influence of the macrocosm, when one of the microcosms (man) above the 66th latitude is left uninfluenced by the cosmos" (Michael Van Buskirk, op. cit., p. 9).

No scientific verification. Probably the most damaging criticism that can be leveled at astrological prediction is the fact that its scientific value is nil. Paul Couderc, astronomer at the Paris Observatory, concluded after examining the horoscopes of 2,817 musicians:

> The position of the sun has absolutely no musical significance. The musicians are born throughout the entire year on a chance basis. No sign of the zodiac or fraction of a sign favors or does not favor them.
>
> We conclude: The assets of scientific astrology are equal to zero, as is the case with commercialized astrology. This is perhaps unfortunate, but it is a fact (Paul Couderc, *L'Astrologie*, "Que Sais-je?" 508; 3rd ed.; Paris: Presses Universitaires de France, 1961, pp. 86-89, cited by John Warwick Montgomery, *Principalities and Powers*, p. 106).

Incorrect time of reckoning. Another major problem with astrology concerns the fact that horoscopes are cast from the time of birth, not from the time of conception. Since all the hereditary factors are determined at conception, it should logically follow that the planets could begin influencing the person's destiny immediately after conception.

The shifting constellations. Astrology is unscientific because of the fact of the precession or the shifting of constellations. Boa elaborates on this problem:

> The early astronomers were not aware of precession and therefore failed to take it into account in their system. The twelve signs of the zodiac originally correspond with the twelve

constellations of the same names. But due to precession, the constellations have shifted about 30° in the last 2,000 years. This means that the constellation of Virgo is now in the sign of Libra, the constellation of Libra is now in the sign of Scorpio and so on. Thus, if a person is born on September 1, astrologers would call him a Virgo (the sign the sun is in at that date), but the sun is actually in the constellation Leo at that date. So there are two different zodiacs: one which slowly moves (the sidereal zodiac) and one which is stationary (the tropical zodiac). Which zodiac should be used? (Kenneth Boa, *Cults, World Religions, and You,* Wheaton, IL: Victor Books, 1977, pp. 124, 125).

THE BIBLE AND ASTROLOGY

The Bible warns people against relying on astrologers and astrology:

> You are wearied with your many counsels; let now the astrologers, those who prophesy by the stars, those who predict by the new moons, stand up and save you from what will come upon you. Behold, they have become like stubble, fire burns them; they cannot deliver themselves from the power of the flame . . . there is none to save you (Isa. 47:13-15).

Other warnings can be found in such verses as Jeremiah 10:2: "Learn not the way of the heathen, and be not dismayed at the signs of heaven; for the heathen are dismayed at them." Elsewhere, the Bible says, "And beware, lest you lift up your eyes to heaven and see the sun and the moon and the stars, all the host of heaven, and be drawn away and worship them and serve them" (Deut. 4:19).

The Book of Daniel gives us a comparison between the astrologers and those dedicated to the true and living God. Daniel 1:20 reveals that Daniel and his three friends would be ten times better in matters of wisdom and understanding than the astrologers because they served the living and true God rather than the stars. When the king had a dream, the astrologers could not give an explanation for it, but rather God alone had the answer, for it is only He who can reveal the future (see Daniel 2:27, 28).

The Bible makes it clear that any type of astrological practice is severely condemned by God, for it attempts to understand the future through occultic means rather than through God's divinely inspired Word.

WHY DO PEOPLE
BELIEVE IN ASTROLOGY?
If astrology is both unscientific and unbiblical, why do so many people believe in it?

One answer would be that it sometimes works, as one book on astrology attests: "When the late astrological genius, Grant Lewi, was asked why he believed in astrology, his blunt answer was, 'I believe in it because it works' " (Joseph Polansky, *Sun*

Sign Success, New York: Warner/Destiny Books, 1977, p. 35).

There is a much better explanation for the so-called accuracy of astrological predictions. If one reads a horoscope, even in a cursory manner, he will be struck with the general and ambiguous nature of the statements, which can be pointed to as fulfilling anything and everything. *Time* magazine observed:

There are so many variables and options to play with that the astrologer is always right. Break a leg when your astrologer told you the signs were good, and he can congratulate you on escaping what might have happened had the signs been bad. Conversely, if you go against the signs and nothing happens, the astrologer can insist that you were subconsciously careful because you were forewarned (*Time*, March 21, 1969, p. 56).

Koch sheds light on the suggestive aspect: "The person who seeks advice from an astrologer comes with a certain readiness to believe the horoscope. This predisposition leads to an autosuggestion to order his life according to the horoscope, and thus contribute to its fulfillment" (Kurt Koch, *Christian Counseling and Occultism*, Grand Rapids, MI: Kregel, 1973, p. 94).

Rachleff tells of a very interesting experiment in which an identical horoscope was mailed to over 100 persons who had given their natal information to a post office box number. The recipients had 12 different birth periods represented by their birth dates.... Each person was told that the horoscope sent out pertained only to him.... Rachleff tells us that "many admired its pertinence and exactitude" (p. 38). (Clifford Wilson and John Weldon, *Occult Shock and Psychic Forces*, San Diego: Master Books, 1980, p. 118).

Astrology is bankrupt both biblically and scientifically. The Bible indicates that all of us have both the capacity and responsibility to choose our road in life. Astrology, since it is fatalistic, would deny us that choice and therefore must be rejected.

CHAPTER

3

Demons

The Bible not only teaches the existence of the devil but also of a great company of his followers known as demons or evil spirits. These demons originally were holy but with the leader, Satan, they fell away from God. Their ultimate end will be eternal damnation when God judges Satan and his host at the Great White Throne judgment (Rev. 20:10-15).

Demons have certain characteristics revealed by the Bible.

1. Demons are spirits without bodies. "For our struggle is not against flesh and blood, but against the rulers, against the powers, against the world forces of this darkness, against the spiritual forces of wickedness in the heavenly places" (Eph. 6:12).

2. Demons were originally in fellowship with God. "And angels who did not keep their own domain, but abandoned their proper abode, He has kept in eternal bonds under darkness for the judgment of the great day" (Jude 6).

3. Demons are numerous. "For He said

unto him, 'Come out of the man, you unclean spirit!' And He was asking him, 'What is your name?' And he said to Him, 'My name is Legion; for we are many' " (Mark 5:8,9).

4. *Demons are organized.* ". . . This man casts out demons only by Beelzebub the ruler of the demons" (Matt. 12:24).

5. *Demons have supernatural powers.* "For they are spirits of demons, performing signs, which go out to the kings of the whole world, to gather them together for the war of the Great Day of God, the Almighty" (Rev. 16:14).

6. *Demons are knowledgeable of God.* "And behold, they cried out, saying, 'What do we have to do with you, Son of God? Have you come here to torment us before the time?' "(Matt. 8:29).

7. *Demons are allowed to roam the earth and torment unbelievers.* "Now when the unclean spirit goes out of a man, it passes through waterless places, seeking rest, and does not find it. Then it says, 'I will return to my house from which I came'; and when it comes, it finds it unoccupied, swept and put in order. Then it goes, and takes along with it seven other spirits more wicked than itself, and they go in and live there; and the last state of that man becomes worse than the first" (Matt. 12:43-45).

8. *Demons sometimes can inflict sickness.* "And as they were going out, behold a dumb man, demon possessed, was brought to Him. And after the demon was cast out, the

dumb man spoke . . ." (Matt. 9:32, 33).

9. Demons can possess or control animals. "And He gave them permission. And coming out, the unclean spirits entered the swine; and the herd rushed down the steep bank into the sea, about two thousand of them, and they were drowned in the sea" (Mark 5:13).

10. Demons can possess or control human beings. "And also some women who had been healed of evil spirits and sicknesses; Mary who was called Magdalene, from whom seven demons had gone out" (Luke 8:2).

11. Demons sometimes can cause mental disorders. "And when He had come out of the boat, immediately a man from the tombs with an unclean spirit met Him and he had his dwelling among the tombs. And no one was able to bind him anymore, even with a chain . . . and constantly night and day among the tombs and in the mountains, he was crying out and gashing himself with stones" (Mark 5:2, 3, 5).

12. Demons know that Jesus Christ is God. "And just then there was in their synagogue a man with an unclean spirit; and he cried out, saying, 'What do we have to do with you, Jesus of Nazareth? Have you come to destroy us? I know who you are—the Holy One of God' " (Mark 1:23, 24).

13. Demons tremble before God. "You believe that God is one. You do well; the demons also believe, and shudder" (James 2:19).

The Effects of a Demonic Attack

From the New Testament accounts of demon possession, along with other examples, we can chart some of the phenomena that can be observed during a demonic attack.

A. Change of Personality

Including intelligence, moral character, demeanor, appearance

B. Physical Changes
1. Preternatural strength
2. Epileptic convulsions, foaming
3. Catatonic symptoms, falling
4. Clouding of consciousness, anaesthesia to pain
5. Changed voice

C. Mental Changes
1. Glossolalia; understanding unknown languages (the counterfeit gift as opposed to the biblical gift)
2. Preternatural knowledge
3. Psychic and occult powers, e.g., clairvoyance, telepathy, and prediction

D. Spiritual Changes
1. Reaction to and fear of Christ; blasphemy with regret as in depression
2. Affected by prayer

E. Deliverance possible in the name of Jesus

As this is a diagnosis in retrospect it falls outside the range of preexorcism symptoms. (John Richards, *But Deliver Us From Evil: An Introduction to the Demonic Dimension in Pastoral Care*, London: Darton, Longman and Todd, 1974, p. 156).

14. *Demons teach false doctrine.* "But the Spirit explicitly says that in later times some will fall away from the faith, paying attention to deceitful spirits and doctrines of demons" (1 Tim. 4:1).

15. *Demons oppose God's people.* "For our struggle is not against flesh and blood, but against the rulers, against the powers, against the world forces of this darkness, against the spiritual forces of wickedness in the heavenly places" (Eph. 6:12).

16. *Demons attempt to destroy Christ's Kingdom.* "Be of sober spirit, be on the alert. Your adversary, the devil, prowls about like a roaring lion, seeking someone to devour" (1 Pet. 5:8).

17. *God takes advantage of the actions of demons to accomplish His divine purposes.* "Then God sent an evil spirit between Abimelech and the men of Shechem; and the men of Shechem dealt treacherously with Abimelech" (Judg. 9:23).

18. *God is going to judge demons at the last judgment.* "For if God did not spare angels when they sinned, but cast them into hell and committed them to pits of darkness, reserved for judgment . . ." (2 Pet. 2:4).

DOES DEMON POSSESSION OCCUR TODAY?

Granting the fact that demon possession occurred in New Testament times, the natural question arises, "Does it occur today?" After extensive study of demonology and years of observing patients, psychiatrist Paul Meier gives his professional opinion:

> I can honestly say that I have never yet seen a single case of demon possession. The main thing I have learned about demon possession is how little we really know about it and how little the Bible says about it.
>
> I have had hundreds of patients who came to see me because they thought they were demon possessed. Scores of them heard "demon voices" telling them evil things to do. It was at first surprising to me that all of these had dopamine deficiencies in their brains, which were readily correctable with Thorazine or any other major tranquilizer. I discovered that all of the "demons" I was seeing were allergic to Thorazine and that, in nearly every case, a week or two on Thorazine made the "demons" go away and brought the patient closer to his real conflicts. (Danny Korem and Paul Meier, *The Fakers*, Grand Rapids, MI: Baker Book House, 1980, pp. 160, 161).

However, there are many others who attest to having witnessed demon possession. Kurt Koch writes, "I was once invited by Dr. Martin Lloyd-Jones to speak before a group of psychiatrists in London. During the discussion which followed my talk, two psychiatrists stood up and stated quite dogmatically that possession as such did not exist. Immediately after this, however, two other psychiatrists present—they were both Christians—rose to their feet and said that they were not only convinced that possession was a genuine phenomenon, but that they had already come across cases of it within their own practice, one of them seven cases and the other eleven" (Kurt Koch, *Demonology, Past and Present*, Grand Rapids, MI: Kregel Publications, 1973, p. 32.)

In the nineteenth century there were some striking cases of demon possession recorded in China by missionary John L. Nevius. When Nevius first came to China, he firmly believed that demons belonged to a bygone era. When he heard firsthand accounts of demon possession, he considered it superstition. However, try as he would, he could not convince the people that what they had heard and seen was a result of their imaginations. Finally, the evidence led him to a change of mind, not only believing the demons existed but also that demon possession was in fact a present reality.

Nevius said this of his experiences:

> I brought with me to China a strong conviction that a belief in demons, and communications with spiritual beings, belongs exclusively to a barbarous and superstitious age, and at present can consist only with mental weakness and want of culture. I indulged Mr. Tu (his Chinese teacher), however, in talking on his favorite topics. . . . I could not but notice . . . the striking resemblance between some of his statements of alleged facts and the demonology of Scripture. This resemblance I account for only as apparent or accidental. . . . (John L. Nevius, *Demon Possession*, Grand Rapids, MI: Kregel Publications, 1968, pp. 9, 10).

A Case Study: Exorcism

Walter Martin relates this fascinating account:

In Newport Beach, California, I encountered a case of demonic possession in which five persons, including myself, were involved. In this case the girl, who was about 5 feet 4 inches tall and weighed 120 pounds, attacked a 180-pound man and with one arm flipped him 5 or 6 feet away. It took four of us, including her husband, to hold her body to a bed while we prayed in the name of Jesus Christ for the exorcism of the demons within her.

During the course of the exorcism we found out that she was possessed because she had worshipped Satan, and because of that worship he had come with his forces and taken control of her. . . . She had married a Christian, was a daughter of a Christian minister, had taught Sunday school in a Christian church, and had appeared on the surface to be perfectly consistent with Christian theology. But the whole time she was laughing inwardly at the church and at Christ. It was not until her exorcism that she was delivered and received Jesus Christ as her Lord and Savior. Today she and her husband are on the mission field serving the Lord Jesus Christ.

Nevius then records his many and varied experiences with demon-possessed people which eventually led to his change of mind on the matter.

I have a psychologist friend who was present with me at an exorcism in Newport Beach, California. Before we entered the room he said, "I want you to know I do not believe in demonic possession. This girl is mentally disturbed."

I said, "That may well be. We'll find out very soon."

As we went into the room and closed the door, the girl's supernatural strength was soon revealed. Suddenly from her body a totally foreign voice said quietly, with a smirk on the face (she was unconcious—the psychologist testified to that), "We will outlast you."

The psychologist looked at me and said, "What was that?"

"That is what you don't believe in," I said.

We spent about 3½ hours exorcising what the psychologist didn't believe in!

At the end of the exorcism he was not only a devout believer in the personality of the devil, but in demonic possession and biblical exorcism as well. He now knows that there are other dimensional beings capable of penetrating this dimension and of controlling human beings! (Walter Martin, *Exorcism: Fact or Fable,* Santa Ana, CA: Vision House Publishers, 1975, pp. 17, 18, 21).

In conclusion, although most cases of alleged demon possession turn out to be in reality something quite different, it does not negate the fact that demon possession can and does occur today. However, one should be very careful before he considers an individual demon possessed when the person's problem may be physiological or psychological.

Only a mature Christian, experienced and seasoned by God in counseling and spiritual warfare, should take an active part in diagnosing or treating alleged cases of demon possession. The human body, mind, and spirit are so complex and interrelated that it takes spiritual discernment coupled with a great amount of knowledge to deal responsibly with what appears to be demon possession.

If you know of someone who appears to be demon possessed and who wants help, you can and should pray for him and direct him to someone who is qualified to help. There is hope for him: God can and will set him free from whatever is binding him, be it demonic, physiological, or psychological.

Parapsychology

Parapsychology is a new branch of either the occult or psychology, depending on whom you consult. It is a discipline that has aimed to put many of the supernatural phenomena associated with the occult on sound scientific footing. The attempt is to create respectability for what has been considered as foolishness.

One of the popular areas in paràpsychology in recent years has been ESP (extrasensory perception). Traditional witchcraft, which assents to the supernatural, has also given way in some groups to this new scientific or paranormal explanation of occultic activity.

Most newer witchcraft groups, however, avoid supernaturalism and prefer instead to speak of *supernormal* or *paranormal* events. Magical laws are seen as effective and within the ultimate purview of scientific understanding, but their emphasis is placed upon pragmatic knowledge of such magical laws and not on their scientific validation or understanding. In this sense, it would appear that there has been a kind of secularization of magic in adaptation to the modern scientific and naturalistic world view. Thus, what were once described in the occult literature as supernatural psychic forces are now examples of extrasensory perception of a kind basically examinable and potentially understandable in the psychologist's laboratory (Marcello Truzzi, "Toward a Sociology of the Occult: Notes on Modern Witchcraft," *Religious Movements in Contemporary America.* Irving I. Zaretsky and Mark P. Leone, eds., Princeton: Princeton University Press, 1974, pp. 635, 636).

In *Parapsychology and the Nature of Life*, John L. Randall comments:

As the 1960s drew to a close parapsychology won a substantial victory in its ninety-year-old battle for scientific respectability. On December 30th, 1969, Parapsychological Association was officially accepted as an affiliate member of that most distinguished body of savants, the American Association for the Advancement of Science (A.A.A.S.). . . . For the first time in its chequered history, parapsychology had been recognized as a legitimate scientific pursuit; and from now on parapsychologists could present their papers at the bar of scientific opinion without feeling that they would be ridiculed or dismissed out of hand merely on account of their subject matter (John L. Randall, *Parapsychology and the Nature of Life*, New York: Harper and Row Publishers, p. 175).

The demand for scientific investigation is a valid quest and should and must be made.

However, in the consideration of parapsychology as science, one must be willing to embrace the most accurate explanation of the data, whether it be fraud, the occult, or a valid paranormal experience.

In most cases, one fruit in the study of parapsychology is an increasing lack of motivation to study the Bible. In fact, it often leads one in the direction of the paranormal or supernatural totally apart from a biblical base. In an interesting preface to his book, *Religion and the New Psychology,* Alson J. Smith writes of the story of a young woman he talked to at length doing research in parapsychology at Duke University:

She was a quiet, intelligent girl from the middle South. She had come to Duke intending to go into some kind of religious work; she had been a "local preacher" in her home-town Methodist church and had occupied the pulpit on many occasions. At Duke, however, she had studied the various sciences and had lost most of her old, uncritical religious faith. She gave up the idea of entering religious work and lapsed into a sort of mournful agnosticism.

In the course of her work in psychology, though, she had discovered parapsychology, the "venture beyond psychology," with which this book is largely concerned. It was a science in which she had learned to put her trust, and yet it spoke to her of the same spiritual world, the same spiritual forces that her old, uncritical religious faith had spoken of; in a different terminology and by a different method, it came out at the same place. The emotional void left by the loss of her religious faith was filled;

her new faith (although I do not think she would call it that) satisfied her intellectually and emotionally. Her laboratory work in parapsychology became for her a sort of religious vocation (Alson J. Smith, *Religion and the New Psychology,* Garden City, NY: Doubleday and Co., Inc., 1951, p. 5).

Smith interestingly enough offers this explanation for the woman's change. He both attributes demise of her Christian faith and the rise of her "parapsychology faith" to the specific method:

Her story, it seems to me, is an allegory on what is happening to millions of nominal Christians in our day. Their acceptance of the scientific method has shaken their religious faith (which, of course, has also been shaken by a great many other things), and they are not very happy about it. But they have to accept the scientific method—its accomplishments are too many and too great to be ignored.

The significance of parapsychology for these millions is that it now takes the scientific method and leads men toward the spiritual world rather than away from it.

Scientists usually accept that similar phenomena occur in both the occult and parapsychology. However, many scientists disagree with the biblical explanation of such phenomena, that it is usually demonic. Often, the new science of parapsychology will discredit any biblical interpretation of the data.

For example, in the book, *Life, Death and Psychical Research: Studies on Behalf of the Churches' Fellowship for Psychical and Spiritual Studies,* authors discredit the biblical admonition against sorcerers and mediums given in the Book of Deuteronomy. They feel this passage does not prohibit the exercise of psychical (demonic) gifts, the prohibition of which has been the historic and traditional interpretation by the church until the modern attempt to give some type—any type—of biblical credibility to the paranormal.

Consider this:

The Deuteronomic "prohibition" (Deuteronomy 18:9 to 12) has long been used by the prejudiced, the ignorant and the fearful as a reason for opposing genuine psychical research by Christian people. In the past, innocent folk have been denounced as sorcerers and witches or of being possessed by evil spirits. Others, who have exercised powers believed to come under the sacred ban, have been tortured to death.

Such attitudes still persist. Those who seek to exercise psychical gifts are often warned of the dangers of divine condemnation. Christians who encourage paranormal investigation are reminded that they are going against the teachings of the Bible and are forbidden to "dabble" in such matters (Canon J. D. Pearce, Higgens and Rev. Stanley Whitby, eds., *Life, Death and Psychical Research: Studies of the Churches' Fellowship for Psychical and Spiritual Studies,* London: Rider and Company, 1973, p. 10).

While it's true innocent people have been denounced in the past (viz., Salem witch trials), it is a logical fallacy to assume, therefore, that historical interpretation of the Scriptures by Christians on this passage has been wrong, when in fact both history and proper biblical interpretation support their position.

ESP

Extrasensory perception, or ESP as it is commonly known, has become very popular today. To know something without the help of the senses is the meaning of ESP.

Lynn Walker states of ESP:

> ESP, or extrasensory perception . . . is the term applied to an ability to know something without the aid of the senses. It includes precognition or what is sometimes referred to as "ESP of the future"; telepathy, which is the awareness of the thoughts of a person without the use of the senses; and clairvoyance, the awareness of objects or objective events without sensory aid (Lynn Walker, *Supernatural Power and the Occult*, Austin, TX: Firm Foundation Publishing House, n.d., p. 90).

ESP is only one major field of parapsychology. Another area of study in parapsychology is psychical research:

> Systematic scientific inquiries concerning the nature, facts and causes of mediumistic phenomena (Norman Blunsdan, *A Popular*

Dictionary of Spiritualism, NY: The Citadel Press, 1963, s.v. "psychical research").

However, what should be noted is that there is a difference between what is often called mental telepathy and ESP. These two often are used interchangeably, but to a parapsychologist they are different.

Mental telepathy is a branch of ESP. In fact, one of the "breakthroughs" in ESP research for parapsychologists was when they made a division between mental telepathy and clairvoyance. In mental telepathy the person is aware of mental images, say symbols on cards, and the cards are shuffled, and he tries through ESP to reproduce the images seen.

Clairvoyance, on the other hand, tries to draw the symbols without any prior sense knowledge of what symbols were on the cards (Pratt, op. cit., pp. 45-54). This distinction led to a new emphasis in psychic research. The psychic researchers were able to formulate better test techniques for telepathy, and to determine precisely what was being tested, as well as what might be fraud, and from our perspective what might be strong occultic influence.

LIMITED-USE ESP?

Dr. John Warwick Montgomery, in *Principalities and Powers,* takes a markedly different approach to the reality and experience of ESP than most evangelical scholars. He

A PARAPSYCHOLOGY TREE

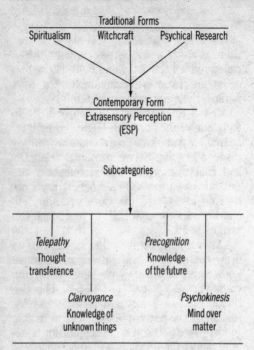

believes that one should not throw out all the experiences of ESP *a priori* as evil without proper investigation. After his investigation of the evidence Dr. Montgomery contends there may be a type of ESP power associated with individuals in various degrees that is not evil in origin.

Another writer, Lynn Walker, who quotes Dr. Montgomery in *Supernatural Power and the Occult,* also holds to this neutral approach, that simply to admit the existence of the power does not mean to admit evil.

In consideration of Dr. Montgomery's approach, if the power is neutral (neither divine nor demonic)—such as atomic energy is neither good nor evil, for its moral value depends on who uses it and what for (e.g., an atomic bomb dropped to murder the Nazis or a nuclear power plant built to heat a hospital)—then it would seem only limited use would be permitted by God, such as the personal experience of the individual.

For example, when a person suddenly realizes that something evil may happen to a friend or loved one, yet at the moment of realization that friend is clear around the world and he has not seen or spoken to him at all in the recent past and something does happen, then he has had a personal experience that may be best explainable at the present by ESP. But that would be the extent of the "use" by the individual.

That experience or any future experiences would not qualify him to be a prophet, for example. Yet, this limited-use idea does not seem completely consistent with the endowment of other gifts given by God, for all gifts from God (of which ESP thus would be one) are created to be used. Yet instead, here God is placing incredible restrictions on its use.

Of ESP or precognitive ability Dr. John Warwick Montgomery offers these remarks:

47

Here we are evidently encountering a mental faculty (analogous to extraordinary vision) which permits some people to look through the temporal haze separating the future from the past. . . .

Where it (precognitive ability) is used as a basis for exaggerated claims in behalf of its possessor—where, for example, the precognitive agent turns himself into, or allows others to turn himself into, a "seer" who can pronounce on the nature of life and the meaning of the universe—precognition becomes a most dangerous quality. Moreover, used in this way, it opens the floodgates of the psyche to supernatural influences of the negative sort (John W. Montgomery, *Principalities and Powers*, Minneapolis, MN: Bethany Fellowship, 1973, pp. 125, 126).

Dr. Montgomery, in his investigation, has completed some important research that will bear close scrutiny.

Lynn Walker sums up the present situation well as he points out that today almost all forms of paranormal activity have no relation to the God of the Bible.

We must conclude that it is when man, through the influence of Satan's direct power, uses a God-given talent or ability to teach religious error (Colossians 2:8-10; 2 Corinthians 11:3, 4), to promote works of the flesh (Galatians 5:19f), to exalt self as specially endowed by God as his agent (Colossians 2:18; 2 Corinthians 10:18), to deny the God of the Bible (2 Peter 2:1), to deliberately aspire to go beyond bounds divinely set (Deuteronomy

29:29)—it is then that man has become an instrument of Satan, a tool of evil supernaturalism. Divination in its multiplied forms and all present-day claims to revelations from God are equally Satan-inspired (Lynn Walker, *Supernatural Power,* op. cit., p. 91).

In summary, except for the unusual experiences reported above, people have no reason to pursue parapsychology. This new discipline does not lead men to God and opens men up to the powers of darkness.

Lynn Walker in *Supernatural Power and the Occult* explains the options:

If Satan did not have the power to create an ability in man, then God must have created man with all his abilities and talents; therefore, the ability to be aware of events or thoughts without the aid of the senses, ESP ability, is of God. Just as some men have, for instance, musical talent while others have none or have it in lesser degree, so do some men have ESP ability, some more, some less, some none. . . . To admit such ability does not admit an evil origin. This is not to say, however, that one's ESP ability cannot be misused (Ibid.).

CHAPTER 5

Satan and Satanism

Satan, or the devil, has been the subject of a multitude of books and discussions for thousands of years. Some deny his existence, saying that he is merely a mythological figure. Others seem obsessed with him, seeing him behind everything imaginable.

HE DOES EXIST

Satan is real. He is not a figment of one's imagination or a mere symbol of evil; he has personal existence! He had a beginning, he is at work now, but eventually he will be judged by God. How do we know he exists?

Since it is our firm conviction that the Bible is a supernatural revelation from the true and living God, correct in everything it affirms, we can go to the Bible and see what it says about the devil and his plans.

The evangelist Billy Sunday was once asked, "Why do you believe the devil exists?"

He replied, "There are two reasons. One, because the Bible says so, two, because I've done business with him."

THE CAREER OF SATAN

The career of Satan begins in the distant past. God created a multitude of angels to do His bidding. In the angelic rank there was one angel who was given the highest position, guardian to the Throne of the Most High. His name was Lucifer.

Lucifer. Information about Lucifer is revealed to us in Ezekiel 28:11-19. This passage is addressed to the prince of Tyre, a man who was vain because of the wealth he possessed and thought himself to be God. While God is rebuking the prince of Tyre for his vanity, He introduces another character called the king of Tyre, the real motivator of the prince of Tyre.

> Again the word of the Lord came to me saying, "Son of man, take up a lamentation over the king of Tyre and say to him, 'Thus says the Lord God, You had the seal of perfection, full of wisdom and perfect in beauty. You were in Eden, the garden of God; every precious stone was your covering: . . . On the day that you were created they were prepared. You were the anointed cherub who covers; and I placed you there. You were on the holy mountain of God; you walked in the midst of the stones of fire. You were blameless in your ways from the day you were created, until unrighteousness was found in you'" (Ezek. 28:11-15).

The king of Tyre is Lucifer. He was perfect in all his ways, the highest ranking celestial being, the most beautiful and wise of all God's creation.

Lucifer, along with the other angels at this time, was in perfect harmony with God. There was no rebellion. There was not any dissent; there was only one will in the universe, the will of God. Everything was beautiful and harmonious.

The fall of Lucifer. Everything was harmonious until one day Lucifer decided to rebel against God. The prophet Isaiah reveals the unrighteousness in Lucifer:

> How art thou fallen from heaven, O Lucifer, son of the morning! How art thou cut down to the ground, which didst weaken the nations! For thou hast said in thine heart, "I will ascend into heaven, I will exalt my throne above the stars of God: I will sit upon the mount of the congregation, in the sides of the north: I will ascend above the heights of the clouds: I will be like the Most High" (Isa. 14:12-14, KJV).

The emergence of Satan. The sin of Lucifer was rebellion. Five times Lucifer said in his heart, "I will."

- I will ascend into heaven;
- I will exalt my throne above the stars of God;
- I will sit upon the mount of the congregation;
- I will ascend above the heights of the clouds;
- I will be like the Most High.

This rebellion brought the downfall of Lucifer, for when Lucifer fell he was transformed into Satan. By bringing another will into the universe, a will that was antagonistic to God, the once harmonious universe was now in disharmony. When Lucifer rebelled, many of the angels rebelled with him, attempting to overthrow the authority of God. This resulted in Lucifer and his cohorts being banished from both God's presence and His favor.

We are often asked, "Why would a good God create the devil?" The answer is, "He didn't." God created Lucifer, the highest ranking of the angels, giving him beauty and intelligence and a superior position to every other created thing. He also gave Lucifer a free will to do as he pleased.

Eventually, Lucifer decided to stage a rebellion against God, and it was at this point that he became known as the devil or the adversary. He was not created for that purpose, nor did God desire for Lucifer to act independently of His will. However, Lucifer did rebel and consequently became the enemy of God and His work.

THE CREATION OF THE UNIVERSE

After the angelic revolt God created the universe as we know it today. We are not told what things were like before God created, so all we can do is speculate. The Bible says, "In the beginning God created the heavens and the earth" (Gen. 1:1). Genesis 1 reveals God's creative efforts. The last and greatest of His creation was man.

THE CREATION OF MAN

The Bible makes it clear that man was created by God in His image: "Then God said, 'Let us make man in our image, according to our likeness; and let them rule over the fish of the sea and over the birds of the sky, and over the cattle and over all the earth, and over every creeping thing that creeps on the earth.' So God created man in His own image, in the image of God He created him: male and female He created them" (Gen. 1:26, 27).

Man was God's crown of creation. He was placed in a perfect environment with everything conceivable going for him. He was in harmony with God, nature, his fellow man and himself.

THE FALL OF MAN

However, Satan was envious of that special relationship God had with man. In Genesis 3 there is an account of what transpired when Satan appeared to Adam and Eve in the Garden of Eden in the form of a serpent.

Now the serpent was more crafty than any beast of the field which the Lord God had made. And he said to the woman, "Indeed, has God said, 'You shall not eat from any tree of the garden'?" And the woman said to the serpent, "From the fruit of the trees of the garden we may eat; but from the fruit of the tree which is in middle of the garden, God has said, 'You shall not eat from it or touch it, lest you die.' " And the serpent said to the woman, "You surely shall not die! For God knows that in the day you eat from it your eyes will be opened, and you will be like God, knowing good and evil" (Gen. 3:1-5).

The result of the yielding to temptation was a break in that special relationship between God and man.

AFTER THE FALL

Since the Garden of Eden episode, God and Satan have been locked into one great cosmic battle with man as the prize. God is attempting to bring mankind back into a right relationship with Him, while Satan is trying to pull man away from God. Moreover, the Bible says that unbelieving man is blinded spiritually by Satan in an effort to keep him from coming to Christ.

And even if our gospel is veiled, it is veiled to those who are perishing, in whose case the god of this world has blinded the minds of the unbelieving, that they might not see the light of the Gospel of the glory of Christ, who is the image of God (2 Cor. 4:3, 4).

Satan is called the "god of this world," hiding the gospel of Christ from the minds

Biblical Titles of Satan

Satan has been given other titles in the Bible that describe his character and his methods.

1. *Devil* (John 8:44) is a Greek word meaning "the accuser and slanderer." By calling him this, one is saying that he makes a false accusation against another, one whose aim it is to harm God and man; one who will tell lies of any kind to achieve his end.

2. *Satan* (Matt. 12:26) is a Hebrew word meaning "the resistor or adversary." By calling him this, one is saying that he reigns over a kingdom of darkness organized in opposition to God.

3. *Tempter* (Matt. 4:3) describes the enemy's manner of acting. Not content with denouncing before God the faults of men, he seeks to lead them into sin, because he himself is a sinner.

4. *Father of Lies* (John 8:44) describes one of his many tactics. Because he makes great use of lies, he is rightfully given this title.

of the unbelieving people. He will do anything to keep people from knowing God.

SATAN'S STRATEGY

One of Satan's plans is to convince the world that he does not exist. Denis deRougemont makes the following insightful observation:

Satan dissembles himself behind his own image. He chooses to don a grotesque appear-

5. *Lord of Death* (Heb. 2:14). The enemy has the power of death because he can accuse sinful man.

6. *Beelzebub* (Mark 3:22, 23) ascribes to the enemy a name meaning "Lord of the dunghill" or "Lord of the flies."

7. *Belial* (2 Cor. 6:15) is a name which originally could be applied to any wicked person. The word itself means "worthlessness," here used as the embodiment of all "worthlessness," the enemy.

8. *Evil One* (1 John 2:13). The total effect of all the biblical references is to present the picture of the enemy as one who is the supreme evildoer.

9. *Ruler of This World* (John 14:30). Since the world, according to the Bible, is mankind in opposition to God, the enemy as the inspirer and leader of that opposition is given this title.

10. *Prince of the Power of the Air* (Eph. 2:1, 2). The enemy's power, in our age, is operative not only on the earth, but in space (David W. Hoover, *How to Respond to the Occult*, St. Louis, MO: Concordia Pub. House, 1977, pp. 13, 14).

ance which has the sure effect of making him inoffensive in the eyes of educated people. For if the devil is simply the red demon armed with a large trident, or the faun with goatee and the long tail of popular legend, who would still go to the trouble of believing in him, or even of declaring that he does not believe in him? . . . What appears to be incredible is not the devil, not the angels, but rather the candor and the credulity of the skeptics, and the unpardonable sophism of which they show them-

Names of Satan
in Other Languages

Arabic:	Sheitan
Egyptian:	Set
Japanese:	O Yama
Persian:	Dev
Russian:	Tchort
Syriac:	Beherit
Welsh:	Pwcca

(Wade Baskin, *Dictionary of Satan*, NY: Philosophical Library, 1972, p. 233).

selves to be the victims: "The devil *is* a gent with red horns and a long tail: *therefore* I don't believe in the devil." And so the devil has them precisely where he wants them (Denis de-Rougemont, *The Devil's Share*, pp. 19-21, cited by D. G. Kehl in *Demon Possession*, ed., John Warwick Montgomery, Minneapolis, MN: Bethany Fellowship, 1976, p. 112).

In *The Screwtape Letters*, a fiction work by noted Christian thinker, C. S. Lewis, the demon is recorded instructing his apprentice as follows:

Our policy, for the moment, is to conceal ourselves. Of course, this has not always been so. We are really faced with a cruel dilemma. When the humans disbelieve in our existence, we lose all the pleasing results of direct terrorism, and we make no magicians. On the other hand, when they believe in us, we cannot make them materialists and skeptics. . . . The fact that "devils" are predominantly *comic* figures in the modern imagination will help you. If any faint suspicion of your existence begins to arise in his mind, suggest to him a picture of something in red tights, and persuade him that since he cannot believe in that . . . he therefore cannot believe in you (C. S. Lewis, *The Screwtape Letters,* New York: Macmillan, 1961, pp. 39, 40).

Satan will use whatever method he can to keep people from coming to God. If a person has done many things wrong in his life and feels guilty about them, Satan will attempt to convince that person he is not good enough for God, that God would never accept him. Many people never come to God because they do not feel God could ever forgive them.

The Bible teaches that anyone may come to Christ regardless of what he has done and receive forgiveness. The Bible says, "Come unto me, all who are weary and heavy-laden, and I will give you rest." The Bible teaches that forgiveness is available to all those who will come to Christ no matter what they have done.

There is another type of person who is also deceived by Satan but who has the opposite problem. That person, rather than feeling he is too bad to come to God, feels that he is too good to need God. Since he has never done anything in his life which he considers horrible, he does not feel that he needs a Savior. This person is willing to go before God based upon his own merit, on the good works he has done in his life, feeling that God will certainly accept him. However, the Bible says, ". . . All have sinned and fall short of the glory of God" and ". . . The wages of sin is death, but the free gift of God is eternal life in Christ Jesus our Lord" (Rom. 3:23; 6:23).

SATAN'S DESTINY

Satan is living on borrowed time. God has promised in His Word that Satan and his angels will receive everlasting punishment for the crimes they have committed against God and man.

> Then He will also say to those on His left, "Depart from Me, accursed ones, into the eternal fire which has been prepared for the devil and his angels" (Matt. 25:41).
> And the devil who deceived them was thrown into the lake of fire and brimstone, where the beast and false prophet are also: and they will be tormented day and night forever and ever (Rev. 20:10).

At that time Satan will be banished once and for all from God's presence without ever again being able to inflict misery on anyone. His eternal separation from God and punishment will be a just end to his inglorious career as the prince of darkness.

C. Fred Dickason in *Angels: Elect and Evil* comments on Satan's destiny.

The Lord Jesus, the Creator and Sovereign, will judge all creatures, including evil angels (John 5:22). He defeated Satan and his demons during His career by invading Satan's territory and casting out demons from those possessed (Matt. 12:28-29). He anticipated the final defeat of Satan when His disciples returned with reports of demons being subject to them through Christ's power (Matt. 10:1, 17-20).

Through His death and resurrection, Christ sealed the final judgment of Satan and demons. The cross reveals God's hatred and judgment of all sin. The just One had to die if the unjust ones were to be forgiven (1 Pet. 3:18) (C. Fred Dickason, *Angels: Elect and Evil*, Chicago, IL: Moody Press, 1975, pp. 210, 212).

WHAT SHOULD BE OUR ATTITUDE TOWARD SATAN?

The Bible exhorts us to take the proper attitude toward Satan in order to deal effectively with his onslaughts. We urge you to observe the following biblical injunctions:

1. Be aware that he exists. The Bible teaches that Satan exists but that he also attempts to hide that fact from the world. We have already indicated that one of Satan's schemes is to have people believe that he is a symbolic figure of evil. He would love people to see him as an "angel of light" or even as a funny little man with a red suit and pitchfork rather than as the dangerous, evil, but ultimately doomed adversary of the Lord God and all mankind.

2. Be aware of his motives. From the time of his rebellion until his ultimate destruction Satan has wanted to be like the Most High. He wants adoration. He wants allegiance. He wants the service of people who rightly should be serving God. He wants people to believe that it is he who is good and it is God who is bad. However, the worship he desires is not informed worship of a god one knows and has seriously considered.

3. Be aware of his methods. From the time he deceived Eve in the Garden of Eden until the present day, Satan has been a liar. The Bible says:

> He was a murderer from the beginning, and does not stand in the truth, because there is no truth in him. Whenever he speaks a lie, he speaks from his own nature; for he is a liar, and the father of lies (John 8:44).

One of his favorite schemes is to try to make a person feel content without Jesus Christ. If someone does not feel a need for God, he will not turn to God. Therefore, Satan attempts to keep people satisfied just enough that they will not turn to Christ.

Another deception used by Satan is counterfeiting. Whatever God has done throughout history, Satan has attempted to counterfeit it. The main counterfeit is religion. Satan loves for people to be religious, to go to church, to think things stand right between themselves and God when just the opposite is true.

If a person believes in some religion without receiving Christ as his Lord and Savior, that person is lost even though he thinks things between him and God are fine. The religious man, trusting in his own works, can be an example of deception by Satan, for God has informed us that to be in a right relationship with Him we must go the way of the cross, the death of Christ for our sins.

Fallen man, often with the approval and help of Satan, has developed a wide variety of religious beliefs in the world as ways to achieve God's favor without submitting to God. Satan is always pleased when people trust in their religiosity rather than Jesus Christ.

4. *Be aware of his limitations.* Satan, the great deceiver, sometimes tries to fool people into thinking he is greater than he actually is. One of the misconceptions that people have about Satan is that he is like God. Nothing could be further from the truth!

God is infinite while Satan is finite or limited. God can be present everywhere at once; Satan cannot. God is all-knowing, able to read our very thoughts; Satan cannot. God is all-powerful; Satan is not. God has the ability to do anything; Satan cannot. However, Satan would like people to believe he has these abilities. Unfortunately, there are too many believers who see Satan behind everything, giving him credit where no credit is due. Basil Jackson makes an appropriate comment:

> Today, I believe we are seeing a most unhealthy interest in the area of demonology so that many of our evangelical friends have, in effect, become "demonophiliacs" as a result of their fascination with the occult. They tend to see a demon under every tree and, thus, quite commonly today, we hear of demons of tobacco, alcohol, asthma, and every other condition imaginable. In this connection, it is noteworthy that, by far, the majority of cases of demon possession which are diagnosed in the deliverance ministry today are mental in phenomenology. This is in marked contrast with the only safe records we have of accurately diagnosed cases of demon possession—namely, the Gospels, in which at least half the people possessed had physical problems rather than any psychiatric difficulties (Basil Jackson in *Demon Possession*, edited by John Warwick Montgomery, Minneapolis, MN: Bethany Fellowship, 1976, p. 201).

We need to realize that Satan is not all-powerful; he has been defeated by Christ's death on the cross. The power of sin over us is broken. Therefore, we need to respect his power but not fear it to the point of thinking he can indwell believers and make them do things they do not wish to do. The power of God is greater, but the great deceiver would have you doubting that. Therefore, be aware of the limitations of Satan and the unlimited power of God.

SATANISM

The worship of Satan has deep historical roots. Known as Satanism, it is found expressed in various ways. Black magic, the Black Mass, facets of the drug culture, and blood sacrifice all have connections with Satanism.

In *Escape from Witchcraft*, Roberta Blankenship explains what two girls, both Satanists, wrote to her as part of their initiation ritual:

> They had had to go to a graveyard in the dead of night, walk across a man-sized cross, and denounce any belief in Christ. Afterwards, a ritual was performed and the girls had to drink the blood of animals that had been skinned alive (Roberta Blankenship, *Escape from Witchcraft*, Grand Rapids, MI: Zondervan Publishing House, 1972, p. 1).

Lynn Walker comments:

> In April, 1973, the battered, mutilated body of a 17-year-old boy, Ross "Mike" Cochran, was found outside of Daytona Beach, Florida. An Associated Press story said, "The verdict of police is that Cochran was the victim of devil worshippers: killed in a frenzied sacrificial ritual."

Lynn McMillon, Oklahoma Christian College professor, reports, ". . . one variety of Satanism consists primarily of sex clubs that embellish their orgies with Satanist rituals. Another variety of Satanists are the drug-oriented groups" (Lynn Walker, *Supernatural Power and the Occult,* Austin, TX: Firm Foundation Publishing House, n.d., p. 1).

TRADITIONAL SATANISM

Until contemporary times Satanism has had much more secretive associations than at present. In the past, the anti-religious and anti-god aspect was prevalent in all aspects of Satanism. Although this is not true of modern Satanism today, traditional Satanism still is associated with black magic and ritualism.

The worship of a personal and powerful devil is central to traditional Satanism. Those involved reject Christianity, yet choose the Lucifer of the Bible as their god. *The Occult Sourcebook* comments:

Traditionally, Satanism has been interpreted as the worship of evil, a religion founded upon the very principles which Christianity rejects. As such, Satanism exists only where Christianity exists, and can be understood only in the context of the Christian worldview. Things are, so to speak, reversed—the Christian devil becomes the Satanist's god, Christian virtues become vices, and vices are turned into virtues. Life is interpreted as a constant battle between the powers of light and darkness, and the Satanist fights on the side of darkness, believing that ultimately this will achieve victory (Neville Drury and Gregory Tillett, *The Occult Sourcebook,* London: Routledge & Kegan Paul, Ltd., 1978, p. 149).

Satanic witchcraft is to be found under this category of Satanism, where witches are involved in the darkest side of evil.

The recent onslaught of drugs and sexual perversion associated with the devil can be found here.

MODERN SATANISM

Traditional Satanism is still very prevalent and growing in society today. However, in recent times, with the growing secularization of society and decline of Judeo-Christian morality, a new humanistic Satanism has emerged and drawn a strong following. The Church of Satan is the clearest example of this new emphasis.

In modern times groups have emerged in England and Europe, and particularly in the United States, which, taking advantage of the permissiveness of modern society, have encouraged some publicity. The most famous of these has been the Church of Satan, founded in San Francisco in 1966 by Anton La Vey, which currently has a membership of many thousands, and has established itself as a church throughout the United States.

Several other groups in America have imitated it, and some groups have also been established as "black witchcraft" covens. The Manson gang, in which a bizarre mixture of

Satanism and occultism was practiced, gained a great deal of unfavorable publicity for Satanism in America, but in fact this resulted in a greater public interest in the subject. With more people rejecting the traditional values of morality, the Satanist movement will inevitably have greater appeal (Drury, op. cit., p. 154).

In a chapter on Satanism today, William Petersen in *Those Curious New Cults* comments on the fact that since the mid-1960s Satanism is making a comeback. He points to the catalyst for the strong upswing as being the box office smash of "Rosemary's Baby." Of the film he states:

Anton Szandor La Vey, self-styled high priest of San Francisco's First Church of Satan and author of *The Satanic Bible,* played the role of the devil. Later, he called the film the "best paid commercial for Satanism since the Inquisition." No doubt it was (William J. Petersen, *Those Curious New Cults,* New Canaan, CT: Keats Publishing, Inc., 1973, p. 75).

Many people are becoming involved in Satanism from all walks of life. They vary in age, occupation, and educational background.

CHURCH OF SATAN

Although the Church of Satan sounds like a contradiction in terms, it was founded in San Francisco in 1966 by Anton Szandor La Vey. The emphasis of the Satanic church is on materialism and hedonism. Satan, to followers of this church, is more of a symbol than a reality. In this emphasis they depart from other forms of Satanism. They are interested in the carnal and worldly pleasures mankind offers.

La Vey is of Russian, Alsatian, and Romanian descent, whose past jobs have been with the circus, an organ player in nightclubs, and a police photographer. All during this time La Vey was studying the occult.

Of the church, La Vey declares it is:

> A temple of glorious indulgence that would be fun for people. . . . But the main purpose was to gather a group of like-minded individuals together for the use of their combined energies in calling up the dark force in nature that is called Satan (Drury, *Occult Sourcebook*, op. cit., p. 77).

Of Satanism, La Vey believes:

> It is a blatantly selfish, brutal religion. It is based on the belief that man is inherently a selfish, violent creature, that life is a Darwinian struggle for survival of the fittest, that the earth will be ruled by those who fight to win (Ibid, p. 78).

La Vey is currently the High Priest of the church, which espouses any type of sexual activity that satisfies your needs, be it heterosexuality, homosexuality, adultery, or faithfulness in marriage.

There is a list of nine statements to which all members must agree:

Satan represents:
1. Indulgence
2. Vital existence
3. Undefiled wisdom
4. Kindness only to those who deserve it
5. Vengeance
6. Responsibility only to those who are responsible
7. Animal nature of man
8. All the so-called sins
9. The best friend the church has ever had, as he has kept it in business all these years.

The Satanic Church is strongly materialistic as well as being anti-Christian. Pleasure-seeking could well describe their philosophy of life. What the world has to offer through the devil is taken full advantage of in the Church of Satan.

Witchcraft

Witchcraft is known as the "Old Religion" and is an ancient practice dating back to biblical times. Witchcraft can be defined as the performance of magic forbidden by God for nonbiblical ends. The word witchcraft is related to the old English word *wiccian*, "practice of magical arts."

It was during the Middle Ages that witchcraft experienced a great revival. It was an age where everyone believed in the supernatural and superstition abounded.

If someone wanted to become a witch, there was an initiation process. Some of the techniques were simple and some were complicated, but there were usually two requirements. The first requirement was that the would-be witch must join of his or her own free will. The second requirement was that the prospective witch must be willing to worship the devil.

Witches are usually organized into covens. "The word 'coven' dates from about 1500 and is a variation of the word convent. It means simply an assembly of people, but it came to be applied especially to the organization of the witches' society" (Geoffrey Parrinder, *Witchcraft: European and African,* London: Faber and Faber, 1963, p. 39).

WITCH HUNTING

One of the darkest periods in European and American history was the time of the "Great Witch Hunt." Although there had been scat-

---

Halloween

The day witches celebrate above all others is October 31, which is All Hallows Eve or Halloween. It is believed that on this night Satan and his witches have their greatest power.

The origin of Halloween goes back 2,000 years before the days of Christianity to a practice of the ancient Druids in Britain, France, Germany, and the Celtic countries. The celebration honored their god Samhain, lord of the dead.

The time of falling leaves seemed an appropriate time to celebrate death, which is exactly what Halloween was to them: A celebration of death honoring the god of the dead. The Druids believed that on this particular evening the spirits of the dead returned to their former home to visit the living.

If the living did not provide food for these evil spirits, all types of terrible things would

---

tered instances of persecution of witches as early as the 12th century, it did not truly get started until the end of the 15th century when two significant events occurred.

The first was a papal letter (known as a Bull) issued on December 5, 1484, by Pope Innocent VIII, which instituted the beginning of official action against suspected witches. This Bull received wide circulation and in it power was granted to men who were responsible for punishing witches. These men were known as inquisitors.

happen to the living. If the evil spirits did not get a treat, then they would trick the living.

Before the introduction of Christianity to these lands, the celebration of death was not called Halloween. Halloween is a form of the designation "All Hallows Eve," a holy evening instituted by the Church to honor all the saints of Church history.

Some Church historians allow the possibility that All Saints' Eve was designated October 30 to counteract the pagan influences of the celebration of death. While All Hallows Eve began as a strictly Christian holiday, the pagan influences from earlier traditions gradually crept in while the Church's influences waned.

Today Halloween is largely a secular holiday, an excuse to get dressed up as somebody else and have a party. However, true witches and followers of witchcraft still preserve the early pagan beliefs and consider Halloween a sacred and deadly powerful time.

How did one describe a witch? William West, an English writer during the reign of Elizabeth I, gave the following description:

A witch or hag is she who—deluded by a pact made with the devil through his persuasion, inspiration and juggling—thinks she can bring about all manner of evil things, either by thought or imprecation, such as to shake the air with lightnings and thunder, to cause hail and tempests, to remove green corn or trees to another place, to be carried on her familiar spirit (which has taken upon him the deceitful shape of a goat, swine, or calf, etc.) into some mountain far distant, in a wonderfully short space of time, and sometimes to fly upon a staff or fork, or some other instrument, and to spend all the night after with her sweetheart, in playing, sporting, banqueting, dancing, dalliance, and divers other devilish lusts and lewd disports, and to show a thousand such monstrous mockeries (William West, *Simboleography*, 1594).

The second event that helped cause the great witch hunt was the publication of a book called *Malleus Maleficarum* (Hammer of Witches) in 1486 by Jakob Sprenger and Prior Heinrich Kramer. This publication was a handbook for witch hunters.

The Papal Bull, along with the publication of *Malleus Maleficarum*, led to a 300-year nightmare. People saw witches everywhere. Those accused of being witches had little or no defense against their accusers. During this period more than 100,000 people in every European state were executed for supposedly being witches.

Witches were supposed to have a variety of different powers which kept the people in fear of them. However, the most feared power thought to be held by the witches was that of bewitchment, the ability to cause sickness and death.

Roger Hart makes an apt comment:

> It can easily be imagined how—in the days when medicine was primitive—various ailments could be mistaken for bewitchment; paralysis, lockjaw, fevers, anemia, sclerosis, epilepsy, hysteria. Such illnesses often displayed symptoms which were extremely frightening to educated and uneducated people alike (Hart, *Witchcraft*, op. cit., p. 54).

To this list we could add Huntington's Chorea and Tourette's Syndrome. Huntington's Chorea is a disease which does not show up in most of its victims until they are past 30 years of age. This disease causes the victim to behave in a peculiar manner, including involuntary body movements, fits of anger, and a loss of intelligence.

The victim may make strange outbursts of laughter, cry like a baby, or talk endlessly. It can easily be seen how a sufferer could be mistaken for being bewitched or being a witch. Huntington's Chorea is also an inherited disease which would convince the superstitious that the bewitchment has been passed to the children.

Tourette's Syndrome is a rare disease which usually begins in childhood. The victim experiences tics—involuntary muscle movements—throughout the body but especially in the face. The sufferer also may kick and stamp his feet. Along with making awful faces, the victim makes involuntary noises which include shouts, grunts and swearing. All of these symptoms are beyond the control of the sufferer but appear to the uneducated as a sign of being a witch.

America did not escape the great witch hunt. Roger Hart comments:

> Perhaps no single witch hunt has attracted so much popular attention as that which took place at Salem in New England in the year 1692. This American witch hunt was remarkable not merely on account of the large number of people found guilty (Salem was a small community), but also because of the late date at which it took place (Ibid, p. 109).

Although Salem was a relatively small town of about 100 households, the percentage of those tried for being witches was enormous. Says historian R. H. Robbins:

> All in all, the toll of Salem, a township of a hundred-odd households, was enormous. During the hysteria, almost 150 people were arrested. A search of all the court records would no doubt add to this number. Because of the

76

time taken to convict each prisoner, only thirty-one were tried in 1692, not including Sarah Churchill and Mary Warren, two accusers who briefly recanted. The court of Oyer and Terminer (hear and determine) sentenced to death all thirty-one, of whom six were men. Nineteen were hanged. Of the remaining twelve, two (Sarah Osborne and Anne Foster) died in jail; one (Giles Cory) was pressed to death; one (Tituba) was held indefinitely in jail without trial. Two (Abigail Faulkner and Elizabeth Proctor) postponed execution by pleading pregnancy and lived long enough to be reprieved. One (Mary Bradbury) escaped from jail after sentencing; and five made confessions which secured reprieves for them (Robbins, op. cit., p. 185).

Fourteen years later one of the accusers, Anne Putnam, retracted her charges, stating she and others carried the guilt of innocent blood.

The great witch hunt of the Middle Ages is remarkable for a number of reasons. First, it lasted some 300 years and took hundreds of thousands of lives. It also took place during a time of renewed interest in learning.

The people who participated in this craze were not all irrational individuals but were rather some of the most brilliantly educated people of that day. Scientists, philosophers and lawyers were among those who participated in the great witch hunt, showing that superstition knows no educational bounds.

It is also unfortunate that much of the persecution came from professing Christians doing it in the name of God. The passages which were used to justify the witch hunt were misread and taken totally out of context. The legal penalties of such Old Testament crimes were part of the then-operating theocracy in Israel.

The Lord God was the King in Israel; He had the right to determine the crimes and punishments against His holy and sovereign state. One who participated in witchcraft was aligning himself with Satan, the foe of God. Such an alignment was treason against the government of Israel, a government directed personally by the Lord God.

Even today treason is often punished by death. However, since no nation today is a theocracy, a nation governed directly by God, the penalties instituted then are not applicable. Witchcraft is still evil and is still rebellion against God. It is not treason. Jesus Christ warned that physical death was not the ultimate punishment anyway.

Those who practice witchcraft, displaying their rejection of Jesus Christ, should heed His warning: "And do not fear those who kill the body, but are unable to kill the soul; but rather fear Him who is able to destroy soul and body in hell" (Matt. 10:28).

WITCHCRAFT TODAY

Although witch hunting and witch trials no longer occur, the practice of witchcraft continues. The modern witch does not fit the stereotype of the old hag, for many people

who are practicing this art are ▓▓▓
mainstream of society. The question ▓
Why a renewed interest in this ancien▓
among both the educated and the ignoran▓
Daniel Cohen lists a couple of possible
reasons:

> First, there is the eternal appeal of magic, the
> promise, however muted, that there are se-
> crets available that will give a person power,
> money, love, and all those things he or she
> desires but cannot seem to obtain. Second,
> witchcraft is a put-down and a revolt against
> some of the establishment beliefs in organized
> religion, science, and rational thinking. The
> historic connection between witchcraft and
> drugs and sex also has undoubted appeal.
> Here is a set of beliefs that claim to be part
> of an extremely ancient religion. Yet this is a
> religion in which drugs and free sexuality are
> not condemned, but might be encouraged.
>
> Despite all the publicity and all the witch
> covens that have been organized, witchcraft
> still is not taken seriously (Daniel Cohen, *A
> Natural History of Unnatural Things*, New
> York: McCall Pub. Co., 1971, pp. 31, 32).

Modern witchcraft bears little resemblance to the witchcraft of the Middle
Ages or to witchcraft in still primitive, prelit-
erate societies. Modern witchcraft is a relatively recent development (the last 200
years), embraces hundreds of beliefs and
practices and has hundreds of thousands of
adherents. The one common theme running
through modern witchcraft is the practice

... n things forbidden by God in ... occultic.

... a couple of decades ago, and for pre-... centuries, there were no admitted ...ches anywhere. Most people have thought of witchcraft as something that only the superstitious gave any credence to. Witch hunts and broomsticks were filed away together in a little-used corner of the mind.

Today, in a massive spin-off from the culture-wide interest in the occult, this has all changed. Tens of thousands across America— some of them with university degrees—are dabbling in witchcraft, Satanism, voodoo, and other forms of black and white magic. Witches appear openly on television. Every high school is said to have its own witch. In Cleveland you can rent a witch to liven up a party. There are some 80,000 persons practicing white magic in the United States, with 6,000 in Chicago alone.

Some of this is a fad. But unfortunately, much of it isn't. Murder after murder has been linked to the craze, with the murderers openly admitting to police or to reporters that they worshipped Satan. Police more and more frequently are finding grim evidence of both animal and human sacrifice (George Vandeman, *Psychic Roulette*, Nashville, TN: Thomas Nelson, Inc., 1973, pp. 99, 100).

THE BIBLE AND WITCHCRAFT
Both the Old and New Testaments make repeated references to the practice of witchcraft and sorcery, and whenever these

practices are referred to they are always condemned by God. The Bible condemns all forms of witchcraft, including sorcery, astrology, and reading human and animal entrails. The following passages describe the various forms of witchcraft which are condemned by God.

1. You shall not allow a sorceress to live (Ex. 22:18).
2. You shall not eat anything with the blood, nor practice divination or soothsaying (Lev. 19:26).
3. Do not turn to mediums or spiritists; do not seek them out to be defiled by them. I am the Lord your God (Lev. 19:31).
4. There shall not be found among you anyone who makes his son or his daughter pass through the fire, one who uses divination, one who practices witchcraft, or one who interprets omens, or a sorcerer, or one who casts a spell, or a medium, or a spiritist, or one who calls up the dead. . . . For those nations, which you shall dispossess, listen to those who practice witchcraft and to diviners, but as for you, the Lord your God has not allowed you to do so (Deut. 18:10, 11, 14).
5. Then they made their sons and their daughters pass through the fire, and practiced divination and enchantments, and sold themselves to do evil in the sight of the Lord, provoking Him (2 Kings 17:17).
6. Stand fast now in your spells and in your many sorceries with which you have labored from your youth; perhaps you will

be able to profit, perhaps you may cause trembling. You are wearied with your many counsels; let now the astrologers, those who prophesy by the stars, those who predict by the new moons, stand up and save you from what will come upon you (Isa. 47:12, 13).

7. But as for you, do not listen to your prophets, your diviners, your dreamers, your soothsayers, or your sorcerers, who speak to you, saying, "You shall not serve the king of Babylon." For they prophesy a lie to you, in order to remove you far from your land; and I will drive you out, and you will perish (Jer. 27:9, 10).

8. And when they had gone through the whole island as far as Paphos, they found a certain magician, a Jewish false prophet whose name was Bar-Jesus, who was with the proconsul, Sergius Paulus, a man of intelligence. This man summoned Barnabas and Saul and sought to hear the word of God. But Elymas the magician (for thus his name is translated) was opposing them, seeking to turn the proconsul away from the faith. But Saul, who was also known as Paul, filled with the Holy Spirit, fixed his gaze upon him, and said, "You who are full of all deceit and fraud, you son of the devil, you enemy of all righteousness, will you not cease to make crooked the straight ways of the Lord?" (Acts 13:6-10).

Conclusion

The existence of an evil, supernatural realm, led by Satan and supported by his legions of demons, is a reality. Satan's devices are many, and his methods are as varied as his devices. Fortunately, there is authority, power, and refuge to be found in the person of Jesus Christ, the Son of God.

If you have not decided to follow Jesus Christ, you can do so now. The Bible says, "[Satan] will completely fool those who are on their way to hell because they have said 'no' to the Truth; they have refused to believe it and love it, and let it save them" (2 Thess. 2:10, TLB). To say 'yes' to Christ—the Truth—pray and ask him to take over your life. God's power, being greater than Satan's, will conquer the evil that has surrounded you and been a part of your behavior. Christ will then take up residence in your life.

If you are already a Christian, be warned: do not become preoccupied with the occult. Preoccupation with Satan's methods is not the best means of approaching our foe, our enemy, the accuser of the brethren.

However, this does not mean we are to do nothing. Rather, we are exhorted in three major areas. First, we are called to *understand*—understand that Satan has already been defeated. Christ's death and resurrection sealed Satan's fate and destruction. That fact becomes reality for those who trust in Christ.

Second, we are called to *know*—know Satan's strategy. Not to know all his methods, but rather his means of operation. This includes his being disguised as an angel of light. Satan's *modus operandi,* aside from a direct assault of lies, also includes the more subtle and often used art of deception. He seeks to lure through the things of the world and the temptations of the flesh. Satan's desire is to replace God's plan with his counterfeit, just as he attempted to do in the Garden of Eden.

Third, besides having a good defense of knowing our position in Christ and recognizing Satan's strategy, we must *be on the offensive* in what we do. This means knowing God and making Him known. When we get closer to our Lord and share the gospel with others, it pierces Satan as with a knife—the Lord uses us to advance His Kingdom and bring Satan's domain to ruin. For our mastery over Satan is not in our power, but in God's power and authority.

Authority over Satan

During Easter week at Balboa, Panama, I first learned of the authority of the believer. About 50,000 high school and college students came down for Easter. With André Kole, the illusionist, in our program we packed out a big ballroom several nights in a row—for two or three meetings a night.

As André was performing, some guy pulled up with his Dodge Dart all souped up. With a deafening sound, he popped the clutch and went roaring down the street. Everyone inside, of course, turned around and looked out to see the commotion. Finally, André got them settled down.

Then the guy went around the block again. As he stopped out front, he revved it up again and roared down the street. By this time everyone was whispering and wondering what was going on. Some stood up, trying to look out the window.

When the guy went back around the block again, I knew that if he repeated his performance one more time, it would break up the meeting. Turning to Gene Huntsman, one of our staff members, I said, "I think Satan is trying to break up this meeting. Let's step out in the doorway and exercise the authority of the Christian." So we stepped out and prayed a very simple prayer.

When the guy came back, he started to rev it up again, and as he popped the clutch— pow! The rear end of his car blew all over the street.

Now, to point out what the authority of the Christian believer is, let's look at Luke 10:19: "Behold, I give unto you power to tread on serpents and scorpions, and over all the power of the enemy: and nothing shall by any means hurt you" (KJV).

Two separate Greek words are used for *power* here, but one English translation. The first one should be translated *authority*, not *power.* The Lord is saying, "Behold, I give you authority over the power of the enemy." The Christian does not have *power* over Satan; he has *authority* over Satan. Let me give you an illustration.

I used to live in Argentina. Buenos Aires, the fourth largest city in the western hemisphere, has six subway lines, one of the longest streets in the world—almost sixty miles long, and one of the widest streets in the world—twenty-five lanes, almost three blocks wide. One street is called Corriente, which means *current.* It is a solid current of traffic—sometimes considered one of the longest parking lots in the world.

One intersection is so busy, about the only way you can make it across is to confess any unknown sin, make sure you are filled with the Spirit, commit your life to God and dash madly! But one day we approached, and an amazing thing took place.

Out in the center of the intersection was a platform on which stood a uniformed policeman. About twenty of us waited at the corner to cross. All of a sudden, he blew his whistle and put up his hand. As he lifted his hand, all those cars came to a screeching halt. With all of his personal power he couldn't have stopped one of those cars, but he had something far better; he was invested with the authority of the police department. And the moving cars and the pedestrians recognized that authority. Authority is delegated power.

THE SOURCE OF AUTHORITY

What is the source of this authority? Paul writes,

> "And what is the surpassing greatness of His Power toward us who believe. These are in accordance with the working of the strength of His might which He brought about in Christ, when He raised Him from the dead, and seated Him at His right hand in the heavenly places, far above all rule and authority and power and dominion, and every name that is named, not only in this age, but also in the one to come. And He put all things in subjection under His feet, and gave Him as head over all things to

the Church, which is His Body, the fullness of Him who fills all in all" (Eph. 1:19-23).

When Jesus Christ was raised from the dead, we see the act of the resurrection and the surrounding events as one of the greatest workings of God manifested in the Scriptures. So powerful was the omnipotency of God that the Holy Spirit, through the Apostle Paul, used four different words for power.

First, the greatness of his power—in the Greek—is *dunamis,* from which comes the English word *dynamite.* Then comes the word *working—energios,* where *energy* comes from—a working manifestation or activity. The third word is *strength—kratous—* meaning to *exercise strength.* Then comes *might,* or *esquai—*a great summation of power.

These four words signify that behind the events described in Ephesians 1:19-23 are the greatest workings of God manifested in the Scriptures—even greater than creation. This great unleashing of God's might involved the resurrection, the ascension, and the seating of Jesus Christ. "When He had disarmed the rulers and authorities, He made a public display of them, having triumphed over them through Him" (Col. 2:15). Satan was defeated and disarmed. All of this unleashing of God's might in the resurrection, the ascension and the seating of Jesus Christ was for you and me—that we might gain victory right now over Satan. The source of our authority over Satan is rooted in God and His power.

HOW TO EXERCISE AUTHORITY

What are the qualifications you must have to be able to be consistent in exercising the authority of the believer?

First, there must be *knowledge,* a knowledge of our position in Christ and of Satan's defeat. At the moment of salvation we are elevated to a heavenly placement. We don't have to climb some ladder of faith to get there. We are immediately identified in the eyes of God—and of Satan—with Christ's crucifixion and burial, and we are co-resurrected, co-ascended and co-seated with Jesus Christ at the right hand of the Father, far above all rule and power, authority, and dominion and above every name that is named.

The problem is that, though both God and Satan are aware of this, most believers are not. And if you don't understand who you are, you will never exercise that authority which is the birthright of every true believer in Jesus. So the first step is knowledge.

The second qualification is *belief.* A lot of people really don't comprehend one of the primary aspects of belief, which is "to live in accordance with." This is not merely mental assent, but it leads to action. You could say it like this: That which the mind accepts, the will obeys. Otherwise you are not really a true believer. Do we actually believe that we've been co-resurrected, co-ascended, co-seated with Jesus Christ? If we do, our actions will be fervent.

The third qualification is *humility.* While

belief introduces us to our place of throne power at the right hand of the Father, only humility will ensure that we can exercise that power continuously. Let me tell you, ever since Mr. and Mrs. Adam occupied the Garden of Eden, man has needed to be reminded of his limitations. Even regenerated man thinks he can live without seriously considering his total dependence upon God.

Yet, humility to me is not going around saying, "I'm nothing, I'm nothing, I'm nothing. I'm just the dirt under the toenail. When I get to heaven all I want is that little old dinky cabin, that's enough for me." That's an insult to Christ. It's not humility—it's pride. Humility is knowing who you are and knowing who made you who you are and giving Him the glory for it. Sometimes, when I hear a person claim he's nothing, I say, "Look sir, I don't know about you, but I'm someone." I *am* someone. On December 19, 1959, at 8:30 at night, Jesus Christ made me a child of God, and I'm sure not going to say I'm nothing. Maybe I'm not all I should be, but I am more than I used to be, and God's not finished with me yet. I know He has made me, and I won't insult what God has made.

The next qualification, the fourth one, is *boldness*. Humility allows the greatest boldness. True boldness is faith in full manifestation. When God has spoken and you hold back, that is not faith, it is sin. We need men and women who have set their minds at the right hand of the Father and who fear no one but God. True boldness comes from realizing your position in Jesus Christ and being filled with the Holy Spirit.

The fifth and final qualification is *awareness,* a realization that being at the right hand of the Father also puts you in the place of the most intense spiritual conflict. The moment your eyes are open to the fact that you are in that place, that you have been co-resurrected, co-ascended, and co-seated with Christ, Satan will do everything he possibly can to wipe you out, to discourage you. You become a marked individual. The last thing Satan wants is a Spirit-filled believer who knows his throne rights. Satan will start working in your life to cause you not to study or appropriate the following principles that show you how to defeat him.

Going through all of the above was necessary to lay a foundation on which you can exercise the authority of the believer. Here is how I do it. Remember, authority is delegated power. Usually I speak right out loud and address Satan directly, "Satan, in the name of the Lord Jesus Christ . . ." I always use this point first because those three names—Lord, Jesus, and Christ—describe His crucifixion, burial, resurrection and seating, and His victory over Satan. "Satan, in the name of the Lord Jesus Christ and His shed blood on the cross, I command you to stop your activities in this area." Or, "Satan, in the name of the Lord Jesus Christ and His shed blood on the cross, I acknowledge that the victory is Jesus' and all honor and glory in this situation go to Him." I speak to Satan in various ways, but I always use those beginning phrases because they remind him that he is already defeated.

Next, I realize there is nothing I can do. I have no power over Satan, I only have authority. And the more I learn of the power behind me, the force behind me, the greater boldness I have in exercising the authority of the believer.

Once the authority of the believer is exercised, though, we must be patient. Never have I exercised that authority that I did not see Satan defeated, but I have had to learn to wait.

Some time ago, for example, I was to speak in a university in South America. Because of the university's Marxist leanings, I was the first American to speak there in four years, and it was a tense situation. Big photographs of me had been posted all over campus and the Communist students, trying to influence the other students to stay away from the meeting, had painted "CIA Agent" in red letters across the posters. I thought CIA meant "Christ in Action." Anyway, it backfired. Most of the students had never seen a CIA agent, so they came to the meeting to see what one looked like, and the room was packed. However, as is often the case when someone speaks in that part of the world, professional Marxist agitators had also come, and their intent was to disrupt the meeting.

When I go to another country I like to

speak as well as possible in the language of that country. So I pointed out to the audience that I was learning their language and that night I would be lecturing in it. Well, I started, and, oh, it was horrible! My back was against the wall—the chairs were about five inches from me. And one after another, these agitators would jump up and throw accusations at me, call me "a filthy pig," etc., and hurl words at me that I didn't even know. Right in front of the audience they twisted me around their little fingers. I couldn't answer them; I didn't even know what they were saying. I felt so sorry for the Christians who were there because they had looked forward so eagerly to my coming to the campus and to seeing people come to Christ.

After forty-five minutes of this heckling, I just felt like crying. I literally wanted to crawl under the carpet. My wife asked me one time, "Honey, what's the darkest situation you've ever been in?" And I said, "It was that one."

By this time I was ready to give up. Every time I even mentioned the name of Jesus they laughed. I had exercised the authority of the believer, and now I thought, "God, why aren't you doing something? Why? Isn't Satan defeated?" Well, I wasn't walking by faith. You see, God works when it brings the greatest honor and glory to His name, not to ours.

Finally, God started to work. The secretary of the Revolutionary Student Movement stood up, and everyone else became silent. I figured she must be someone important.

She was quite an outspoken woman, and I didn't know what to expect. But this is what she said. "Mr. McDowell, if I become a Christian tonight, will God give me the love for people that you have shown for us?"

Well, I don't have to tell you what happened. It broke just about everyone's heart who was there, and we had fifty-eight people decide that day to follow Christ.

I've learned to exercise the authority of the believer and then to walk by faith and to wait. Sometimes I have had to wait six months or a year, but in the long run, when I look back on a situation and see how God has been glorified, it is beautiful.

And I never repeat the exercise of the authority of the believer in a given situation. Satan only needs one warning. God will take care of it from there. Jesus said, "All authority has been given to me in heaven and earth. Go therefore, and make disciples of all nations."

THE ICE SERIES

Hunt for Evil
Body Shot
Mach One

*To Monique Daoust, Anna Gibson, and AnnMarie Spiby
for helping me with beta reads. Thank you for helping me
catch the little things that mean so much!*

1

I'm free?

Henri's gut whirred like a boomerang, though she showed no outward sign of triumph. That's right. She kept her face expressionless. If only she could jump on the table and start dancing. But freedom came with a backhand so vicious, her thoughts darted in a gazillion directions while volts of wariness shot up her spine.

Yes, she'd expected this day to come. *Eventually*. But she also expected the news to be delivered by a Delta Force commander, an elite member of the United States Army. They owed her that much. Presently, she trusted the suit sitting across the conference room table less than she trusted the lamebrained attorney responsible for landing her in the pen.

A sergeant in the elite Delta Force counter terrorism unit, Henri had learned in the trenches to suspect first, question later. And her internal suspicion radar was firing on red alert. Still, ten years of ingrained military discipline prevented her from telling the windbag he was full of shit. Besides, her throat had closed. Hell, even her hands perspired.

WTF?

She wiped her palms on her orange coveralls.

I'm free, dammit. This guy's not my CO. I could tell him to go to hell.

She closed her eyes and inhaled a calming breath. "Do you need my answer now?" He'd just dropped a bombshell, offering her some international job that would make use of her "special talents". And it paid more money than she'd ever dreamed of earning. The rub? The suit refused to tell her where she'd be going or the details of what she'd be doing until she committed. What if he wanted her to murder someone? The man just sat there, his intense eyes staring at her from across the table. He was pasty, sweaty and overweight. Worse, agreeing to his clandestine request was like blindly slicing her palm with a dagger and dripping blood on a signature line just because her commanding officer told her to do it.

"*Ja*, that would be preferable," he said. The man had introduced himself as Anders Lindgren and spoke with an accent that sounded Scandinavian. The fact he was sitting in a conference room in a highly-restricted military operation denoted some credibility, but that did zilch to lower Henri's wariness meter. His face gave away nothing. Lindgren could pass for a seedy politician—the type who wouldn't think twice about sending her tiptoeing into a minefield filled with IEDs.

"After all," he continued, "until three minutes ago, you were still planning on being a guest here."

Here, being military prison, a lifetime guest of Uncle Sam. Henri swallowed, forcing back bile bubbling up her esophagus. Two years rotting in a goddamned hellhole because of a setup by a terrorist who wanted revenge. A bastard who'd entered the US illegally for the sole purpose of murdering the Iranian

Ambassador and pinning the kill on Henri. "Who figured out I was innocent?" she asked.

The corners of Lindgren's mouth turned up. "We began to suspect you were framed when my expert came across certain...ah...internet chatter."

"Where?"

"That's classified."

Pursing her lips and inhaling through her nose, Henri glanced at the folder he'd handed her. She'd wasted two lousy years of her life and, out of the blue, they admit to her innocence? Wasn't she entitled to a few details? And why had the news been delivered by a foreigner? He wasn't even military.

Lindgren inclined his head to the folder, still lying unopened on the table. "You've been given an honorable discharge. But your country and the world need you now more than ever."

With a groan, she opened the cover and skimmed the top memo. "They're not bothering to offer a return to my squadron?"

"The major felt it was time to move on." Something in Lindgren's tone told her he wasn't giving the full story.

More lies.

Henri squared her shoulders. "What if I disagree?"

The man's features pinched. "He said you'd be difficult."

"Oh, yeah?" Every muscle in her body clenched. Was the suit's collar buttoned too tight? *Difficult?* She was madder than a honey badger fighting a cobra. If it weren't for the cameras in the four corners of the conference room, she'd reach across the table and slap the smirk off the dude's face. "Tell me, Mr. Lindgren, who wouldn't be bitter after spending two years behind bars for a crime she didn't commit?"

He shook his head with a pinch to his brow. "Your situation is a grave travesty, indeed. But now that the truth has been uncovered, we see *great* potential in you."

After giving him an exaggerated roll of her eyes, Henri tuned the man out. She read the damned papers, including the details of her discharge and a letter from the President, first apologizing, then explaining that he wanted her to follow the Scandinavian. *The President?* She examined the signature. How the hell was she supposed to know if it had been forged? She held the paper up. "Is this authentic?"

"It is."

No.

No matter how sober the suit looked, Henri wasn't about to trust him. At the rear of the folder was a paycheck with the notation "two years' back pay". Great. Practically half of it was taken out for taxes. She swiped a hand across her mouth and stared at the figures. With this much money she could go home and restart her life. The other alternative? Go to God knew where with this pompous stuffed-shirt? Because the commander-in-chief of a country that had stripped her of her rank, thrown her to the wolves and locked her in a cell suddenly said, "*Oops, sorry, you can have your Medal of Honor back now*"?

No fucking way.

She shoved the chair out from the table and stood. "Sorry, sir, but the letter says I'm a free woman. I've been discharged with two years' back pay and the only place I want to go is home."

Not waiting for his response, Henrietta Soaring-Eagle Anderson tucked the folder under her arm, marched past Anders Lindgren and out the conference room door.

"Please ensure your tray tables and seatbacks are in their locked and upright position," the flight attendant's buttery voice announced over the jet's intercom.

What felt like hurricane-force wind whipped and jerked the 65 passenger CRJ700 jet around like it was a glider.

"Lord save us!" cried the woman beside Mike Rose as she grabbed his arm with both hands.

Chuckling under his breath, he rubbed his eyes while trying not to roll them. The woman held on with the strength of a sumo wrestler, her face white as bed linens. That's why Mike hadn't politely un-wrapped her fingers from his bicep. The turbulence was nothing to him. He'd touched down in far worse conditions than this windstorm. On occasion, he was known to hop off a transport between bursts of enemy fire. He even had a few battle scars to prove it.

Danger came with the job and it wasn't for the weak at heart like this bird with the iron grip.

Stealing a glimpse out the window, he leaned away from his terrified seat-mate. Bloody oath, he hadn't been this far west in yonks. Years ago, he'd attended a joint US/British training session at Area 51 in Nevada, the sort of barren terrain he was expecting. But this Utah town was different. With few trees in sight, the crags surrounding Saint George looked more Martian than Earthlike. Though stark, the cliffs and rock formations held a beauty all their own as if the town had been erected in the middle of an offshoot of the Grand Canyon.

Mike was a Scot, Highland born and bred. After university he'd joined the SAS, but he'd been an ICE asset for the past eight years—headquartered in Iceland. Neither Scotland nor Iceland was known for balmy weather and the further the plane descended, the starchier his collar grew. *Brilliant.* It was May and the outside temperature was in the high eighties according to the flight attendant's pre-takeoff announcement. Unheard of in Mike's neck of the world.

He checked his watch while the floor rattled with the lowering of the plane's landing gear. The ICE-issue mini-computer read eleven p.m.

The woman beside him tightened her grip as the plane tottered. "Holy heck, why don't we just land already?"

"The local time is one minute after four p.m.," announced the flight attendant.

After switching the display to Mountain Time, he patted the woman's hand and twisted his arm free. "Not accustomed to flying are you, ma'am?"

She shook her head. "I don't like turbulence."

The wheels touched down with barely a jolt. Nice work on the pilot's part, especially given the gusty wind.

Mike glanced out the window at the small, regional terminal. "Och, it looks as if you've survived this wee flight."

The woman cringed. She looked to be middle-aged with a friendly face. "I'm sorry for grabbing you."

"Not to worry. You can count on me to lend an arm any time."

"It's quite a sturdy arm at that." Leaning in, she gave him a quizzical stare. "Are you English?"

Bloody hell, he sounded about as English as an Afrikaner. "Scottish."

"Really? My ancestors were Scottish."

"Aye?" Now why didn't that surprise him? Practically everyone in America could claim Scottish heritage—but that's what bolstered the Highland's tourism industry so he tried to seem interested.

"What brings you out to Saint George?" she asked.

"Meeting a friend." Not exactly the truth, but close enough. At least he was meeting someone, then high-tailing it back to headquarters for his next assignment.

"Golfing?" she continued to probe. Now they were safely taxiing, the woman developed a yen for a chat. "Or is it mountain biking? You know Saint George is the mountain biking capital of the world."

"That so? I'll have to give it a go." Honestly, Mike would rather be mountain biking than on this bloody assignment. It was a waste of his time and a waste his skills. Why they'd picked him for this detail was a quandary. Sure, the Head of Field Operations, Garth Moore, had said no woman could resist Mike. But he knew Garth was just feeding him a line to stroke his ego and get him to board the plane.

Mike didn't consider himself a lady-killer. In fact, it was the other way around. The lassies always found a way to pull the trigger on him. And after the last messed up affair, he'd had enough of the fairer sex to last a lifetime. And it had been too convenient for ICE that he'd been between assignments. Mike would rather be hunting terrorists any day.

But as the boss, Garth usually got what he wanted, smooth talking or nay. And then, of course, the schemer had tipped the scales by placing a wager. He'd bet a hundred quid that Mike would fail this mission. Och aye, that riled him.

Failure was not in Mike's vocabulary. And with a hundred quid on the line, he couldn't fail. *No bloody chance.*

The rental company didn't have much of a selection of hire cars and after settling for the only four-wheel drive on the lot, Mike pulled up the address he'd keyed into his GPS app. Aye, he was jetlagged, but there was no use wasting daylight. And the sooner he accomplished his mission, the sooner he'd be back to ridding the world of evil with an extra hundred pounds in his pocket.

It took about a half-hour to drive across town and out to the country—as the crow flies, about forty miles east of Area 51. When he turned onto the sparse residential area of the Shivwits Paiute Reservation, weatherboard houses didn't surprise him. The place looked much the same as the satellite images he'd examined. The yards were filled with red dirt and sagebrush. Some homes were caravans and others looked to be no larger than two-bedroom units, but there weren't many. He turned left at the second block—a nondescript road posted as 3765 North. It only had one house the same matchbox size as the others. He rolled to a stop and checked out the place. There was an old Chevy truck parked out the front. Beneath the caked-on dirt, it appeared to be white.

Mike checked the rearview mirror and raked his fingers through his mop of red hair. His effort didn't result in much success. It sat there like it always did—thick and unruly. At least he'd had it cut before he'd left Iceland and he no longer looked like a pirate. He slipped off his black wrap-around sunglasses but after a gander at a pair of overtired and bloodshot eyes staring back at him in the mirror, he decided to leave them on.

Before hopping out of the car, he noted an advertisement for a local restaurant on the jacket of his hire car agreement and committed the name to memory—the Black Bear Diner. The silver Jeep Laredo already sported a sheen of red dust. Mike didn't care. He'd experienced far worse conditions in Syria just a few weeks ago. Tugging down the sleeves of his starchy sports jacket, he strode to the door and gave it a solid knock. A television shut off. Footsteps lazily pattered across the floor before the door cracked open, held by a security chain. The face peering up at him, however, looked nothing like his target. Round and careworn, the woman blinking with big brown eyes was far older and heavier.

"Good afternoon, madam." Mike bowed his head respectfully. "I'm looking for Miss Henrietta Anderson."

The woman's eyes widened just enough to express surprise *and* recognition. "She's not here." Aye, this was the auntie for certain. Mike had memorized the details Henri's file which included a much younger picture of this woman, Anderson's only claimed next of kin. The file included a picture of the lassie's father as well, but that slimy piece of shite hadn't made contact with his daughter since she was a wee child.

As the door started to close, Mike slid his foot into the gap. "I beg your pardon, madam, but I just flew over eight thousand miles to meet with Miss Anderson and I'm afraid I'm going to need a bit more information."

"I-I don't know anyone by that name." The fear filling the woman's eyes betrayed her.

Liar.

"Och, I'm afraid acting isn't your strong suit, madam." He pulled out his phone and, with a few flicks of his finger, tapped on a picture of the auntie with Anderson, taken twelve years past. "This is you, Chenoa, standing beside your niece. You are her only claimed next of kin. Miss Anderson was honorably discharged by the army three months ago and headed here. And dunna tell me I canna see her. I've come all the way from Scotland for this meeting, and I'm no' about to tuck my tail and head for home without having a wee conversation." Mike gestured to the chain. "And if you think that bit of metal will protect you from the likes of me, you are sorely mistaken."

The woman tipped up her chin as if daring him to try something. "Are you threatening me?"

"Nay. I'm speaking my mind is all. Now please, call the lass. I'll have my say and be on my way."

"She's not here."

Exercising restraint, he cracked his knuckles rather than breaking the damned chain. "Where is she?" he asked, his voice as calm as the pleasant expression he cemented on his face.

"Someplace no white man will ever find her."

Mike heaved a sigh and pocketed his phone. "I might be white, but I'm no' the enemy."

"Then why are you here?"

"I aim to offer her a job."

"What kind of job?"

"One that will make good use of her talents."

"She had a job like that and ended up in prison on false charges for two years."

"Aye, but I can guarantee her immunity—*ongoing* immunity."

The woman frowned, her eyes narrowing with distrust.

Mike pulled a business card out of his top pocket. Four copies had been made for this mission. Since ICE was a clandestine organization, it only contained his name, a phone number and the words Intelligence Consulting Services. They meant nothing but might help Henri understand the nature of the job he'd come to offer.

No, he didn't want to use the cards at all—because he wouldn't be there if Garth hadn't made that bloody wager. No one in their right mind would want to be chasing the woman. Not after the rebuff she'd given Lindgren at Miramar. However, now that Henrietta had a few months to cool off, she might reconsider. At least that was the plan.

"Tell her I'll be at The Black Bear Diner at o-eight-hundred tomorrow morning. I'll buy her breakfast. If she doesna like what I have to say, she can walk away with a full belly."

Chenoa took the card, read the front and turned it over to find the back blank.

"Will you tell her?" Mike asked.

"I can't make any promises."

"It's just breakfast, madam."

The woman pursed her lips, making her face look like a prune. "You know the army ruined her life. She won't want to speak to anyone."

"I dunna represent the Americans or the military."

The woman looked at the print on the card again.

"This says you're a consultant. Who do you represent?"

"The good guys."

She snorted, giving him the evil eye as if she wasn't impressed. "I'll do what I can."

Mike bowed. "Thank you." The door closed as he walked away. Before he hopped into his Jeep, he pulled another device from his pocket and attached it to the wheel-well of the Chevy where it would be out of sight. Dammit, he no intention of leaving the success of this mission in the hands of Auntie Chenoa.

3

Henri slammed her pickaxe into the bedrock of the mine wall with every ounce of strength she could muster and added a healthy dose of anger to boot. Why couldn't the bastards leave her alone? Now the suits had traveled all the way to Utah? Aunt Chenoa had said this guy wasn't wearing a tie, but he wore a sports jacket and looked sharp. This one was from Scotland. And evidently they'd sent a taller, younger person in to butter her up. According to Chenoa, Scottie-boy was a stud. But then, dear old auntie had an eye for anything young in trousers.

She took another swing with the pick. *Or a kilt.*

But why not send in an American? What was it about these foreigners? Didn't they realize that no meant no, nada, uh-uh, no freaking way?

Did they think that if a mob of overseas schmucks tried to pour on the charm, she'd melt and go all gooey?

"Screw them!"

Henri wasn't about to drive into town for a breakfast and sit there while she listened to a line of drivel. Jeez, the last guy refused to tell her anything about the job before she committed. They were *insane!* She'd probably shove her syrup-drenched pancakes in the dude's face—even if he did end up looking like a million bucks—which she doubted. Besides, hot men were always self-centered assholes.

And Henri didn't have time to listen to anyone at the moment, especially an arrogant, *Scottish* asshole. She had a list a mile long of all the things the mine needed. Shoot, it had taken her a month to clean the house—well, it wasn't a house. But the two-room apartment carved out of sandstone. Her home. Her hideout. Her pad. It had been Grandfather's home and he'd willed it to her. The mine was what she'd always wanted, what she'd dreamed of. Up there in the hills no one bothered her. And, aside from a few trusted Paiutes, no one even knew the mine existed—probably because in forty years, Grandfather had only found a handful of gold dust and hadn't tried to sell it —he even kept it quiet from the Paiute band.

"*No use getting our people excited,*" he always said.

The gold dust was hidden and only Henri knew where to find it. Henri. Not Aunt Chenoa. In truth, the only person Grandfather had ever trusted was Henri. Her mother had been an alcoholic who drank her life into an early grave. Aunt Chenoa stayed away from the sauce, but never expressed interest in the mine. She'd never expressed interest in much of anything aside from the odd trip to Mesquite to play the slots or to pick up any passing white dude who flashed his wallet.

Henri smashed the pick into the bedrock, making rock chips and dirt shower to the ground. Her aunt had pissed her off more than anything. The woman couldn't keep her opinions to herself. It was bad enough that the only time Chenoa visited the mine

was to tell Henri she'd had a visitor from Scotland—
with her eyes full of awe, no less.

But the thing that stung the most was that after
Chenoa blurted out the news, dear old Auntie had not
so tactfully reminded Henri about her family outside
the reservation.

Family, my ass.

Henri had never told anyone that she'd tracked
down her worthless father—blond-haired, blue-eyed
Jarrod Anderson. He'd abandoned Henri's mother in
Saint George and Mom never recovered. Dear old Dad
now lived in Chino, California with his new wife and
kids. The jerk had pictures of his new family plastered
all over Facebook. Yeah, the proud father. Why in
God's name hadn't he shown a modicum of pride in
Henri? Because she had brown eyes and black hair?

Henri smashed the pick into the wall again, the
reverberation jarring her arms as she hit solid rock.
The only person who'd ever believed in her was
Grandfather. He'd treated her like she meant something. They had shared good times and developed a
bond that went deeper than any human relationship
she'd ever experienced. He'd died right after Henri
joined the Delta Force CT unit. Thank God he hadn't
been alive to witness her bogus trial and the humiliation of her conviction. No wonder she'd gone into hiding. Anyone who'd endured the hell of JRC would
want to shut out the world while mindless war raged
in the Middle East.

I don't need anymore shit!

She drew back the pick once again but the low
hum of a motor stopped her from smashing it into the
rock wall.

The mine was hidden in the southeast corner of
the Paiute reservation. Fences and no trespassing signs

were posted everywhere. Aunt Chenoa had been up there once in three months and that had been the extent of Henri's visitors.

But no mistaking it, a motorized vehicle was nearing. Henri slung her rifle over her shoulder and jogged up toward the entrance until she took a sharp left and headed through the escape tunnel. Her back door, so to speak—a ladder leading out an old fissure, serving as a way out in case the cave entrance collapsed. Pulling herself up, she quickly ascended then pushed out the camouflaged grill and climbed onto the rocky plateau above her spread. On her belly, she crawled to the edge right above the mine entrance—as well as the entrance to her pad. The barrel of her rifle slid nicely between a pair of sagebrush. The spot provided good camouflage, though no barricade to stop a bullet.

A hundred feet down below, her red Ford F-150, Old Red, was parked in its usual place, not that anyone ever bothered a beater, 1977 truck. In the distance, dust rose and curled with the breeze. As the vehicle crested a hill, Henri used the scope on her rifle to home in on it. A four-wheel drive. Silver. Jeep Laredo. Not familiar. The SUV dipped behind a hill.

It didn't take a mastermind to know who was driving. The Scot had expected company for breakfast. But how the hell had he discovered the mine's location?

Had the jerk followed Aunt Chenoa yesterday? But how? No vehicle had approached aside from auntie's Chevy. And if Rose knew her location, why had he waited to pay a visit? Had he been acting gentlemanly by waiting for their breakfast date? Was he pissed that she'd dissed his invitation? Probably.

Let him be pissed.

She waited patiently while the SUV neared until it pulled to a stop beside her truck. Henri kept the man in her sights while he got out of the Jeep and looked up the hill. Christ, the stud had a mop of red hair just like a Scot. She snorted. Redheaded guys always looked pallid and bloodless. In fact, after ten years in the Army, she had come to the conclusion that red-headed dudes lacked the toughness bone. They were better suited for office jobs.

Odd, though, he'd ditched the sports jacket and was wearing boots and camo. She let him approach until she was sure he'd be able to see the muzzle of her rifle peeking between the sagebrush. "I could shoot you for trespassing," she said, using her badass sergeant voice.

The man took off his sunglasses and grinned. Good Lord, maybe not all the redheads on the planet were pasty. True, he had fair skin, but he looked buff—healthy, even. "Henrietta Anderson," he said in a deep brogue, waving as if they were old pals. "'Tis good to see you've lived up to your reputation." Jesus, he rolled his "rs".

Cute grin or not, she didn't buy the friendly approach. "And what might that reputation be?"

"Sharpshooter. Someone who doesn't take shite."

At least he had that right.

He took a step. "Did your auntie tell you I visited?"

"She did."

His eyes narrowed. "I missed you at breakfast."

"I had no intention of going."

He stepped again.

"That's far enough." Henri pulled back the bolt, making a loud click.

The man chuckled and raised his palms, though

he didn't move any closer. "Och, I just want to talk, lass."

"How did you find me?" she demanded.

He looked skyward. "I can find anyone on the planet."

Damned satellites. "It's dangerous to sneak up on me."

"Aye."

"But you did it anyway."

"I've faced danger before." His eyes narrowed and when his auburn-bearded jaw hardened, she didn't doubt he was telling the truth.

Two could play his game. "Where? You been to Afghanistan?"

"Aye, Iraq, Syria, Russia. You ken, I hang out wherever the bad guys are."

"So, you're a real soldier. Wow. Pretty impressive for a redhead."

He didn't smile this time. "How about you invite me in for a coffee and we have a wee chat?"

"I think we've talked enough."

"Right-o." He saluted. "You'll need money eventually."

"Not much."

"Too, bad, 'cause I can offer you a sweet deal." He rubbed the back of his neck. "So, you intend to hide up here? Pretend the big bad world doesna exist?"

"What do I care about the world? No one cared about me after they threw my ass in the slammer for two fucking years."

"Bad break." He looked away, chewing his lip. "One I'm sure you'll nay forget. It's a shame you willna have the chance to chase after the asshole who set you up."

Henri's heart stuttered while her breath caught.

She'd thought about revenge. Thought about it a lot. She'd endured two miserable years where all she did was think about tracking down the real killer and making him pay. And now he'd planted a seed that made all the animosity boil to the surface.

All I need is one shot. One shot and I'd end Fadli's reign of terror.

But before she replied, Mr. Rose skittered back down the hill—if the name on his card was real. Looking through her sights, she watched him return to his SUV and, right before he got in, she closed her finger on the trigger and fired a shot. It hit exactly where she'd aimed—a pebble three feet from his boots. And for added effect, it flew up and struck him in the leg.

The man didn't even flinch. He simply glanced over his shoulder, shifted his gaze to her hiding place and saluted once more, the bastard.

He was ex-military for sure. Nonetheless, Henri wanted nothing from that man. Anything he had to say would lead to no good. Her shot was a warning. He knew it. Moreover, he'd better not try to come back or else she'd pull out her shotgun and fill his ass with buckshot, or rock salt. Nothing stung more than twin barrels full of salt in the backside.

Henri climbed back down the mine shaft and headed for her pad. Sure, it wasn't much, but she loved the place. Calling to her soul, it reminded her of living in the time of her ancestors—those on the Native American side of her family. Though it had modern comforts. Grandfather had rigged a generator deep into the mine so only a low hum made its way to the cave, and it gave her all the electricity she needed. She cooked on an old RV range that used propane. She had an old TV—no reception, but she had stacks of DVDs, a table, two chairs, a recliner and in the back room was a wardrobe, a dresser with a mirror and a bed.

Life was good.

Anything was better than the JRC at Miramar.

And I don't need to be a hero. Been there, done that and was paid in misery. I am to flipping the Army the bird and moving on.

She opened the cupboard and pulled out a can of chili. Cranking the can opener, she sighed. Life was lonely, too. But that's how Henri wanted it. She'd had enough of COs barking orders—of sleepless nights in some Afghanistan hellhole. She'd had enough of jail cells and enforced daily routines.

She lit the burner and dumped the contents of the can into a pot.

Her mine may only yield a bit of dust, but it was hers. No one told her what to do and no one ever bothered her—Mike Rose being the exception. But he'd go back to Scotland soon enough.

After stirring the chili, she moved to the picture of Grandfather on the wall and reverently brushed her finger along the bottom of the frame. "Your spirit is still here. It lives in these walls. And you were the only person who ever cared."

Henri's shoulders tensed while she returned to the stove. What if she could chase after the asshole who'd set her up?

She raised the spoon to her lips and tasted while her mind churned with the possibilities and all the ways she'd dreamed of hunting him down. To nail Omar Fadli would be sweet revenge. Fadli was the assassin—the schmuck who'd pinned Henri with the hit on the Iranian ambassador. He'd come to Washington DC just to frame her because she'd provided cover for a regiment of Delta Force black ops and one of her bullets had killed Fadli's brother—a terrorist who Henri stopped from throwing a grenade that could have taken out the entire squadron.

The chili started to boil.

No, she wouldn't think twice about revenge if she was the only person whose life he'd ruined. But the guy was a mass murderer. Al-Umari's right-hand man, Fadli was the muscle behind the terrorist executions that plagued the Middle East and beyond.

Was she bitter about doing time? Was she slighted because no one, not even her CO believed in her innocence? *Hell yeah*. But Henri would pay the price again if it meant saving the lives of the soldiers in her unit. Fadli was upset because she'd stopped his brother from killing dozens of peacekeeping American soldiers? Those men were her brothers—the force had been more like a family to Henri than anything. And Fadli deprived her of it.

SITTING on the bed in his hotel room with an open bag of Cheetos, Mike reviewed Henri's file. He'd told Garth he'd have the lass on the plane in three days and the boss had wagered it would take at least a week, maybe two. Stretching the odds, Mike had held out his hand and they'd shaken on it. He'd have Henrietta Anderson in Iceland in a fortnight or he'd be the one paying up.

Not that Mike needed a hundred quid. He just couldn't stand to lose.

The boss was right. There were a few things in Mike's arsenal that Anders Lindgren didn't possess. First of all, Anders had a good-sized paunch and was about sixty. A twenty-nine-year-old woman who was fit enough to be a Delta Force sniper wouldn't be attracted to the Icelander, but at thirty-five and fighting fit, Garth insisted Mike would be more convincing. He hadn't argued. Usually he was fairly lucky where the ladies were concerned, though not lately.

The last bird had flown the coop after he'd departed Scotland for an op in Syria. Before that, he'd been on leave for a month and really thought Sabrina might be the right one for him—she was smart and had a fantastic career as an investment banker. It didn't hurt that she had a body like a diva, either. She traveled a lot, which was another boon. At least he'd thought it was a boon. He'd thought a lot of things. Most of all, for the first time in his life, he thought he might have met a woman compatible enough to put a ring on her finger.

But he'd been wrong.

Sabrina's traveling led her into the arms of a Spanish billionaire. She'd been two-timing for months before Mike found out. Hell, the hole she ripped in his heart still burned.

Good riddance. He popped a handful of Cheetos in his mouth—not that a hardened spy like Rose needed comfort food, but they sure tasted good.

Maybe Mike just wasn't the marrying type. Sure, every time he was on leave he found women who were fantastic—beautiful birds who would have done anything for him, yet not one of his countless relationships had panned out.

Truth be told, it was about time he faced the fact that he was married to the job. He operated in a sphere of high-speed and dangerous ops. The rush fed him, made him feel alive. He couldn't ask a woman to sit around and wait while he risked his neck in every country that ended in "stan".

Bye, sweetheart, I'm going into Kazakhstan to track down a load of missing uranium. I'll be off the grid. See ya in three to six months.

Tipping up the Cheetos bag, he poured the rest into his mouth.

God help him, he needed to convince Anderson to give ICE a go so he could return to risking his neck— immerse himself body and soul in the next incredibly dangerous op. He liked pushing it to the edge. The riskier the mission, the sweeter the rush.

Once the bag was empty, he shifted his focus back to the file on his lap.

At the mine, he hadn't seen anything of Henrietta Anderson aside from the muzzle of her .300 caliber Winchester Magnum sniper rifle. It was the perfect choice for a woman, only fourteen pounds and as accurate as a laser.

But guns aside, Mike had seen enough pictures of Henri to know she was bonny. The woman was five-ten and all legs. She wore her hair tied back in a braid in most of the photos, but it was so long it touched her well-formed arse. She had exquisitely chiseled features and an intelligent arc to her brow. And reading her file, she had what it took to make a good spy. About one in 100,000 had the moxie to be an asset and, according to her dossier, Henri was a rare find. *If* Mike could convince her to join ICE. She'd been on multiple tours with the 3rd Delta Force Detachment and her file was chock full of heroism. Mike would relish having a soldier like Henri Anderson watching his back any day. She'd even earned the Medal of Honor, receiving a gunshot wound to the calf in the process. The hit had gone in her file as a graze because after an injection of penicillin and field dressing, she was back in action.

She was tougher than bullets and Mike had learned firsthand she was about as stubborn as a curly nose hair as well.

He paged through her army report. Two could play the stubborn game and few could beat him once he dug in his heels. Besides, he'd made the bet with Moore, a wager Mike wasn't about to lose. Once the woman agreed to go to Iceland, she'd be Garth's problem, end of story. Mike could collect his hundred quid and leave her training to the fine folks at ICE.

Unfortunately, the one thing missing from Anderson's file was what made her tick. Sure, she was hiding in the mountains because she'd been slighted by her country. Her aunt was a bit of a cold fish as well—didn't come across as someone Henri might confide in, or even warm to. What did Henrietta Anderson love? What were her interests? At one time the lass would have put her life on the line for her squadron, but what about now? What kept her awake at night? What was her passion?

Mike needed to find a way past her rifle and past her badass facade.

Their interests were about as similar as her red desert was to his green Scotland. He liked fast cars. He owned a red Porsche 911 and an old, stone manor on the hill that overlooked Oban Bay. He liked nice things. He liked it orderly. Though he wasn't home much, he kept his place tidy like a show home. And then there was Henri. She lived in a rickety mine shaft.

After reading until his eyes crossed, trying to find anything he might be able to use to connect with the lass, he decided the only thing they had in common was an appreciation of weapons.

With that decided, he drove to a gun shop, used an ID indicating his last name was MacLeod and he was a US citizen, bought a Remington 700 sniper rifle, ammo, a headlamp and a canteen. Not ideal, but it was the best civilian gun he could purchase without drawing attention to himself.

The next morning, Mike headed back to the reservation. This time, he parked the Jeep a mile away from the mine. By the way Henri had ambushed him, she'd been alerted of his approach long before he'd arrived.

The first rule of war? Strategy. And when the commander is strategizing, his greatest tool is the element of surprise.

4

Mike treated the tire tracks leading to the mine as if they were a dusty goat trail in the Middle East filled with IEDs. Since the lass had obviously been alerted to his approach the day before, this time he intended to invoke the element of surprise. This was a mission just like any other and it was time he realized it. He must handle it no differently—just like he was in Syria slipping into an enemy camp and targeting his quarry. Somehow, he needed to get in Henrietta Anderson's head and he couldn't do that by reading her damned file.

Going bush, he climbed the hill across from Henri's old Ford truck. If the condition of that heap of metal was any indication, she ought to pay more attention to what ICE had to offer—*if* she'd let him get a word in edgewise. Damn, he wasn't a fan of tough women. Sure, Henri might be bonny with all the right female equipment, but Mike liked women who were a little flirty when they first met—who appreciated his, *might as well say it*, when they appreciated him for being a goddamned man.

But this wasn't about a female piece of arse hiding on a Paiute reservation in the middle of nowhere. This was about a sniper, a Special Ops soldier who'd proven she had what it took to be in the field. And Mike wasn't going back to Iceland without her.

Yesterday, he'd studied the satellite images before he chose his approach. Peppered with sagebrush, the place was desolate or some might call it pristine with no trees and little sign of human life. By the lack of tracks in the stills, it was clear few people frequented Henri's mine intentionally or by accident. Besides, the barbed wire fence and no trespassing signs were a sure-fire deterrent for most of the locals.

The sun beat down like a blast from a welding torch. By the time Mike reached top of the hill over the mine, his face and arms were working up a burn. Stupid. He always wore a cap and long sleeves in arid climates, the same common sense should have prevailed in Utah.

Next time.

Stepping carefully to minimize his tracks, he circled the terrain on the hill. The first thing he found was Henri's back door, the one she'd used to ambush him the day before. The ground was still streaked where she'd crawled to the edge of the cliff and watched him through her scope. Footprints surrounded the hole, covered with a bit of grill that had a big tumbleweed tied to it. Funny she hadn't covered her tracks, though given the isolation of the mine, there was probably no point.

After Mike took a drink from his canteen, he slipped his torch onto his head, shouldered his rifle and climbed down. At the bottom of the shaft, he took a deep breath, relishing the reprieve from Utah's torturous sun. It was a good ten degrees cooler down there and darker than a cup of Turkish coffee.

He stood for a moment and listened. Nothing

honed his hearing like being sightless. A low hum came from below, carrying a slight vibration. It was a motor, no question. Whether it was from mining equipment or a generator, Mike couldn't tell. Though it sounded like a field camp generator, he hadn't spent any time in a mine before.

Rule number two of war? Don't make or act upon assumptions unless you're given no choice.

As he reached up to turn on his lamp, something rumbled beneath him, making the ground shake. He froze and listened. A hiss echoed in the distance, sounding like debris giving way. Silence followed. Mike smiled to himself. Henri was down there working. Was the lass a gold digger after all? But that didn't make sense. If she was interested in money, she might have listened to Lindgren back in San Diego, or at least probed a bit when Mike met her yesterday.

He adjusted the light and started through the passageway, moving in a crouch to protect his head. Whoever carved out this tunnel wasn't six-three, not even close. He came to a juncture with a shaft to the right leading downward. Blinding sunlight beamed in from the left, but beyond the mine's entrance was a door. Wooden, it was paneled like an old house door, the frame fitting into the sandstone as if it belonged there.

A house door was an invitation to someone like Mike. The third rule of war? Know your enemy. Gather information in any way you can. Make use of spies.

Hell, Mike was a spy. A damned good one. And it didn't take a sleuth to guess Anderson's living quarters were behind the rickety portal.

He turned off his headlamp before he tried the knob. It wasn't locked. No surprises there—the lass wasn't exactly in the middle of metro US. Though a bit of paper sailed to the ground when he opened it. Henri must be suspicious enough to rig the slip to leave a sign if she had an intruder.

Mike picked it up and, after he stepped inside, replaced it while shutting the door. The hum he'd heard must have been a generator because the lights were on.

The place was like stepping into a Hobbit hole filled with Native American art, or perhaps a cave out of an *Indiana Jones* movie. The red-rock walls weren't smooth. They'd been carved by a pickaxe and dynamite. But it was clean. The floor was stone as well but smoother and covered with woven Navaho rugs. There were old lanterns and relics on the wall. It reminded him of a prospector's hovel, except for the recliner and television. Mike moved to the shelves of DVDs and read the spines. It was a mishmash of action-adventure, Disney, romance and westerns. Interestingly, the *Pride and Prejudice* jacket showed the most wear. Maybe, deep down, Anderson was a romantic. Right? Tough girl, soft heart?

It could happen.

In the center of the room were a rustic table and two chairs. Beyond that, a hob for cooking and rows of pictures on the wall.

The photographs interested Mike the most. The largest was a black and white of an old Native American man standing at the mine entrance with a pick in his hand. He had to be the grandfather who'd bequeathed her the mine. The frame was made from dozens of tiny colorful beads in zigzag patterns. Moving along, there was a picture of Henri in uniform receiving her Medal of Honor, another of her a bit younger, wearing traditional buckskin dress and standing with a group of other Native American dancers. Anderson stood out. She was taller and fairer, and by far the prettiest, in fact, something seemed off, as if she didn't fit in and the others resented her.

Is that why she lives in isolation? She doesn't fit in with her clan...er...tribe?

The rest of the pictures were either of Henri or her grandfather and most of them appeared to be taken near the mine. There were no photos of Aunt Chenoa, no sign of Henri's deceased mother, and definitely no photo of her father.

Mike moved to the bedroom. It was stark, but what drew his attention were the books on the nightstand—one on prospecting and a thriller.

He picked up the prospecting book and leafed through the dog-eared pages. So, the lass did want to find gold. A piece of paper fell to the floor. Mike picked it up and sat on the bed, unfolding a map of the mine which included the escape route he'd used to get inside. Down the shaft where he hadn't been there was an X with the notation "small vein here".

His reading was interrupted when the hair stood up on the back of his neck. He froze. He didn't even breathe. Years of living on the edge had taught him to always trust his gut and, right now, his internal hazard meter hit the red zone.

In a nanosecond, Mike's heart rate spiked. He hadn't heard footsteps. He hadn't heard the door open, but never in his life would he mistake the sound of a rifle bolt moving a bullet into its chamber. He looked up in time to meet Henri's eyeball glaring through her Win Mag's scope.

Springing to his feet, Mike faced her.

"Do you make a habit of breaking and entering?" she asked, using a tone that clearly said she wasn't about to take shite—the same tone she'd used yesterday.

With his next blink, he took it all in. She'd been working, all right. She was covered in powdery dust. Jeez, she looked like she'd been buried in it—all five-feet ten of pure, solid woman staring at him along her deadly sights. Only her eyes were swiped clean, as dark and shiny as wet slate. Given other circumstances, he wouldn't mind spending a candlelight dinner staring into browns as hypnotic as hers. But he wasn't there for fun.

Mike glanced to the open door behind the woman, his mind calculating his odds of escape given her finger caressing the rifle's trigger. "Ah..."

"Put the map back in the book and set it down." Her braid slipped around her shoulder as she spoke— a thick rope at least three-feet long and caked with dirt. Whatever happened down there, she'd been in the wars.

He did as she asked while watching her out of the corner of his eye. If she wanted to shoot him, he'd already be dead. He had no doubt she could do it. A trained killer, she was like a panther ready to pounce, daring him to make the first errant move. The thought of taking her on made him hard. God save him, the woman was a freaking Amazon sprung from the dust of hell and ready for battle. Mike bit back a grin—now was no time to tell Anderson how sexy she looked dirt and all.

"You couldn't leave me alone, could you?" she demanded, the harshness of her voice snapping him from his wee fantasy.

"No' until you hear me out." He inclined his head toward the gun slung over his shoulder and gave her a challenging squint—one that usually worked with the ladies. "I thought you might enjoy a bit of target practice."

"Yeah, with you as the target." She slid her foot back. "Now you're going to walk out of here nice and slow."

Jesus Christ, terrorists were easier to crack than this bird. But the more she talked the more he relished the chase. He even took a step toward her, watching that trigger finger for a twitch. "Come, lass. I'm no' here to rifle through your gear. I just want a word."

"You've already had a lot more than one, and I'm not interested in anything you have to say."

He shook his head. "I dunna give up easily."

She made a pretense of inching up her Win Mag and peering through her scope. "Then you're going to die."

"Bloody hell." Mike headed for the door, but when she shifted her rifle as he passed, his instincts kicked in. The wildcat had a loaded gun in her hands and had just threatened him. Mike might be trained to take a lot of shite, but when it came right down to it, self-preservation trumped kissing the arse of a woman who refused to allow him the courtesy of listening to what he'd flown 6500 miles to say.

Moving with the speed of an asp, he reached back and pushed the muzzle away. Her eyes flashed wide as he twisted the Win Mag until it broke from her grasp.

He tossed the rifle on the bed, ducking as she spun and threw a roundhouse kick aimed at his head. The gun over his shoulder clattered to the floor. Before he could counter her attack, she nailed him in the ribs with a spinning side kick while her thick braid whipped around and dragged across his face. A world karate champion, taking a solid hit only served to hone Mike's senses. Gaining his balance, he went on the offensive throwing rapid fire strikes, hard enough to stun, but not a one hard enough to cause any serious damage. Henri wasn't dazed. She attacked like a badger, blocking, jabbing, all the while as Mike backed her to the wall.

And he didn't let up. He had a mission to accomplish and if the woman wanted to play rough, so be it. Anderson had no idea with whom she was messing. Mike blocked her every kick, her every sucker punch. Sweat beaded on her forehead and turned the dust to mud.

She shrieked like a cat when he trapped her against the wall with his body, staring into those enormous, brown eyes now looking as tasty as melted dark chocolate. She squirmed against him, full breasts pushing into his chest. He blinked, but not before he pinned her with a choke hold. The woman could fight better than most men. Because of that, Mike knew better than to give her inch. Not yet, anyway.

"All I want is a bit of your time," he growled, ignoring the rock-solid erection below his belt while Henri panted, her breasts crushing into his chest with her every inhale. Christ, he'd worked with women before. Beautiful women, and he'd always been able to control the ole cannon before. Now was no different. That's right. He didn't like hard-arsed women—ah— even if they had eyes that could melt a heart of granite.

"Why?" she asked in a sultry tone she hadn't used before, tipping up her fine-boned chin. "So you can fill me with the same bullshit as that Dutch suit?"

"He's an Icelander."

She squirmed against him. "Whatever."

Damn. Too much heavy-breathing woman was addling his mind. He needed to back off. Fast. "Look, let's do some target practice. No pressure."

"Oh, yeah? I'm lethal. I could kill you with my eyes closed. In fact, I might enjoy it."

He chuckled. Och aye, he knew exactly the enjoyment she was talking about. *The rush.* It was what every field agent lived for—what made her ideal for the job. "That's what makes it fun."

"Why would you trust me?" she asked, wriggling against him. Hell, she just might do him in right there —death by hotness.

"Because you were brave enough to win the Medal of Honor."

Henri's pupils dilated, then her lips formed a thin line. "They stripped it from me."

"But they gave it back."

"I was framed and they didn't believe me."

"No question." If only he could release her, but it would be stupid to give her an inch until she offered something to show she was bending. At least she'd stopped talking about killing him. Regardless, he still couldn't back down now. No chance. What he said in the next thirty seconds was critical to this op. *I'm not going to lose.* "You were mistreated, you got the raw end of the deal. I'd be out for blood if I were you. I wouldn't trust me either...not yet, at least."

Her body relaxed a bit—good sign. "So, are you going to keep me in a choke hold all day?"

The corner of his mouth inched up. "Are you going to attack again?"

"Mmmm-aybe." She swallowed, shifting those damned hips and brushing him where she shouldn't. Not that he was giving her any room to move. If she realized what she'd done, she didn't let on. The woman just narrowed her gaze and snorted. "I'm not interested in anything you have to offer." This time, Henri's conviction didn't sound quite as determined as it had the day before.

Grinding his teeth against his ill-timed male response to having a lean woman's body crushed against his, Mike decided it was time to go in for the kill. "Tell you what. Let's just shoot few rounds—no pressure. I'm booked into the Hilton Garden Inn for a fortnight."

"Fortnight." She rolled her eyes, but the hard-ass routine was gone, thank God. "You Scots and your weird words."

He released his grip. "The same can be said for you Yanks."

Stretching her neck, she wriggled her body again. Mike cleared his throat and stepped back. Her gaze meandered downward. A wee pink tongue slipped out the corner of her mouth. She'd noticed.

So, she is human.

Mike took another step away. Damn, of course she'd noticed. His cock behaved like a bloody teenaged appendage. So, shoot him. He was a man. Besides, she'd felt too good pressed flush against him with nowhere to go. Had the circumstances been different, he could have used a dozen different moves to coax the woman to her back, especially with the bed right behind them. But this was business. And she wasn't interested. And he bloody well better not be. This Delta Force sniper had proven herself to be a walking fighting machine not to mention she was covered in dust—which was now smudged down the front of his clothes. He cleared his throat. "I guess mining work is pretty dirty."

She brushed off her jeans, making clouds of red powder billow around her. "Yeah, it's kinda like

fending off heavy fire from a foxhole in
Afghanistan."

"Been there."

"So," she said, retrieving her rifle from the bed.
"We shoot a few rounds and then you'll leave me
alone?"

Mike retrieved his gun from the floor. "That's the
deal. At least today." He mightn't have convinced her
to join ICE but, in his book, he'd just earned a victory,
and that was far more than he'd accomplished
yesterday.

The fourth rule of war? Success will be achieved
only through one blood-shedding battle at a time.

∼

HENRI DIDN'T KNOW why she'd agreed to target practice—aside from being locked in a choke hold by a
man who looked like a descendant of Eric the Blood-
axe, a Viking who pillaged Scotland in the Middle
Ages. Rose had to be at least 6'3" and as solid as a
mountain of granite. And his crystal-blue eyes were
too damned disarming. How was a girl supposed to
fight a guy who attacked like a linebacker with Chris
Pine eyes?

On top of all that, maybe she'd backed down because she needed a diversion from nearly being
buried in the mine right before she walked in on Rose.
Not only was she shaken down to her boots from the
cave-in, she'd been covered in rocks and dirt clear up
to her waist. Another foot and she wouldn't have had
such an easy time clawing herself out. And she'd bet
her savings the intelligence consultant wouldn't have
ventured down the mine shaft to lend a hand. Worse,
God only knew how long it would take to shovel out

the debris just to get back where she'd started that morning.

She was already mad, then finding Rose looking at Grandfather's map had set her blood to boiling. Henri should have shot him, not agree to shoot *with* him.

Maybe she'd gone along with it because she needed him to stop pressing that delicious male body against hers. Yeah, she might be angry, she might be resentful, but she was still a woman. Rose had scared the shit out of her—not because he was in her pad, but because of her own startling, nothing-short-of sizzling response. After two years in the pen and three months in isolation at the mine, Henri was no longer used to big, muscular, masculine bodies being in such close proximity. No longer used to breathing in spicy male scent. No longer impervious to sparring with hot, brawny dudes. Christ, her knees had even wobbled. And, oh, how the man could fight. He was a pro all the way. Made being a member of Delta Force look like being a Boy Scout. She'd given him everything she had and he'd just toyed with her. He'd backed her against the wall and pinned her there with...*God*! He had muscles where no one else on the planet had sinew.

And she wasn't about to let herself think about sex or the rock-hard piece of anatomy that made men so...

No!

Mike Rose had needed to get the heck off her just so she could think.

In truth, Henri should be madder than a mama bear defending her cubs from a hunter. Come to think of it, now the oxygen was once again flowing to her brain, she was good and pissed. How dare this arrogant, Scottish bastard break into her pad and poke around as if he had a warrant? As if he had a right to look at her personal effects?

After they'd climbed to the top of the ridge above the mine, Rose pointed to a Joshua tree about four hundred meters out. "Let's start with that spindly old thing. It looks like something out of Dr. Seuss."

"The Joshua tree or the leaves?" she asked, cocking her head and looking at it critically, fairly certain that Rose's eyesight wasn't as sharp. Grandfather had named her Soaring-Eagle for a reason, which had everything to do with her 20/7.5 vision.

The Scot gave her a sideways glance. "I'll take the clump on the right."

"Suit yourself." She swung an exaggerated gesture with her palm. "This was your idea. You go first."

He winked with a cocky grin, raising the Remington to his shoulder. "This isn't a Win Mag, but the best I could do without putting in a special order at the local store."

Snorting, she crossed her arms. "Now you're making excuses."

"Bloody, smartarse Yank," he mumbled under his breath.

Yeah, try to charm me with your brogue, dude.

The problem? No matter how much she wanted to resist, he was too damned charming and she suspected he knew it. What guy who looked like Rose didn't? That's why they were all bad news.

Henri watched him fire off four solid rounds, each one hitting its mark and devastating the poor Joshua tree's branch. A yucca unique to the Mohave, Henri wasn't overly excited about damaging a gift from Mother Earth. Regardless, Rose proved that, if nothing else, he was an adequate marksman who'd be an asset in a Delta Force shit-storm.

He turned to her with a grin, making her stomach spring into calisthenics. Caught off guard, she snapped her gaze to the ground. Jeez, she couldn't take those damned electric-blue eyes. "Don't look at me like that."

"Like what?"

She flicked her hand at his face. "Like that—grinning as if you're planning to seduce me into doing whatever it is you want me to do."

"That could be arranged, lass." Dammit if his smile didn't get bigger, the ass. But then he snorted and shook his head like the hot guy routine was all a joke. "Go on. Let's see what you've got, ace."

She pulled her Win Mag off her shoulder. "Tell you what. Four leaves. Joshuas are fragile."

"Leaves? From here? No one would be able to make them out, let alone shoot them."

"Right." She raised the gun to her shoulder and peered through the scope. This guy might have read her file, but he'd never been in combat with her.

The tips of Henri's fingers tingled as she honed her senses. Before she ever took a shot, she became one with her rifle. As she breathed, her weapon breathed. The breeze, every gust of wind affected her the same as it did the steel molding into her grip. In Henri's hands, her rifle was an extension of her arm; another appendage honed and trained for precision.

She flicked off the safety and pulled back the charging handle. Her heart fluttered with the sound of a sleek, hollow-point, copper cartridge slipping into the chamber ready to dance.

The caress of the trigger always brought the same shot of adrenalin. Time slowed. Her breathing became steady. Henri could even hear her heartbeat echo in the barrel. When she blinked, it happened at the pace of a desert tortoise. She eyed the first long, spiked leaf. Her finger closed in.

Crack, crack, crack, crack. Before she blinked, she shot through four leaves.

Lowering her rifle, she gave Rose a grin of her own.

His brow pinched, he looked at the Joshua then back at her. "Did you?"

"Can't see worth shit, can you?"

"I don't have a scope."

Groaning, she rolled her eyes again. Guys never believed a chick could shoot until they had their faces shoved in the evidence. "Come."

Henri led him to the tree and gestured to the frond Rose had obliterated. "Here's your handiwork—managed to ravage the poor tree. Do you have any idea how long it takes a Joshua to grow? That one would have taken about sixty years to attain such *spindly-old* glory." Not waiting for Rose's response, she pointed to each of four leaves, elegantly pierced with individual bullet holes. "One, two, three, and four. And the tree will live."

The man raked his fingers through his tangle of auburn hair. "Holy smokes."

"Thanks."

"I mean, I've never seen shooting like that and I've been around the block a few dozen times."

She shrugged. "Yeah, well Fadli must be pretty impressive, especially if he made everyone think the ambassador's murder was my work."

"Too right, and that bastard's still out there."

Henri's stomach squeezed. She didn't want to admit it to Rose, but ever since Lindgren had visited her with the news, dreams had crept into her mind about facing the man responsible for sending her to the pen. She wanted to nail him. Bad. She just didn't want to kiss anyone's ass along the way.

Mike arched his eyebrow and gave her a look as if he knew what she was thinking. Before he said anything, he let a pause dangle in the air. The space between them swelled as if electrically charged, but Henri wasn't about to be the first to move, to speak or even blink.

"Your talent is going to waste," he said point blank without the sales pitch.

Her shoulders tensed. She'd expected more charm, more dancing around the issue. Rose just laid it out there. And Henri was not fool. Her life *was* going to waste—but, didn't a girl deserve a chance to lay low and nurse her wounds for a while? "No one bothers me here."

"I'll give you that. And I'd wager your contact with the world is all but nil."

She shifted back, refusing to allow any emotion to show on her face. But Rose was right. Isolating herself from the world had become her way of coping. Jeez, she hadn't even seen a news headline in three months. Did she want to find Fadli and introduce him to the fires of hell? God, yes. But on her terms.

Was she ready to leave the mine and let an organized mob of military zealots tell her what to do?

No. Fucking. Way.

Mike sucked in a breath like he was about to say something, but Henri held up her palm and jumped in first. "I'll tell you right now. I'm not going anywhere."

"Even with Omar Fadli out there plotting his next target? Maybe he'll hit the western US next—figure out a way to pin it on you."

"Shut up." She was still recovering from the last

time that bastard had ruined her hopes, her entire military career, her life—even if she did dream of lodging a bullet between his eyes. "I like it here. I have everything I need. No one bothers me."

The Scot gave a nod. "Aye, and by the looks of it, this place will always be here for you." Glancing away, he casually slung the Remington over his shoulder. "I'll tell you this. My organization isn't the military. We're a highly specialized, highly secretive group of experts. Every man and woman in the field runs his or her own op and none of us are subject to any country's laws." He started off but stopped and looked back. "You'll have two months off a year to do your prospecting or whatever it is that recharges your engine." He gave her a card that said Hilton Garden Inn with the number 322 hand-written on the back.

Henri took it, then stood motionless while she watched him walk away until he disappeared behind the hill.

Did she want to believe him?

Hell, the mine had just collapsed and nearly killed her in the process.

My life is a fucking mess.

5

S he'd put it off for weeks, but when Henri opened the cupboard and all she found was a stale Pop Tart, it was time to go to town for supplies. Aside from being out of food and low on drinking water, she'd spent last night going over the items needed to repair the cave-in. The list would cost her big. Every time she turned around, something else failed. Last month she'd had to replace the generator, then the batteries, then the pump motor for the well. Would it never end?

After a shower, she slapped on a bit of makeup and brushed out her hair, leaving the thick mop down so it would wind-dry on the way.

Heading outside, debris crumbled beneath her boots as she climbed down to her truck, Old Red, another relic inherited from her grandfather. But it worked. At least she thought it did until the damned thing growled like a two-week old Labrador and died —five times.

Grinding her teeth with a frustrated grunt, she hopped out and looked under the engine. The thing had always leaked oil, but this time, it looked like a tanker had dropped its load. The dipstick confirmed it, too. But when a person owns a 1977 Ford, they always kept a few quarts of 10W-30 behind the seat.

She added all three quarts and, in addition to writing motor oil to the shopping list, she decided to make a pit stop at Martin's repair shop on the rez. Martin could fix anything.

Still, even after adding oil, the truck was reluctant to start. Worse, as Henri drove along the rocky and rutted dirt road to Shivwits, Old Red pinged and knocked all the way to the highway. Afraid of a breakdown, she pulled into the Shivwits neighborhood and found Martin. At least she found his legs—the rest of him was under the hood of a Mustang.

"Hey," she said. Having been in the same grade in school, Henri had known Martin most of her life.

"That you?" he asked before he straightened and wiped his hands on a rag.

"Got engine trouble."

"I figured." He looked at her with brown, puppy-dog eyes like he always did, the big flirt. The only problem was there was no spark in Henri's heart aside from the friendly kind. Martin had asked her out a gazillion times. They'd even gone to the senior prom together. The problem was they were too much like brother and sister. Martin always had her back. In fact, he was the only guy on the rez who didn't call her Whitey on account of her worthless dad. "The only time you come around is when you need that old heap of junk fixed."

"Hey, this Ford was Grandfather's. He'd turn in his grave if he heard you diss his wheels."

Martin tossed the rag and headed for Old Red. "What's wrong with it this time?"

"Aside from leaking oil like a sieve, it's knocking and it's got that 'eau de burning oil' thing going on."

"Knocking isn't good."

"At least it's not blowing smoke."

"The new radiator I installed is warrantied for five years."

Henri nodded. When she'd first returned from the slammer, she'd had to shell out two hundred fifty bucks because Old Red had a rusted-out radiator. She kicked the rear tire. "How long do you think the repairs will take?"

"That depends on what's wrong."

"Okay, how long until I can drive to town for supplies?"

"Give me an hour—then we'll see." He shook his head. "You really need to trade this thing in."

Henri cringed. She'd looked at truck prices and even used ones were outrageous. "Yeah, but I like this one."

Martin raised the hood and pulled out the dipstick. "How many quarts of oil did you put in before you left the mine?"

"Three. That's all I had."

Shaking his head, he blew out a sigh. "You need a new truck, Sister."

"Just figure out the damages and get me on the road." She threw her thumb over her shoulder. "I'm heading to Aunt Chenoa's for a minute."

"See ya. And, Sister?"

"Yeah?"

"You look nice with your hair down."

"Thanks."

Awkward.

Heading off, Henri hoped her aunt wasn't home so she could just pick up her mail without having to be sociable, but Chenoa opened the door as Henri walked up the dirt path. "What brought you down from your gold mine?"

"I'm out of food."

Chenoa held the door and ushered Henri inside. "Figures. Otherwise you'd never pay a social visit."

"Do I have any mail?"

"In the kitchen where it always is."

While Auntie rambled on about all the gossip on the rez, Henri leafed through the pile of junk. Some things never changed. The only thing she didn't chuck was a bill from her credit card company.

"So, I saw the silver Jeep head toward the mine yesterday." Auntie said, raising her eyebrows. "What did the Scottish man do at your place? It seems like he was up there an awfully long time."

"Target practice."

"He's a sharp-shooter?" Chenoa hated the word sniper. She thought it was akin to assassin...which it was.

"Sort of."

"What's the job he's offering? It sounds promising. Where would you be working?"

Henri shrugged, her head starting to pound from the interrogation. "Not around here, that's for sure."

Auntie leaned on the counter, squinting like she was about to give some unwanted advice. "Goodness, you're not attached. Why don't you take it? I worry about you holed up there in that mine all by yourself. What if something happened?" she asked in an accusing tone. "You could be trapped for weeks before anyone even realized you were in trouble!"

Well, that had almost happened yesterday. Regardless, Chenoa had a way of making Henri want to hit something. Without even knowing what Rose was offering, good ole auntie was encouraging Henri to take a job. It could be a one-way ticket to Syria and the woman would tell Henri to go. Heck, Rose could be asking her to assassinate the President of the United States.

Secret organization? Answering to no country? WTF?

But Henri knew better than to disclose anything to her aunt, lest it be broadcast to everyone in Southern Utah. "Yeah, well, I want to stay around here."

"So, is it a civilian job?"

"Sort of."

"That wouldn't be all that bad..."

Thank God the doorbell rang.

Henri answered.

Martin stood on the porch with a frown. "You want the bad news or the really bad news?"

Cringing, she rubbed the back of her neck. "Shit."

"Your engine's shot. The camshaft is no longer working in time with the pistons and it can't be fixed."

"What's that going to set me back?"

"Five grand, but I'm not finished. Your undercarriage is rusted through. You need a ton of body work —I tapped the rear fender and it fell off. The springs in the seat are shot. Your steering column is a wobbly mess." He stopped and took a breath. "You want me to go on?"

Shaking her head, Henri jammed her fist into her hip. "Just tell me the damages."

"That's what I'm trying to say. You need a new goddamned truck. It'll be a miracle if that heap makes it to town for you to get your supplies...and if it does, there's no way it'll make the return trip."

No one needed to tell her that after buying a truck, the equipment she needed for the mine and to keep feeding herself, her back pay wasn't going to last.

Henri held out her upturned palm. "So, can I borrow your Tacoma to drive to town?"

Martin crossed his arms. "Did you listen to anything I said?"

"I can't buy new wheels if I can't get to town."

He dug in his pocket and pulled out the keys. "I need it back by five."

"Fine."

~

AFTER HENRI HAD BEEN to the big-box hardware store, to the mining equipment shop on the other side of town, and to five different car yards, she sat in Martin's Tacoma and blankly stared out the windshield. She'd never been much for crying, but right now she wanted to bawl her eyes out and scream.

She pounded her fist on the steering wheel.

"Dammit...Arrrgh!"

She pummeled the thing repeatedly while strands of hair flicked into her eyes and across her mouth. Tenser than a wound spring, she shoved her fly-aways out of her face.

She'd been working her freaking ass off and had absolutely nothing to show for it aside from a gargantuan list of bills and a crap-ton of dirt that would take three months to move by hand.

Why did everything have to fall apart at once? Henri had jotted the figures onto a slip of paper. The truck she liked was sixty-four grand. There was a used model she could buy for fifteen, but it already had well over a hundred thousand miles on it. Then there was the mining equipment she'd need—if she ever expected to find anything other than sandstone and basalt. No one had to tell her she could swing her pick and shovel for the rest of her life and maybe come up with a couple hundred dollars in gold dust. Her grandfather had done it—though mostly as a hobby. He'd worked as a ranch hand and retired to the mine. The place couldn't even support a damned mouse.

Shoveling for the rest of her life wouldn't be a bad thing, except she needed to live. A person could only cut food costs so much. Her boots might last her another two years if she was lucky. She made her own bullets, but casings and lead weren't free. Gas wasn't free. Mining equipment wasn't effing free. The constant need to repair *everything* wasn't free.

After swiping away a stupid tear, Henri picked up the piece of paper with her scribblings. If she wanted to do things right, buy a decent truck that would last, and set up the mine so she wouldn't break her back by the time she was thirty-five, she'd have to fork out a minimum of seventy grand and that didn't include food. Worse? She only had fifty grand and some change in her bank account.

She'd be wiped out and then some.

Another option would be to buy the truck for fifteen, the hardware for a grand, and shovel out the dirt from the cave-in by hand. Once that was done, she could get by for a couple of years swinging a pick like she'd been doing. The downside of that was the risk of more cave-ins.

On one hand, she liked the solitude of the mine. No one bothered her. No one told her what to do...

No one cared, either.

Aunt Chenoa was right about one thing. If Henri had been trapped in the cave-in, no one would have even noticed anything amiss for weeks. Maybe months.

Maybe forever.

She could have been buried alive and no one would have known.

Would her life ever be normal? She'd learned to like being alone all the time. She'd been an outcast since the day she was born. The only place she'd ever belonged was in the army—because she was a damned good assassin. She was good enough to be accepted into Delta Force and pass their rigorous tests. Though, even in the service, people were afraid of her. Who wouldn't be afraid of a sniper who could hit a bullseye at two miles? She was a freak, a loner.

Yeah, there'd been friends and boyfriends. Though the latter was always fleeting, and nice guys like Martin never ignited that spark. Henri only ever got that rush of passion from a bad boy—a guy who flew by the seat of his pants with his hair on fire—the daredevil type.

Not that she'd seen any action...*in forever*.

Maybe there was something wrong with Henri's internal ignition switch. What would be so bad about shacking up with Martin? He was a Paiute. He'd been Henri's friend since they were in kindergarten. Sure, he was about six inches shorter, but she was five-foot-ten. Most the guys on the rez were shorter, though most of them treated her like an outsider. Not Martin. If only she had the hots for him.

Eew.

The thought of kissing him was just plain gross.

I mean, who kisses her brother? Right?

Henri had to face the fact that she'd been an oddball all her life. Until Mike Rose broke into her pad and smashed through the barrier she'd built around herself, she'd been content enough to accept loner-dom. Heck, no normal guys *ever* thought girls who worked as snipers were hot. And most guys didn't like half-white, Native American girls who could beat them at just about any sport on the planet, or pin their butts to a sparring mat. Not to mention, she couldn't cook worth beans. If it counted, she did keep a tidy house. She was even pretty good at bead work. That was a girly hobby.

Henri shook her head.

Who am I fooling? There aren't any guys out there for me.

She'd known it for years. In fact, everything would be just fine if Grandfather were still alive. She'd always enjoyed working with him in the mine, playing cards and watching DVDs. He didn't care if she cooked a can of chili or barbequed a steak on the charcoal grill. The old man would have eaten burnt eggs if she'd put them in front of him.

The old man.

She looked toward the looming Red Cliffs of Saint George.

Grandfather would have asked the spirits for guidance.

In five minutes, Henri had driven up the steep hill, parked and was now ascending the Chuckwalla Trailhead at a fast march. Once she reached the summit, she gazed over the town that had always been her home. The white Mormon temple stood out as a testament to the first settlers, but what moved her was the sculpted red sandstone that gave Saint George its character—rock which endured through eons of time. Beyond the crisscrossing streets and houses lay the land of Arizona, the land of her ancestors, the Anasazi. And to the east, the jagged cliffs of Zion Canyon peeked above the hills.

Using her wide-angle vision, a sense of calm spread from Henri's chest through her limbs. Taking in a deep breath, she sat cross-legged and let her palms rest on her knees. After two deep, reviving breaths, she became one with the heartbeat of Mother Nature. The spirits of her ancestors calmed the fire in her blood.

Above, a hawk called. Henri saw it in her minds' eye but she didn't move.

I hear you.

The hawk called again, the high pitch sending a shiver through her limbs.

Grandfather walked with pride and with honor. His granddaughter was Soaring-Eagle of the Paiutes. She was not afraid of anything. No one would make her fear the night, and no one could take away her soul. Soaring-Eagle would always walk with pride and honor as a tribute to the man who had raised her.

The hawk's next call was but a whisper on the wind as the tension completely melted from Henri's body. She didn't move as she breathed in tandem with the gentle breeze, soaking in life-giving heat from the sun.

When she finally opened her eyes, she knew her purpose. Her gaze homed in on a hotel not far from the shore of the Virgin River. The Hilton Garden Inn. The place where Mike Rose said he was staying.

He'd offered her a chance to stop Omar Fadli from his reign of terror.

If she could accomplish one thing in this life, it would be to ensure that man never killed again. Fadli craved power. He made weaker people suffer to feed his psychotic need to feel important. How many people had he killed since the Iranian ambassador? How many people had he tortured? How many women had he raped?

Could she stop him?

6

Staying focused on a computer screen wasn't Mike's forte. Put him in the field and give him a target and his focus would hone like a leopard tracking its prey. But right now, Mike wiped his fingers across his eyes and blinked at the hooked-nosed image of his boss staring at him on the screen. Garth Moore was a battle-worn ex-Marine. An American with an impressive dossier, the boss didn't take shit, but sure as hell knew how to dish it out.

"I knew sending you out there was going to be a waste of time, but Lindgren was adamant." Garth chuckled with an arrogant grin that said, "I told you so".

Mike cracked open a pistachio nut and popped it into his mouth. "I didn't say I was giving up. I just said she was tough."

"Well, buck up and pay up. Face it. I won the bet. Lindgren has a line on a guy who won't be such a pain in the ass."

Mike arched his back against a jabbing pain. He'd never met an operative who wasn't a handful in one way or another, especially a woman. But he knew as much as Garth that ICE needed female operatives.

They brought an entirely different dynamic to the world of espionage. Some were worth the headaches, like Olivia Hamilton who just brought down an ISIS harem in Syria filled with European kidnap victims. She and her partner, Logan Rodgers, were now in Pakistan chasing a lead on Fahd al-Umari, the elusive, radical leader of the Islamic State. Mike should be there now. But he didn't lose wagers. He'd find a way to convince Anderson to become a spy if it killed him.

"No bloody way," Mike said. "You gave me a fortnight. That was the deal. If you turn yellow and back out now, you owe me a hundred quid, asshole."

"Hey, watch who you're talking to."

Mike used the touchpad to move the pointer to the "end call" button. "Pardon me, sir." He sniggered. "Same time tomorrow?"

"You'd better have something to report, smartass."

Chuckling, Mike clicked off and headed for the shower. As he turned on the hot water, he was already planning his next attack on the Anderson mine. Nothing like fielding sass from Garth to make him want to win all the more.

He stripped off his shirt and examined the foot-sized bruise over his ribs. It was tender, but he didn't think Henri had broken anything with the vicious side kick she'd planted during yesterday's impromptu sparring round. He pulled back the shower curtain. The lass had some moves, he'd give her that.

Bloody oath, Mike had never seen anyone with her talent, either. She shot perfect holes through four slender leaves as if she could create art with her rifle. Hell, if she didn't make it at the mine, she could start a new art genre—go on the road and give demos at county fairs.

But complimenting the woman on her talent with

a rifle wasn't the way to get through to her. Nope. Spending a bit of time in her place had given Mike a few ideas, though. Make no bones about it, he wasn't about to lose his goddamned bet.

It took him less than five minutes to lather up and rinse off. But he didn't expect to hear a knock at the door when he reached for a towel. His heart skipped a beat. Damn, his Glock was beside the bed. Who knew he was in Utah? Mike had a gazillion enemies, but he doubted anyone would have followed him to the ends of the earth, especially since his passport read Michael MacLeod—an American.

He wiped his face and tucked the towel around his waist. Looking through the peephole was a sure-fire way to get his brains blown out. He cracked the loo door open. "Yeah?" he asked with a growl in his voice.

"It's Henri."

His stomach pulled a handstand then back flipped off the high dive. There was a God after all. In two strides, he opened the door. "Hiya—"

Something made him stop talking. Not that he was planning to pull the lass into his arms and plant a kiss on those delightfully pursed lips but, nonetheless, Mike suddenly was at a loss for words. Henri looked much the same as she did the day before, sans the red dust. *Scratch that*, she looked a gazillion times hotter than the day before. Her lips were shiny, her eyelashes feathery and long and, good God, she had a mane of gorgeous black hair that spilled over her shoulders and down to her waist. Goddess wasn't the right descriptor, though. Boots, jeans, flannel shirt unsnapped low enough to catch a peek of cleavage made her look more like a country western goddess.

She stared at him expectantly. It might have been the light in the corridor, but her eyes were incredibly expressive. And those precisely arched eyebrows slanted over deep pools of liquid chocolate—not milk chocolate—this woman's eyes had the depth of intense, dark, smooth, delicious...

Her lips parted and a sexy tongue tapped the corner of her mouth. "Ah..." Her gaze trailed down to Mike's abdomen as those eyebrows arched higher. Then she stared at his bruise. "Did I do that?"

He glanced down. "Nah...well, aye."

"Sorry." She cleared her throat and started backing away. "It looks like I've caught you at a bad time."

Mike raised his palms and shook them. "No, no, no. I was just about to head to the mine for a friendly visit."

She pointed to the bruise. "You mean I haven't scared you off?"

He chuckled. "If anything, you've made me more determined."

"That makes about as much sense as a bee sucking nectar from a plastic daisy."

"I ken, but you're going to give me an opportunity to explain."

She crossed her arms and shifted her weight to one hip. "I figured I owed you that."

"What changed your mind?"

"I need a new truck and the mine caved in on me yesterday."

"The red dust?"

"Yeah." She crossed her arms. "But this doesn't mean I'm joining you. I'm just considering my options."

Mike glanced to his towel. "I'll be in the lobby in five. Can you wait that long?"

"Five's stretching it."

"Three."

Heading for the lifts, she threw a smirk over her shoulder. "I'm timing you."

HENRI'S FINGERS were still shaking when she hit the lobby. Why hadn't she just picked up a phone and called his room? *I spend three months alone and suddenly I go brain dead?*

She coughed out a groan. Who showers at eleven a.m.? Jeez, it was as if Rose had been sitting around in a towel all morning waiting for her to stop by. Except his hair was wet. *Maybe he just kept wetting it?*

Not.

By the time she sat down and opened a complimentary newspaper, the big Scot slid in beside her on the couch and held up his watch. "Under two minutes."

He could stop with the grin. Now.

She gave him a pointed stare. How men could look like a million bucks by combing their hair, she had no idea. Her gaze trailed down from his jeans to his sneakers. "No socks?"

"Hey, when a woman says she's timing me, I cut every corner possible."

Henri folded the paper and set it on the side table. "I want a steak."

"The Chop House okay, or do you ken of another place in town?"

"The Chop House is fine." At least it was adjacent to the Hilton Garden Inn and they could walk.

She kept him at arm's length as they strode across the parking lot to the restaurant.

"Hey, Anderson," he said like they'd been teammates in boot camp.

"Yeah?"

"Your hair is...ah..."

She brushed it back. "Too long?" She'd never worn it down in the army—against regs.

"No." He shook his head. "Cutting that mane would be a sacrilege."

She pursed her lips to avoid smiling. She might be able to get along with Rose.

After they stepped inside the Chop House, they followed the host to a table in the bar at Mike's request. It was Thursday and there weren't any people in there. As soon as Henri put down her menu, Mike signaled the waiter, they ordered a couple ribeyes and then Mike told the man to leave them alone until the food was ready. As soon as he disappeared, Mike looked across the table. "What do you remember of your meeting with Anders Lindgren?"

"Was that his name?" Henri asked, thinking back. "To be honest, as soon as he told me Omar Fadli had killed the Iranian Ambassador and I was a free woman, I tuned him out."

"Understandable. I probably would have done the same." Mike sipped his glass of water. "Lindgren never has much to say. And he does things bass-ackwards of you ask me."

"He was pretty brief. Wanted a commitment I wasn't half-ready to give." She chuckled. "Was the letter from the President authentic?"

Mike glanced behind him before he answered. "Aye. That's the tool Lindgren uses to get his man—or woman. Truth be told, verra few people ever have the opportunity to meet the Icelander, let alone receive a letter from the leader of their country."

"How were you recruited?"

"Much the same. I was in the SAS. Twenty-second

regiment. Did a fair bit of time in Iraq. Flew home from a tour and happened to be sitting beside Lindgren on the flight."

"Was that a coincidence?"

"Oh, no. Nothing is a coincidence when it comes to ice—ah—I mean Lindgren's operation."

"So, what's the job?"

Mike scratched his neck and twisted his mouth. "Mostly classified. I canna tell you much."

"You've seen my place. I don't even have a dog to tell secrets to."

"What about your auntie?"

"I talk to her as infrequently as possible." Henri huffed. "Look, I'm not signing on for something I know nothing about, otherwise you'll be blowing as much smoke as your Icelandic boss."

The big Scot leaned in, his blue eyes honed like crystal lasers. "Headquarters is not in the US. The ops facility is in a cold and out-of-the-way place."

"Like the North Pole?"

"Close." He gestured with a karate chop. "Only heads of state are aware of our existence, though we're unofficially beneath the NATO umbrella. Because we're an unknown entity, we operate under the radar, so to speak."

"Do operatives have diplomatic immunity?"

"Aye. When they can. And I'm no' going to tell you the work isna dangerous. There aren't many jobs more dangerous, in fact."

"What about money?"

"About three times your service pay for starters. Bonuses for achievement."

"What kind of bonuses?"

He waggled his eyebrows. "Bigger than your salary,

but that depends on who you bring in and how many toes you step on whilst doing it."

Lord knew she needed the cash. "And you said two months off a year."

"Aye. More if you need it, or less if you're in the thick of a shite storm. Our goal is to have people in the field who are focused on one thing."

"The job?" Henri asked.

"Aye, the job."

Two ribeyes with loaded baked potatoes arrived.

Licking her lips, Henri picked up her steak knife. "What if I don't like it?"

"It's a Viking burial, complete with a burning ship. Death is painless and quick." Mike's eyes shifted as he took a sip of water.

If Henri hadn't been trained in Special Ops, she might have bought his line of tripe. Instead, she threw back her head and laughed out loud. "Are you entirely full of crap?"

"Nah." He grinned. Again. God, he could stop doing that. "I couldna help the last line—had to see the look on your face."

"Did I disappoint you?"

"Nope."

She gave him a pointed frown. "Well?"

He shoved a bite of steak in his mouth. "There's an exit plan for retiring operatives, but it does include signing a gazillion nondisclosures on penalty of death."

"Committing treason to...?"

"The world."

"What about training?"

"It's like the military. It's extensive and never ends. But you'll initially receive the spy stuff." Wincing, he rubbed his side—the one with the enormous bruise. "You've got combat maneuvers down pat."

She snorted. Had the little sparring session at the mine been some sort of test? "So, Rose, where do you fit in to all this?"

"I'm a field operative. I go where I'm told...mostly."

"Mostly?"

"We're all big lads and lassies. When I'm in the field, I run my op. There isna much need for orders, except the general ones...'this is the goal, now go achieve it'."

She cut her meat and popped a bite in her mouth. "Why did *you* come to Utah and not someone else?"

"I'm a closer. Garth figured if anyone could recruit you it would be me."

"Because you're a smooth talker or a smooth looker?"

"Neither." He shrugged as if he didn't realize he was hotter than hell on wheels—not just a good-looking dude with muscles, but a jaw-dropping stud with brains, even with the auburn hair. "I just get the job done and I dunna like to lose."

Henri had to admit she was similarly minded. And she wasn't giving up on Grandfather's mine. She was just rearranging her priorities so she could afford the place. She took another bite and her eyes rolled back. "Umm." But she didn't revel in the deliciousness of the meal for long. "If I join you, I want a shot at Fadli. Guaranteed."

"Garth decides where operatives are placed. I canna promise—"

"Whoa." She sliced her hand through the air and stared him down. "You're a closer, but you can't influence this Garth person?"

The corner of Mike's mouth twitched. "Verra well,

I might no' be able to make broad-brush promises, but I can tell you this: If you stay at the mine, you'll never get your chance at Fadli or any of the other scum responsible for the death of your mates in Afghanistan. If you go with me, I'll do my best to make a pitch on your behalf. Besides, ice—ah—I mean this branch of NATO always takes advantage of an asset's talents." He thrust out his palms. "Good God, Anderson, you can pierce the leaves on a Joshua tree from four hundred meters and make it look artful. I have no doubt that's why Lindgren wants you."

"Not good enough." She pointed at him with her knife. Negotiations needed to take place before she signed on the dotted line. "So, we go after Fadli, right?"

"Ah—"

"Don't bullshit me. *You* will make sure I get a crack at him?"

He gave her a point-blank stare. "Yeah. I will after you're trained."

"That's fair." Henri was liking the odds better all the time. "If I agree, then what?"

"I take you to headquarters. You'll have training on gadgetry and spy techniques."

"How long until I'm in the field?"

"That's up to you."

"Will we be training together?"

"Probably no'." Rose shook his head. "You're a rookie and I've been an operative for eight years. Besides, I'm a lone wolf and dunna hang around headquarters much. None of us do 'cause there're too many bloody terrorists and government crooks out there." He scooped a heap of baked potato with his fork. Then his face took on the hard stare of a field general not about to take no for an answer. It was a look that shouted: tell me what I need to hear or I'll kick your sorry ass all the way to hell and leave you there to burn. "What do you say, lass?"

Henri's jaw twitched. Not about to be intimidated because she could kick some ass of her own, she met his stare with one equally as intense. She let the silence hover. It was a good thing there wasn't a candle on the table. It would explode form the tension sparking between them. "I need an open-ended roundtrip ticket."

"That can be arranged."

7

"Hello?" Omar Fadli asked in Arabic, as he answered his cell phone.

"Three months you make me sit in this hellhole scanning millions of airport pictures every day. I swear, this is the most monotonous job I've ever been forced to endure," said Melvut Amri, a young man Fadli was grooming to be part of the Islamic State's inner circle.

"Is that why you called? You should be enjoying the *vacation*. Anyone can do your job, it just takes patience."

"That's the problem," Amri said.

"All young men need to learn patience before they can truly be moved into the limited realm of the elite." Fadli sipped his coffee. "I sense this isn't a social call."

"No. We finally had a hit. Henrietta Anderson flew out of Saint George, Utah on a private jet this morning."

"To where?"

"That's the strange thing. There's no flight plan logged in the database."

A tic twitched above Fadli's eye. Something wasn't right. "Was she alone?"

"No. She was with a man. I'm running his picture for facial recognition now."

"Anything?"

"Still waiting."

The coffee in his gut churned. "I want to know where that plane is headed."

"Wait a minute...."

"You got something?"

"Not sure. It's an old picture from 2003. Computer says it's an 80% match..."

"With?"

"It's an SAS officer. British...that doesn't make any sense."

Fadli's gut squeezed. It made sense all right. It meant Miss Anderson was back in business. "I need to know that woman's location. Make sure our people are on full alert at every airport in the US, Europe and the Middle East."

"Yes, sir."

"And Amri?"

"Yes?"

"It's time to hand the reins over to your assistant. I have a more important task for you."

~

HENRI SHOULD HAVE GUESSED headquarters was in Iceland. Mike had even told her Anders Lindgren was an Icelander. He'd also let the word "ice" slip a couple of times, so it didn't surprise her to discover that ICE was the acronym for the International Clandestine Enterprise, an elite world spy association to which she now belonged. What did surprise Henri was the high-tech environment converted from an underground Cold War bunker in the remotest part of the island country.

The world could suffer a nuclear holocaust and ICE would be unaffected—at least until supplies ran out. Literally everything was state-of-the-art from the situation room, to the command center, to the training center, to Henri's suite.

That's right. She had a suite as if she were staying in a five-star hotel. Everyone did.

Aside from the food being outstanding, it was like something out of *Star Wars*—a sprawling, underground city complete with a PX-type store, a bar and a movie theater.

When Henri boarded the private jet with Mike back in Utah, she'd had her misgivings about traveling to Iceland with him. Still, she'd been at ICE a week and hadn't seen the country. The jet hadn't stopped in Reykjavik or in any town. They'd landed on a glacier between mountains. Batman would have been impressed when they drove a RaptorTrax—a pickup with tank tracks for wheels—into an ice cave. Once inside, they stopped on a frozen platform that looked like it was part of the cave floor. Then Asa, the driver who turned out to be a mega cyber genius, pushed a button and down they went, truck and all. No one on the planet could possibly know ICE ran an entire underground city in the middle of Iceland, forty-five meters beneath a glacier. In fact, not many people even knew of ICE's existence.

Just like the military, they'd thrown Henri into the thick of training as soon as she'd passed the physical. But unlike the military, a fast-track program had been developed specifically for her. At the moment there were a half-dozen computer programmers in training for the cyber counter intelligence division. It was a new dynamic to be training among a bunch of nerdy wiz-kids, but Henri liked it. Since she could run circles around them in military tactics, the trainees looked at her like she was a rock star.

Thus far, mornings were spent on surveillance, gadgetry and languages with the nerds. Surprisingly, Rose was still there. Until he was reassigned, Mike had taken over Henri's afternoons to give her the fast-track, which she quickly learned included lifelike situational traps and involved bruising. Adding to the pain, they always ended the day in the sparring ring.

Henri wasn't about to admit it to anyone, but she hadn't regretted her decision to take the job. Yet.

Of course, her feelings had nothing to do with her trainer being Mr. Stunner. And, better, Rose had shown her moves she'd never seen before. When Henri graduated from spy school she was going to be one badass Paiute.

This afternoon was a little different because her training with Mike would include the cyber nerds. The greenhorns had progressed enough for a face-off in the paintball court. The gym-sized room was military-like, with derelict buildings, stairs, cement columns and it even had a car shot up with a psychedelic pattern of paint. Today's exercise was lights out, using night vision. It was Mike and Henri against Asa and her six cyber trainees. The goal? Eliminate their targets and secure Building 1.

They were suiting up in the blue dressing room while the whiz-kids were at the other end of the paintball court in the red dressing room. "Test," said Mike into the comm.

The sound came through like a blast from a rock concert speaker. Henri clapped a hand over her earpiece. "Hey, whisper, dude."

The big Scot winked. She'd been doing her best to ignore his charm, but Rose was damned irresistible—

especially when he winked. And how the man could make a paintball getup look sexy was bewildering. But he pulled it off just like he pulled off the whole red-headed too-sexy-for-his-shirt thing.

He scraped his teeth over the corner of his lip and looked down, picking up a whiteboard marker. Jeez, part of what made him attractive was he'd throw a cavalier wink and then blush and look away. Yeah, he knew he shouldn't be flirting, the rogue. "Here's the plan," he said, his voice now deep and commanding. He drew a quick diagram of the paintball court and made an X. "We're here. Building 1 is halfway. But across from it is a platform we call the treehouse."

"I'm heading there, right?" asked Henri.

"Yeah. I'll cover you. Make a beeline straight for it, climb up and hide behind the barrier—it's a wall meant to be bulletproof. Once you're in place, give a ready signal."

"Let's tango?"

"Sounds good." Mike drew a line to Building 3, which was nearer the red dressing room. "My guess is the rookies will head directly for Building 1, try to take control and ferret us out from there."

"But we're not going to let them get close." Henri picked up a marker, nudged him out of the way with her shoulder and circled her lookout point. "From here I have a direct shot at Building 1. No one will be able to get inside unless they take me out."

"You got it. And once they realize it's not going to be easy, they'll try to get to you."

"But you'll head them off." Grinning, Henri examined the whiteboard. "It looks good. What are the pitfalls?"

Mike capped his pen. "Their numbers, mainly. Trevor's a pretty good shot."

She rolled her eyes. "Please."

"Well, he's better than the others."

Henri gave him a playful smack on the arm. "They don't have a chance."

He clapped a hand on her shoulder, squeezing his fingers. "I ken."

Sparks of electricity tingled beneath his palm. Henri's breath caught as she met his gaze—blue eyes shinier than a swimming pool in the sunshine, and so very off limits. Tensing, she slipped from under his grasp and shrugged as if he hadn't made her knees turn to Jell-O. "Can't stand to lose, you?"

"Absolutely abhor it." He gave her a long don't-let-me-down look before he put on his helmet and moved to the door. "You ready?"

Taking a deep breath, she pulled back the bolt on her paintball rifle. "Ready yesterday, dude."

As soon as the buzzer sounded, they slipped into the arena. In a crouch, Henri started for the treehouse. Movement to the left caught her eye. Holy hell, the newbies were catching on. They'd split up and fanned out. Not what was expected but, if nothing else, a soldier was trained to improvise. She ducked behind a barrier made to look like a cinderblock fence. Pointing her weapon toward the movement, she locked on her target and took a shot. One down. More movement. Shot two.

"Five to go," Mike said over the comm.

"They're quick studies."

"What did you expect from a mob of glasses-wearing MIT hounds?"

"Heading to the treehouse now. Cover me?"

"I'm all over you like a flea on a rat."

Henri checked 360, then headed off. "You need to work on your analogies, dude."

"I have hundreds of them...it's just some wouldna be workplace appropriate."

Henri almost laughed out loud, but that would have given away her position—way too rookie a move for an ace. The light taps of the enemies' footsteps rang out from the direction of Building 2. No one came close, but the nerds were maneuvering, no doubt. The sooner she got to her spot, the sooner she could eliminate the rest.

Arriving at the bottom of the ladder, she reached for a rung.

Crack!

A ball of paint exploded right above her hand.

Pop, pop. Two more shots came from behind.

Henri hit the ground and rolled behind the ladder. At her six, Mike took out one of the attackers. "A little late on the trigger," she sniped.

"You're still alive, aren't you?"

"Smartass." After checking to ensure no one else had their laser sights trained her way, Henri climbed the ladder. "Let's tango."

"On my way."

Slipping her rifle over the barrier, she used her scope to home in on Mike moving toward Building 3. As she zoomed out, another flicker drew her attention. One of the skills that made an elite sniper was the ability to sense activity by using her peripheral vision. Most humans couldn't perfect it, but Henri had earned the moniker, Psychic Mama by her Delta Force squadron because she was a peripheral vision ace. Could she see things before they happened? No, but she could see them before most everyone else. She shifted the rifle barrel to the right. Before she blinked, she took out enemy number four. The perp stumbled backward, discharging his weapon. Paint splattered on the wall above and behind Mike's head.

"Now who's lagging on the trigger?" he whispered into the comm.

"That one missed you by a mile. Three to go, sport."

Mike disappeared into Building 3 to the sound of ambush fire.

Henri focused, panning her gun across the scene. "Report!"

The big Scot didn't respond, but someone dashed out of Building 3. Henri homed in. *Red-vested enemy, target acquired.*

Crack.

Number five down.

"Mike?"

Still no answer. She could only assume he was down. And by the gunfire from Building 3, she guessed there were at least two red teamers in there.

Henri caught a flicker at Building 1.

Crack. Six down, one to go. Henri's heart rate spiked.

Now it's just you and me, Batman.

The problem was whoever was out there knew she was on the tower. The perp knew she was a sniper. Worse, the mastermind had to take Henri out before he or she could take Building 1.

The hair rose on the back of her neck, the sensation warning her to duck behind the wall. How to stay alive in hell? Henri always, always trusted her intuition.

Pop!

A bullet of paint smacked her hideaway, right where she'd been scoping. She closed her eyes and envisioned the enemy's angle in her mind's eye. Whoever fired the shot had to be near the car. That's right, the perp must have slipped out the back of Building 3.

Henri held her breath and listened. Then she continued to breathe soundlessly while she waited for the perp to move. Ready to pounce, in her mind's eye, she focused on the green, glowing NV image of the vehicle. The shooter was waiting her out.

But Henri was patient. She could wait all day.

"Time to make a move," a deep voice boomed over the loudspeaker. It was Garth Moore, Head of Field Operations. No one in the compound sounded as menacing as the boss. Henri looked to the rafters. If only she'd known the big cheese was watching the exercise go down, she might have been a bit more aggressive. Especially since waiting all day had just been nixed.

Not about to lose against a handful of new recruits, Henri tightened her grip on her weapon. She knew where her target was hiding. Silently slithering to the far corner of the platform, she inched over the wall with her rifle. Firing a barrage of repeating shots, she rose high enough to spot the tip of her target's helmet.

Crack, crack, crack, crack, crack.

The perp didn't have a chance.

The lights flickered on.

Nearly blinded by the sudden burst of fluorescents, Henri slipped her NV goggles up and rubbed her eyes. "What the hell happened to you, Rose?"

"Ambushed." He walked out of Building 3 with a massive splotch of red paint in the center of his vest and another on his thigh. "I think they bugged the blue dressing room."

"Too right," said Trevor from the car while his helmet dripped blue. "The first rule of war is to use spies."

"That's the third rule," Garth barked over the loud-speaker. "But I'm impressed. Rose, you'll have to step it up a notch."

Henri had to laugh. Mike was the best damned combat ad libber she'd ever seen. He had an answer for everything, and the respect he received from the seasoned veterans during meetings in the situation room confirmed it.

Asa sat up from where she'd been shot, blue paint covering her helmet. "That was amazing."

"We'll make a field agent out of you yet," said Garth.

One of the few Icelander's on the team, Asa looked up to the observation window where Garth was still standing. "Who will monitor all the chatter?"

"Multitasking."

Mike gave Henri's elbow a nudge as he headed back to the blue room. "Ready for your sparring session?"

Tingles crackled up her arm and across the back of her neck. Sparring with Rose was invigorating and unbearably frustrating. But it was the best part of every day—the part she looked forward to—the part that made fire thrum through her blood. She sensed today's sparring would contain an added challenge. Then those darned tingles fired across every inch of her body, even in places where they had no freaking business being remotely worked up.

8

Mike's rules of war were based on his past experience and the writings of Sun Tzu. Garth had liked them so much, he'd allowed Mike to introduce his rules into the curriculum for new ICE recruits—at least the first two-dozen rules. The list was lengthy—Mike had developed over a hundred. Since he'd become a spy, one of his favorites was number twenty-six: All warfare is based on deception.

He sat cross-legged in the middle of the sparring mat. The training center was a labyrinth, from the paintball court to the weight room, from the flight simulator to the running track on the mezzanine that surrounded the sparring arena where he did his most intense training. On one wall were mirrors. Off to the side, a myriad of weapons including nunchucks, bow staffs, sparring swords and knives hung from hooks on the walls. Mike liked to spar weaponless the best. A man needed to be able to defend any attack with his hands—that is, as long as he wasn't facing a gun further than ten paces away.

Henri was already a minute late, which gave him time to sink deep into a meditative state. After years of training in martial arts, Mike could reach a level of deep calm even when being smacked in the face, but sitting in the middle of an enormous space with no other sound was a rare and idyllic treat for transporting his mind, body and soul into a level of consciousness akin to floating. Eyes closed, his every breath rushed in his ears. His heartbeat hammered a rhythm in a slow cadence that kept time with the harmony of being.

A door to his right opened and closed. Soft, shoeless footsteps neared and stopped a good six feet away.

There was no need to open his eyes. Mike knew it was Henri. Her walk was like a gazelle's, feminine and light. Men planted their feet harder and slapped the mat.

The air whooshed ever so slightly and Mike pictured her stretching in his mind's eye.

"I think the paintball contest went well," she said. "Natalie told me Garth intervened—gave them about two hours of coaching. It's a wonder we weren't obliterated as soon as we stepped onto the court."

Mike inhaled deeply, keeping himself at his present level of consciousness. He already knew Garth had something to do with the paintball maneuvers. There was nothing the Head of Field Operations liked better than taking seasoned operatives down a notch or two, though it would take a lot more than a two-on-seven match to bruise Mike's ego.

Henri took a step nearer, her gaze boring into the side of Mike's head like a laser. He'd never started a session like this before. The air again whooshed slightly when she sat. "Okay, so we're meditating today. I'm cool with that," she said—almost whispered.

Breathe in. Breathe out.

Mike continued to rise the level of consciousness

until he felt weightless. His breath, his heartbeat intermingled and laced with Henri's. He sensed her aura as it surrounded him. He'd grown to know her scent and it filled him, almost completed him. As their breathing became united, so did the rhythm of their hearts. His mind floating, his body grew aroused. Not exactly the level of consciousness he'd been aiming for but, nonetheless, he wanted to stay there on that plateau. Indeed, the physiological reaction below his waistband wasn't supposed to happen. In fact, it never had happened while meditating. And if there was one thing martial arts had taught him, it was to conquer all his mortal weaknesses.

Time to move.

He opened his eyes to mere slits and gauged the distance between them. If he raised his arm straight to the side, he would be able to brush her shoulder with the tips of his fingers. But any movement on his part would be immediately sensed by Henri. Mike's attack needed to be lightning fast and deadly.

Taking one more deep inhale, he closed his eyes and swallowed.

With a sudden burst, he sprang into action. Rising to his knee, in one fluid motion, he stretched for her shoulder, gripped it in his right hand and swung a roundhouse kick at her face. Knowing her only counter would be a crouch and block, he held back to avoid a crushing impact.

Henri surprised him. Dropping down and twisting toward his thumb, she slipped from his grasp and caught his thigh with an upward heel bump.

Thrown off balance, Mike ran his fingers along Henri's arm and pulled her down to the mat. On his back, he wrapped her up with his thighs and clamped tight. God, his knees nestled in the arc of her slender waist as if they belonged there. His cock lengthened, but he ignored his body. Sexual reactions when sparring with a female weren't new to him, only this surge of lust was so powerful, it pushed his self-control to the ragged edge.

Placing his hand against her elbow, Mike used a tad of hyperextension to roll Henri to her back. He pinned her hands above her head while his body turned to fire.

"You ass," she seethed, her eyes drilling through him. The woman sounded like she was about as turned on as a hippo protecting her young. So much for lustful urges. Gnashing her teeth, she bore down and circled her arms, making Mike fall forward. Then, after planting a knee to his backside, she broke away with her braid following like a bullwhip. In one move, Mike was on his feet facing her.

"Not bad, Anderson," he growled menacingly, making damned sure she didn't think he'd even dreamed about being aroused. If two weren't ready to tango, there'd be no dance.

HENRI CHUCKLED as she circled her opponent. She'd known Mike had something up his sleeve when he didn't respond when she walked in and told him about Garth's intervention. Expect the unexpected— that was the rule to staying alive in this business whether you were working as a combat sniper or an ICE asset.

If she hadn't sensed his attack, he would have nailed her in the face, the turd.

But Mike Rose was a quandary. It was both exhilarating and frustrating to work with him. She'd learned more in the past week than she had during her entire basic training—cool methods of smuggling weapons across enemy borders she'd never dreamed of, makeshift weapons, dismounted surveillance. Every day made her thirst all the more to be out there. And in the sit room, she'd heard the chatter about the free world's greatest enemies with Fahd al-Umari and Omar Fadli topping the list. The excitement pulsing through her veins almost made her forget about the mine. Almost. Every night Henri looked at Grandfather's picture beside her bed and was reminded of her purpose.

Mike lunged.

Henri skittered back, making him miss, but he stopped himself before he stumbled forward.

She threw a roundhouse at his head to distract him, followed immediately by a jab to the sternum. He blocked both. Dropping, he swung a kick at her ankles —trying to make her fall. Henri jumped, but his foot caught her toe. She landed off balance and stumbled backward.

True to form, Mike advanced, giving her no quarter. Before she knew what happened, she was on her back with her wrists pinned but, this time, she couldn't move.

Struggling, she looked into those electric blue eyes staring at her with intensity as well as amusement.

"What are you planning to do next, Anderson?" he teased with a wriggle of his hips. Didn't he know how much that affected her? Damn, the guy made her knees grow weak just by being in the same room. When they sparred, she had to mask her feelings behind a tough-bitch, sergeant persona.

Typical, Mike embodied the bad-boy alpha—the type who always made her melt. All it took was a grin. He perfectly played the part of the smartass flying by the seat of his pants. But that was the draw. Who could resist a guy on top of his game and knew it?

Mike was good.

Too good.

Worse, he constantly needled Garth about getting back into the field. He could be on a plane out of there tomorrow. They had no possible future together. For the love of God, she was half-Paiute and he was a Scot. They had absolutely nothing in common.

"Well?" he persisted.

"Come closer."

He narrowed his eyes. "A head-butt to the snout? I like it."

Henri's tongue slipped to the corner of her mouth. "I dare you."

A low chuckle rumbled from his throat, making vibrations swarm across her skin. But a man like Rose never shirked a dare. As soon as he dipped his chin, Henri stretched up and planted a smooch on his lips.

Mistake.

Major mistake.

With the flash of his eyes, his body crushed over hers as his mouth dove in for the kill with a full-contact, wet-tongued, disarming kiss that would make any woman swoon. Thank God Henri was on her back, otherwise she would have melted into a heap of boneless limbs. Within two swirls of his tongue, she was ready to tear off her clothes and offer to bear his children.

She didn't have a hope of weaseling out of this one. Big, hard male covered every inch of her body. His chest molded into her breasts. But the most shattering feeling of all was his rock-hard cock rubbing back and forth along her crotch. Henri was dizzy with desire and, as he released her wrists, she wrapped her arms around him and clung on for dear life.

His fingers plunged into her hair as his hips relentlessly rocked, disarming her of any thought of attack.

Of course, the bad-boy ace from the Highlands could kiss. He was like a walking advertisement blasting out, "take me ladies, there's none better". He'd probably made love to every woman he'd ever worked with. But right now, Henri didn't care. She tugged up his t-shirt and sank her fingers into the thick bands of muscle on his back. No one was around. He could take her right there on the mat and she'd let him.

He trailed kisses to her ear. "Round, set and match to you, lass."

Could she melt a bit more? Sighing, she chuckled. "I should have known your weakness from the first time I laid eyes on you."

"I—"

A door closed.

Mike rocked onto his haunches, moving faster than a cobra. "Garth?" His voice shot up like an adolescent. "What news from the upper deck?"

After Garth curtly dismissed Henri, Mike swiped his hand across his mouth and faced the CO. Nothing like being caught by the big cheese with your proverbial pants down. How much had Garth seen?

God, he was an idiot. But damn, he'd expected a head-butt, not a kiss. Henri wasn't the type of woman who flirted around, either. The woman was far more likely to deliver a kick to the balls than a friendly pat on the shoulder—or a mind-blowing kiss.

And Mike had fallen for it. He'd not only fallen for it, he'd played right into her hands, practically fucking her right through those blasted yoga shorts that hugged her ass like a second skin.

Garth eyed Mike like he did when he had something up his sleeve—though this time it was probably an assignment in Antarctica. "She's something else."

Those words could mean anything.

"She is," Mike replied.

"Then it's a good thing I need you to leave for Pakistan in the morning. Jesus Christ, what is it about a mop of wild, red hair that women can't resist? You look like Andy Capp on steroids if you ask me."

Mike couldn't help but smirk. "I'd rather think of it as Jamie Frazer on steroids, sir."

"Who the hell is Jamie Fazer?"

"It's a Scottish thing." Avoiding an explanation of the American popularity of the *Outlander Series*, Mike batted a dismissive hand through the air. "So, are things heating up with Rodgers and Hamilton?" he asked, attempting to deflect the focus away from him.

"They are, and I aim to ensure they don't do the same between you and Anderson."

"No, sir." He could bloody kick himself. Lord, he knew better than to get too close to an asset. What the hell was he thinking?

"Good to hear. By the speed with which you were moving when I entered the gym, I had my doubts."

"I thought I was done when I collected my hundred quid." Mike shook his head. "You can bet it's time for me to head back out in the field. I've had enough recruiting and training. Besides, you could put Anderson in the field tomorrow and she'd be fine."

"I'll decide when she's ready."

"Of course." Mike excused himself and headed for the showers. He couldn't get out of there fast enough. Garth frowned on fraternization at ICE, though it happened all around him. Look at Hamilton and Rodgers —they'd spent their entire holidays together at his ranch in Montana. And dammit, who wouldn't go off their trolley after being cloistered underground at ICE for a few months? None of the operatives were robots —possibly aside from Garth. The men and women who risked their necks for the clan were living, breathing people with human needs. They were all young and vibrant and smart and that included being sexually healthy.

If Garth didn't like the idea of Mike kissing Henri, then he could go bite himself on the bum.

After a shower and a rare steak in the mess, Mike headed to the only place he could get a cold beer. The last crew had dubbed the bar the "Ice Cave" and the moniker had stuck. The director of administration even had a sign made and posted outside the door, though it wasn't neon. It was silver and business looking, and followed the same font, size and standard as every other door sign in the compound.

The techie recruits were gathered around the bar, with Ed Sheeran blasting from the red jukebox that played tunes nonstop. But the music was barely louder than the tequila-swilling crowd pounding on the bar and shouting.

Moving closer, Mike homed in on the cause of the brouhaha. Natalie, the Brit from Liverpool, was on her back on top of the bar with her belly exposed. Aaron from Colorado was straddling her legs with a bottle of tequila in his hand while Pam swiped a lime along Natalie's throat and sprinkled on some salt, then squeezed the juice into the lassie's navel.

"Hiya, luv," Natalie yelled from her back, grinning at Mike. "Come have a body shot."

Aaron pumped his arm like a bodybuilder, which he was not. "I'm the body shot challenger of the world!"

Pam from Texas grabbed the bottle of tequila and held it up. "Are you ready?"

"Hell yeah!" Aaron shouted while Natalie sucked in her gut and Pam poured in the tequila.

The crowd pounded the bar shouting, "chug, chug, chug," though all Arron did was lick the salt from Natalie's neck, then slurp the tequila from her belly button. Roaring, he sat upright, flexing his muscles. "I'm the baddest man in town!"

Shaking his head and laughing, Mike moved behind the bar, pulled out an Icelandic Red Ale and popped the top. "You lot are having a piss up without me?"

"Only way to drown our sorrows, mate," said Trevor.

"We nearly had you," said the German.

Mike took a swig. "It'll never happen."

"Not as long as you have Hawkeye watching your back," said Pam.

"You mean Soaring-Eagle?" He leaned his elbow on the bar, unable to stop himself from taking a long visual examination of Natalie's shiny, wet navel.

Still on the bar, she rolled to her side. "Is she really an Indian, luv?" she asked with a slur to her Liverpool accent.

Aaron slid down from the bar and a pulled a beer out of the fridge. "Native American." By the looks of the squeezed limes piled up in a glass, they'd been at it for a while.

"Her mother was a Paiute," said Mike. He took a drink. ICE policy was not to disclose too much about an asset's background, though they already knew Henrietta Anderson's middle name was Soaring-Eagle. Garth had let that one slip.

Natalie ran her finger up and down Mike's bicep. "She's an anomaly."

"She's fucking unbelievable," said Aaron.

Mike nodded and took another pull from his beer, hiding his smile. Unbelievable was right.

"Do sharpshooters turn you on?" Natalie's tongue slipped out the corner of her mouth while she poured a shot of tequila and held it up to him. When Mike refused, she chugged it.

He gave Arron an elbow-nudge. "How long have you lot been at it?"

"Came straight here after Garth chewed us out."

Mike chuckled. He should have known Garth would have had something to say. "Got an old-fashioned, military arse-whipping, did you?"

"Not only that, we're hitting the slopes in the morning—ice climbing."

Gesturing to the near-empty tequila bottle and countless empty beers, Mike shook his head. "Do you have a death wish? All of you will be knackered and chundering up your guts."

Trevor raised his beer bottle. "This is the last round."

"Good thing." Mike lifted his beer to his mouth, but Natalie caught his wrist.

"I dare you to have a body shot," she said, raising her eyebrows and giving him a suggestive bat of her eyelashes.

He gulped, his gaze shifting to her abs—pretty nice abs at that. But he wasn't fooled. This was a bad idea on too many fronts. Though it almost killed him to turn down a dare, Mike shook his head. "Maybe some other time."

"You got it bad for Henri. I knew it," said Pam.

"Beg your pardon, but she's an asset." Mike gestured with his beer to make his point. "And I'm training her, mind you."

Natalie rolled to her back. "Then you need this, luv. It'll help you sleep." She glanced down to his crotch and waggled her eyebrows. "Or not..."

The bloody team started in smacking the bar and shouting "chug, chug, chug."

Mike hesitated while he guzzled his beer. He shot a glance toward the door. He couldn't slip away now. Doing so would make him look like a coward.

And I'm no bloody chicken liver.

Pam swiped the lime along Natalie's neck and sprinkled salt, then picked up the tequila. "Are you afraid, Scottie boy?"

"This Highlander isna afraid of anything." He climbed onto the bar, straddling Natalie while Pam poured the poison.

Natalie gazed at him with half-cast eyes, looking like she wanted a lot more than a lick in the umbilicus. "Come get me, luv."

"Bottom's up." Mike dove in, licked the salt off her neck and slurped the tequila from her stomach, then tried to sit back. Unfortunately, Natalie wrapped her arms around his neck and pulled his face to her lips. He opened his mouth to object and she shoved her tongue inside, giving him a sloppy kiss and finishing it off with a snarky bite to his lip.

Dazed, Mike pushed himself up and rocked back on his haunches. "Didn't see that coming."

Pam slammed the tequila bottle on the bar. "Next time, instead of paintball, we should have a kissing contest—maybe we'd win."

The music stopped.

Everyone looked.

Henri stood beside the silent, light-flashing jukebox looking like she was about to kill something —namely Mike.

Aaron pulled Natalie off the bar. "Come on, Ringo, I'll walk you to your bunk."

Ignoring her teammate, Natalie ran her hand down Mike's thigh and gave his knee a pat. "They call me that on account of my Liverpool roots." She blew him a kiss. "See you later, stud." With a self-impressed snort, she sauntered out the door with the others, waving to Henri.

The problem?

The woman Mike had been dreaming about every night for the last few weeks stood akimbo, her arms crossed, her lips disappearing into a white line, and her eyes looking like they were about to shoot laser beams. Rather than give him an earful, she emitted a dissenting grunt, turned on her heel and headed for the door.

Hopping down, it took Mike three strides to stop her before she made it into the hallway. "Whoa there, lassie."

She jerked her arm from his grasp. "Don't call me that, you goddamned jerk."

"It's no' what it looked like."

"No? So you weren't on the bar straddling a woman, doing body shots, then licking her tonsils."

"You dunna understand." He threw his thumb over his shoulder in the direction of the bar. "They dared me—and Natalie was shitfaced."

"Oh, so you only take advantage of women if you're on top of them in the sparing ring, or if they're steaming drunk."

Mike thrust his palms out to his sides. "I didna—"

"You did. I saw you."

"No. Natalie grabbed me by the neck and kissed me."

"And you kissed her back."

Jesus, if only he could grab her by the shoulders and show her *again* what a real kiss was bloody like—if the angry Pocahontas didn't knee him in the balls in the process. "What was I supposed to do, throw a fist?"

Henri looked to the ceiling and groaned. "What

should I care?" she shouted. "You're my trainer. And you'd better not kiss me with that filthy mouth again. Not. For. Fucking. Ever!"

Mike's jaw dropped as he watched her disappear out the door. A chasm spread through his chest while he stared, silence roaring in his ears.

What the hell just happened?

And like she said, what should she care? They weren't an item.

Maybe this misunderstanding was for the best. They hadn't pledged their undying love. They'd shared a single kiss. A hot, bone-melting, passionate kiss that had set his balls on fire, but it had only been one. Anyway, he was leaving in the morning. God only knew when their paths would cross again.

He moved behind the bar and opened another beer. When that was gone, he drank another. Nothing helped. He'd still be a lout come morning, no matter how much alcohol he consumed. He popped one more top.

The thing that really bit was leaving in discord. It was like walking away from unfinished business. Quarrels always made the muscles between his shoulder blades tense and needle at the back of his mind for bloody months.

Damn it!

10

H enri spent the following two months focused on her training. Money had started going into her bank account and that was all she needed to care about. At least that's what she tried to convince herself. However, not long after Mike disappeared, she'd learned that Natalie made a habit of imbibing in the sauce after a hard day's training and the English chick didn't appear to be discerning as to who she flirted with. If Henri had such intel under her belt at the time, she might have been more inclined to listen to Mr. Rose on what ended up being the last time she saw him.

Every time she replayed the incident in her mind's eye, her gut clamped into a lead ball. If she'd known he was flying out before dawn the following morning, she mightn't have been in such a hurry to leave him in the dust.

Henri's shoulders sagged.

The Scot was all wrong for her anyway, even if hindsight had a way of making people wise. She'd turned her back on the man and he was gone. Since, Henri had thrown herself into training and Garth had invited her to sit in on operations management in the situation room, which was a daily rush. Jeez, she should have sidestepped the Army and joined the CIA. The sit room was like being in the middle of a ten-way virtual reality game, except everything was live and as real as it got. ICE had its talons sunk into every corner of the world. Even Washington.

But today, all the wall monitors in the sit room were displaying scenes from Lasbela, Pakistan. It was dark aside from an illuminated hotel sign in front of a rundown building. Infrared cameras focused on two sides of the hotel with a storefront down below. Above the ground floor, all the room windows had bars...and online the hotel was touted as three-stars.

I'd give it a half-star at best.

Henri had enough experience in the Middle East to know that inside the place had to be a wreck. The beds would be cots covered with frayed linens. The walls would be dingy and covered with holes. If they were lucky, the residents might have the luxury of a bathroom complete with a squatting toilet, comprised of a ceramic hole in the floor. Given the intel, she hoped they weren't lucky. She hoped the place stank like a sewer.

"GoPros going live," Mike's voice announced from the spherical speaker sitting in the center of the teak conference table. A jolt of energy shot up the back of Henri's neck. She knew Mike was in Pakistan, but all the intel they'd received recently had been from either Olivia Hamilton or Logan Rodgers. She had no idea the three had teamed up.

Before she spoke, she insured the mute light was illuminated on the speaker. "How many assets are going in?"

"Three. Rose, Rodgers and Hamilton," said Garth, taking his usual seat at the head of the table and rubbing his hands. "There's nothing like watching an op go down and these pros will make you appreciate what it's like to be in the middle of a shit storm."

"With all due respect, sir, shit storms are what Deltas are made for, much like Marines."

Garth gave her a wink. "I knew I'd like you, Anderson. Once you came around." He picked up his screen highlighter pen and drew an orange circle on the map in front of him which was mirrored by monitor three that took up the entire north wall. Number three was always used for the hottest action, though there were ten enormous monitors lining the room. "Intel has it al-Umari is on the third floor."

"Why is he staying in such a hellhole?" asked Henri. "He's loaded."

"It's a smoke screen. Hell, bin Laden lived in a cave. You know that. You were there." Garth pointed to the circle he'd drawn. "Our team is here, across the street from the Al-Khalid Hotel."

More monitors lit up, showing the feed from the GoPros attached to each operative's helmet.

"We're locked and loaded, sir," Olivia's voice came over the intercom. "Sniper's on the roof."

Henri's heart rate sped. She should be on the roof. She was the only person she knew who could keep Mike safe. "Who's up there?"

"Stephan," said Garth. "A German. Good but not as accurate as you."

"No one is." Dammit, why hadn't Henri been told about this? She could have hopped on a flight to Pakistan yesterday.

Garth gave her a scowl and pushed the button to unmute the microphone. "Green light. Kick some ass!"

Henri gripped her leather armrests and leaned forward, looking at the GoPro feed from each of the three operatives. Not a word was said as they scurried single-file through a narrow passageway.

Someone opened a door for them.

Henri pushed the mute button. "Who's that?"

"One of our insiders."

"A local?"

"Yeah. Recruited by Hamilton. Damned brilliant how she got inside—an example for the classroom."

But there was no time to ask more questions. The team darted up a flight of stairs without a sound. Henri's gaze shot from one dim image to the next as she frantically tried to determine which picture was coming from Mike's camera.

A hand went up in front of camera two.

All three stopped.

The hand pointed—it was a masculine hand.

Henri leaned forward, clamping her fingers tighter.

The asset with camera three traversed to the opposite side of the stairs. They were moving in a crisscross pattern, obviously setting up to pass through some kind of doorway or corner.

Camera three focused directly on the lead man.

Mike!

Henri's heart flew to her throat and stuck there. Why did he have to take the lead? The leader was always the most likely to be shot.

"Breathe, Anderson," Garth growled.

"I should have his back—I mean their backs."

"Mm hmm."

Mike darted into an open space. His camera sent back the image of an empty corridor. Camera two dashed for the next flight of stairs, followed by camera three. In a few seconds, all three of them had climbed up to the third floor. Henri had figured out that Logan was camera three and Olivia two.

This time, Mike crossed the stairwell to provide cover from the left while Olivia moved, M4 muzzle first into the corridor.

Something metallic flickered on camera one's screen.

"Stop!" Mike's urgent voice boomed in a strained whisper.

Eyes popping wide, Henri's gaze flashed across the monitors.

WTF?

"Shit!" Olivia's feed spun back to the men.

"What?" asked Logan.

"Trip wire," said Mike, his cam focused on the thin string.

Henri gasped.

Olivia's pant leg was brushing the wire.

"Back down," said Logan.

"What if it goes off?" asked Olivia, her whisper crisp and urgent.

"It would have already blown." Logan sounded awfully sure of himself.

Henri looked to Garth and asked, "What are the chances it's motion sensitive?"

The CO's eyes shifted her way. "I don't like it."

"I don't either." Henri's mind raced. "What choices do they have?"

Garth flicked on the speaker. "Logan's right."

Logan moved down the flight of stairs then turned and focused his GoPro on Olivia. "Turn and dive. I'll catch you."

She nodded. "Count of three?"

"Three," said Mike. "Two, one."

A brilliant flash of light lit up all three screens followed by darkness.

"Report!" bellowed Garth.

Nothing came back, not even static.

Henri didn't breathe while she and Garth stared at the dim and cloudy monitors. It was impossible to discern anything.

Mike's finally showed movement—a hand swatting away dust.

Someone coughed.

"Report!" Garth boomed again.

"Lionheart here." It was Mike.

"Cowboy crushed but not broken," said Logan.

"A miniscule flash bang can't take down the Duchess." Olivia grunted. "But I have one hell of a sore arse...not to mention a bloody leg."

Thank God, they'd all survived.

"Checking for enemy snoops." Mike slowly ascended the stairs. After verifying the corridor was empty, he focused on the damage. "Looks like a crappy IED."

Garth let out a quick breath. "It's a good thing, otherwise I'd be down three assets."

Mike's camera nauseatingly moved back and forth. "The place looks deserted."

"A trap?" asked Henri.

"Looks like it." He moved down the corridor and opened one of the doors to an empty room. "There's nobody up here."

Henri glanced to the outside monitors. They all looked clear.

"God dammit," Garth barked. "Get the hell out of there, now! They just might have a backup plan. Eyes, you see any spooks?"

"No, sir." A different voice with a heavy German

accent came through. The reply must have come from Stephan on the roof across the street.

"We'll rendezvous when we get back to the Ponderosa. Roger and out," said Logan.

"Keep your comms on and don't be a damned hero. If you need support, ask for it. I've got a line on a few helos itching to fly in and save your butts." Garth pushed the mute button.

"You think they'll see more trouble?" Henri asked.

"Doubt it. Whoever set that IED wasn't a pro—probably some lackwit they pulled off the street as an afterthought."

When Mike's monitor went black, Henri turned her attention to Garth. "So, Olivia's lead didn't pan out?"

"That's their next problem. They'll have to start from ground zero." He slammed his fist on the table. "Damn. Six months of work down the shitter."

The door to the sit room swung open. Asa strode inside with her laptop under her arm. With a thin line to her lips, she moved straight to Garth and opened the computer in front of him. "There's just been a bank heist in Avignon."

"Jesus Christ, can't you see I'm in the middle of a crisis here?" Garth shoved his chair back and scowled. "What would I care about a heist in France?"

Asa shot an eye-roll to Henri. Letting out a deep breath, the ICE whiz-kid made a few clicks on her laptop and brought an image up on the enormous north-wall monitor. Blurry, it looked like three men dressed in ISIS black were running out of a bank. "You know I wouldn't march in here without a reason, sir." She grabbed the CO's laser pointer and directed it at the guy carrying a briefcase. "See the tat?"

Garth drew a hand down his mouth. "Holy shit. In Avignon?"

Henri homed in on the tattoo. It was an insignia of the ISIS flag. "But that doesn't make sense. Islam forbids body art."

"Not when it's a recruit," said Garth. "There are plenty of tattooed rebels out there who've gone to the dark side."

"Do you think it's al-Umari?"

"I think he ordered the heist, at least." Garth looked between the two women. "The bastard is everywhere."

"The chatter says over million euros in uncut diamonds and precious stones were stolen."

"That ought to keep the bastards in guns and ammo for a while." Garth thrust his finger at Henri. "Anderson. I need someone in Avignon ASAP. It's a fact-finding mission. Meet with the banker, do some digging with the locals. Find out if this is ISIS or wannabes. I'm not throwing ICE assets at this until I know for sure that Fahd al-Umari and his radicals are behind it."

11

fter landing at *Avignon Provence Aéroport*, Henri rented a car and drove straight through the medieval fortress walls of the city. She'd been on a half-dozen tours of duty overseas, but had never seen roads as narrow as in France. At least they were paved, albeit with cobblestones and definitely were not built for cars. She parked in a miniscule spot several blocks away from the *Banque Palatine*. One of the perks about being an ICE asset was the IDs. She'd been issued with several, some of which were in a safe deposit box set up for her in Reykjavik. For this trip she was using an American passport in the name of Samantha Smith and it had been accompanied by an Interpol badge.

Her stomach erupted with a case of butterflies as she stepped out of the car and straightened the jacket of her black pantsuit. It had been awhile since she'd dressed up—just about two-and-a-half years and now she'd swapped out her Army uniform for the suit of a spy. Henri might be ready to fly solo with an op but, for some unknown reason, nerves decided to hit. Maybe because she was a tell-it-like-it-is gal and now she needed to walk into the bank pretending to be someone else.

Taking a deep breath, she squared her shoulders and proceeded to walk through the narrow lane. The bank was situated behind a cement wall in the narrowest road Henri had seen yet. Why anyone would try to stage a heist there was insane...though that's what everyone else must have thought as well, which could be why the thieves had been successful.

After taking a good look around the exterior, she proceeded through the front door. She stood for a moment, using her wide-angle vision, noting everything from behind a pair of sunglasses. The *Banque Palatine* looked as small on the inside as it appeared on the outside, though across from the tellers was an iron gate with marble stairs leading to a lower level. A small, brass plate read *voûte*—vault.

A security guard stepped in front of her. "*Puis-je vous aider?*" he asked if he could help her.

Henri's French had improved at ICE and she'd memorized a few phrases on the flight. "*Le directeur?*" She flashed her badge. "Interpol."

"*Attendez ici,*" he said, telling her to wait there. "*Êtes vous Anglaise?*" he asked if she was English.

"*Oui.*" It was easier to say yes than to explain that she was an American.

Henri's fingers drummed her thighs as she waited. Three tellers were on shift and they all checked her out, stealing curious glimpses from their work. The tension in the air was thicker than smoke. But that was understandable. Everyone must be totally nervous considering the bank had just been robbed.

Asa had only shown Henri the one still of the suspects getting away, but there were cameras everywhere, even one directed straight at her with its red recording light on. She turned her back and watched the activity on the street—not that anyone would be looking for her. After all she'd been in the field as an ICE asset for about two hours.

Five minutes later, the manager came out and greeted her in English as he led her to his office. He introduced himself as Richard Laplante. "I'm surprised to see Interpol brought in. Are the thieves part of an international crime ring?" he asked, gesturing to a leather chair. Richard was a short man, gray hair, glasses and a paunch he hid under his coat and tie.

"That's what I aim to find out." She sat, taking in everything from the Dell computer to the empty cup and saucer on the man's desk. "I just stepped off the plane and this is my first stop. Do you know if there are any leads?"

He shook his head. "There were no prints."

Henri thought back to the hand in the photo. The tattoo had been on the man's wrist. "Were they wearing gloves?"

"*Oui*, rubber gloves."

"What about the cameras? Have you given the footage to the police?"

"The cameras were disabled."

"And that didn't set off an alarm?"

"If it had, we'd be a million euros in gemstones richer, would we not?" He crossed his arms and sat back. "You can collect all this information from the police. The suspects came into my bank with guns after they'd disabled the entire security system—including the teller crisis buttons."

Henri mirrored his position. "How easy is that to do, Mr. Laplante?"

He shook his head. "I wish I knew. We had the latest system installed only a month ago."

Henri pulled out a notepad and started writing. "Do you have footage of the workers?"

"They were all licensed and bonded."

"That may be, but I'd still like to see the footage. Can your IT person send me a file with the recordings from the dates of the installation?" She handed him one of the business cards she'd received right before she'd left ICE.

His gaze shifted sideways. "I suppose it wouldn't hurt."

"No, it wouldn't, would it?" She thought about asking if he'd given the information about the new system to the local police, but decided against it. If Asa came up with anything that would interest the local authorities, it would be shared through NATO. It was best for Henri to play her hand close to her chest—keep things as wrapped up as possible. She gestured to the card balanced in his fingertips. "When can I expect the file?"

"You're an American are you not?"

"I'm an Interpol officer, and I'm trying to uncover clues to retrieve your million euros in gemstones." She slid her finger across her phone's screen and opened the photo Asa had put up in the ICE sit room. "How was this photo taken?"

His eyebrows arched as he examined the shot. "The security guard snapped it with his camera phone as the thieves were leaving."

"He had use of his phone?"

"Only after they stopped pointing their guns at him."

∼

LIFE HAD BEEN good to Omar Fadli over the past few years. Though he'd been through hell to get there. An orphan of war, he'd endured conditions far worse than most of his brethren. He'd been taken by Fahd al-Umari at the age of twelve and from that time he carried an AK-47 in his hands. The caliph had taught him to be a soldier and the rigid values of the Islamic State. Fadli had been given increasing responsibility and chances to prove his use to the cause until he'd become a part of al-Umari's inner circle.

And his successes were on the rise. So was his power. In fact, Omar had carefully laid plans to build a dynasty.

After the assassination of the Iranian ambassador to America, Omar had been rewarded with a villa near Baghdad. He sat beneath the awning on his veranda with his feet up. His laptop was opened but he ignored it, preferring to enjoy his coffee.

The computer dinged, announcing an e-mail. He considered turning off the volume but chose to take another sip of coffee and enjoy the view of his pool down below. Who would have ever guessed the boy who begged on the streets of Aleppo would grow rich enough to own a home with servants for his wives and a pool?

He was blessed by Allah and, for that, he should be working twice as hard as he'd done before his rise to wealth. After all, al-Umari was growing old. He needed a strong successor in whom the ideals of the Islamic State could be truly realized. With that thought he heaved a sigh, sat forward and tapped the touchpad. He took another sip as he opened an attachment from the ISIS surveillance group.

Then he spewed coffee across his monitor.

Swiping the liquid away with a napkin, he leaned closer and read the e-mail.

Facial recognition flagged this picture of an ISIS enemy exiting the Avignon airport at 20:00 yesterday afternoon.

Snatching his phone from the table, Fadli made a quick call.

"Hello?" the voice asked in Arabic.

"How soon can you get me on a plane to France?"

"I'll need to have papers made first. Could take a week."

"You have a day."

12

Since it was clear the trail had gone cold in Pakistan, Mike headed for ICE and a new assignment. Hamilton and Rodgers could pick up the pieces in Lasbela and Mike was only getting in the way.

The problem? Henri wasn't in Iceland.

Mike wouldn't admit it to a soul, but he kinda missed the hotshot. He'd felt terrible about the way they'd parted, even though Henri was the one who'd walked away in a snit. Worse, he hadn't had a chance to say goodbye, and then it had felt too awkward to send her an e-mail. God, he was a wanker. They'd shared a kiss. So big deal.

Another reason for not e-mailing was Mike didn't like using internet communication when in enemy territory. No matter how much the gadget geniuses told him no one could crack ICE encryption, Mike didn't buy it. Anything could be cracked, and the moment he veered from his hard and fast rule, he'd end up with a bullet in his brain.

Now back at ICE, he took his laptop to the lab for a scan—maintenance all operatives did when they were at headquarters. "Hiya, Asa. What's the chatter about today?"

The lass looked at him through black, plastic-framed glasses that made her eyes appear enormous. "There are more thugs out there every day." Her screen was processing data a gazillion bytes a minute and she stared at it as if she could read every word.

Mike slid his laptop in the docking station and started his scan. "You need the speed of a quantum computer."

"Jà, tell me about it." She sat back, still watching her screen. "I'm running facial recognition on a file Henri sent."

"Where is she?"

"Following up on a bank heist." Asa switched her monitor to a blurry picture of men in black, one with a briefcase in his hand.

Mike leaned closer. The man's sleeve had hitched up, exposing his wrist. "Is that—?"

"A tat of the ISIS flag."

"You dunna see that every day. Where was it taken?"

"Avignon, France."

"What did Henri send you?"

"Footage of men installing a new security system in the *Banque Palatine* right near the town center."

"She thinks they're the culprits?"

"Could be."

Mike scratched his chin. "You think it's an ISIS job?"

She gave him a look over the rims of her glasses. "Ask Garth. I'm just a techie."

"Right, and I'm just a grunt."

Asa snorted as she reverted to the other screen. The data had stopped and two pictures stared back at them. One of a worker, and the other of a guy who looked identical to the first, wearing a black jihadi uniform and brandishing an AK-47. "This says his name is Melvut Amri. From Turkey. Suspected ISIS recruit. Before he went loco, he worked as technician for a security company in Istanbul."

Mike's gut twisted. Garth had sent a newbie asset into an ISIS firestorm? "Can you find a picture of his wrists? Who does he work under? Where is he now? How the hell did he get to France? Christ, is Anderson safe? Who has her back?"

Asa's fingers flew across her keyboard. "You bark worse than Garth—and you'd better talk to him about Henri. As far as I know he sent her on a fact-finding mission and that's what she's doing, finding the facts."

Mike headed for the door. "I want every tidbit of information on that bloke as soon as it crosses the wire. Make it your top priority."

Asa's fingers didn't stop. "I'll do what I can but—"

"I'm off to have a word with Garth right now." Mike could have blown steam out the top of his head. What was Moore thinking, sending a rookie into a hostile situation? He stormed up the stairs and down the long passageway to the command center and burst through the doors. It took half a second to spot Garth standing with his arms crossed, looking up at a monitor. Mike forwent a greeting and jumped straight to the point. "What have you heard from Anderson? Did you know an ISIS militant installed the security system at the bank in Avignon? Who's got her back?"

Garth straightened, giving Mike a quizzical look. "Whoa, back up there, soldier. What did you say about the security system? Have you been talking to Asa?"

Mike thrust his fists into his hips. "I have and the guy's name is Melvut Amri. He's a recruit from Turkey.

Asa's digging up more intel now, but it stinks like terrorist shite, and we've put a greenhorn in over her head."

"Don't get your panties in a twist. Anderson is only gathering intel." Garth pulled his phone from his belt. "But if what you say is true, the pot just started to boil."

Damned straight.

Mike paced while Garth put his phone to his ear. "Asa. Why is it Rose knows the name of the Avignon robber before me? And he's confirmed ISIS? On our most wanted list? Good God. What about the tattoo? It belongs to Melvut Amri? I need details! Faster! Why the hell didn't you tell me about this sooner? Oh? That's not an excuse!"

By the time Garth tapped the end button, his face was scarlet. He sucked in a deep breath and regarded Mike with a pair of enormous eyes. "This just went to DEFCON I, my friend."

Mike headed for the door. "Order me a private jet. I'm going in stealth."

13

Sitting in an antique, French Provincial chair in her hotel room, Henri clicked off an encrypted video call with Garth. She couldn't help but take a moment to revel in her achievement. First job out and she'd gotten a dynamite lead. And now they had proof ISIS was in the middle of the bank's security system install. She'd know it from the moment Richard Laplante had mentioned the work had been done. The concerning part was that Melvut Amri seemed to have disappeared along with the gemstones. Since the heist, there had been no major arms purchases or movements, at least none that ICE had uncovered as of yet.

From the intel provided by Asa, the local police hadn't turned up anything either. For the time being, Henri had opted to stay away from local law enforcement and Garth agreed. The sooner the cops found out that Amri was involved, the sooner every journalist in the free world would be turning him into a celebrity headliner. If Amri hadn't gone underground yet, he'd go into hiding when his face popped up in newsfeeds across the world. Then they'd never find him.

Now that she had a picture of his face on her phone, she could do some snooping of her own, maybe uncover a line on Amri's whereabouts before Mike arrived.

Yeah, Mike.

Her stomach fluttered. Rose was already on a jet headed for Avignon. And she didn't want to come across looking like a rookie twiddling her thumbs waiting for the seasoned operative to arrive. She might be new to ICE, but she had years of warfare under her belt, which included being a sleuth.

She shook her head. So, Garth thought she needed backup. Didn't he know she could handle herself? Delta Force soldiers routinely handled sticky situations. She had firsthand experience in interrogation and surveillance. Heck, her education at ICE had only served to enhance skills she'd already honed years ago —aside from walking into a foreign bank pretending to be an Interpol officer—and she'd pulled off that ruse just fine, by the way.

Wearing a pair of jeans, black boots with two-inch heels and a light jacket, Henri headed out. While she'd been waiting on information to return from Asa, she'd spent some time walking the streets of Avignon. It was a relatively small city with much of its medieval architecture unchanged—in fact the city was awe-inspiring, a cool place to explore even if she was on the job.

She headed for a café she'd found in the shadier side of town. Middle Eastern music had resounded out to the sidewalk and as she'd gone past, she saw women wearing hijabs inside. At least it was a place to start.

When she arrived, it was 4 p.m. A little early for dinner, but that also meant they wouldn't be busy.

And she was right. A group of men sat at table in the back and when she stepped inside, their conversation stopped. All heads turned her way. Henri smiled and waved at a woman standing near the cash register and wearing a pink hijab. "*Bonjour*," she said doing her best to impersonate a tourist. "This looks like a cool place to eat. Mind if I take a seat?"

The woman glanced back to the men before she picked up a menu and gestured to a table. Henri sat in a chair where, if she turned her head right, she could see the men and, to her left, she had a clear shot at the door. After ordering grilled eggplant with feta cheese and pomegranate sauce, she pretended to use Instagram while she took a couple of pictures of the men who had reverted to their conversation.

The waitress brought her food and Henri licked her lips. "This looks delicious." When the woman glanced sideways with uncertainty written on her face, Henri gave her rudimentary French a try. "*Merci. C'est très bon.*"

"*Bon appétit*," she responded, though she didn't smile.

The meal was good and Henri took her time. Another man came in and, after giving her a once-over, headed back to join the men. They were speaking Arabic, though not loud enough to make anything out. Her biggest language focus at ICE had been Arabic.

To buy time to draw out her surveillance, she ordered dessert and more water. By the time the woman brought the bill, she even smiled. Henri paid in cash and, right before she stepped outside, she showed the waitress the picture of Melvut Amri. "*Avez-vous vu cet homme?*" Have you seen this man?

The waitress' eyes widened and she glanced back to the men before she shook her head with no trace of a smile. In fact, there was no mistaking the fear in her eyes. "*Non.*"

Henri pocketed her phone. "*Merci.*"

As she left, the hair at the back of her neck prickled. Obviously, the woman had lied. Moreover, something sinister appeared to be brewing. Before Henri crossed the street, she glanced over her shoulder at the café, then again when she turned the corner. It wasn't until she reached the next block that she saw him—a man following. Of Middle Eastern descent, he stood about her height, stocky, sunglasses, black slacks, white shirt with a collar.

Thinking fast, she slipped into a pub. The air was hazy with cigarette smoke. The patrons had their eyes glued to a game of soccer on a big screen over the bar. Henri spied the *Toilette* sign and strode toward it with purpose. She even smiled and waved at a complete stranger on the way. The bathrooms were down a dimly lit hall that ended with a door to the alleyway. Henri pushed outside and looked both ways. The man on her tail wasn't in sight. She ran westward, taking a circuitous route to her hotel, checking all directions at every turn. She didn't see the tail again.

At the café, she'd paid in cash and hadn't given her name. If those men were friends of Melvut Amri, there was no way they'd be able to find her. On the other hand, if they had been watching the bank, there could be a remote possibility that someone involved in the heist had seen her there.

But people go to banks, even tourists.

After Henri was absolutely positive she'd lost the tail, she walked in the door of the Hôtel La Mirande. The place was fancier than any accommodation the army had ever supplied, and stepping inside was like traveling back in time to an era that moved at a slower pace. Classical music softly floated through reception. Antique furniture filled the vestibule. Even Henri's room had been decorated with French Provincial furniture; it even had quaint, yellow wallpaper with roses.

Regardless of the relaxed atmosphere, she remained on full alert. As she headed for the stairs and straight up to her room, every flicker of movement processed through her mind with the speed of a microchip. Adrenalin still pumped through her blood. She needed to send the pictures she'd taken to Asa to run through ICE's system. First thing in the morning, she'd set up surveillance of the café. Good thing Mike was coming in. He could help with that.

After swiping her keycard, Henri opened the door and switched on the light.

A flicker of movement made the hair on the back of her neck stand on end. Gasping, a jolt of electricity shot through her blood. She ducked. But her flinch wasn't fast enough to completely avoid the thrust of the fist aimed at her face. As she moved, knuckles grazed her ear.

In a heartbeat, four things about the assailant flooded her mind: a ski mask, a man, her height, sixty pounds heavier.

Henri blocked his next strike with a downward heel pump while she threw an elbow into his temple.

As the man recoiled, she went on the assault with a jumping side kick to the ribs. He doubled over with the impact and spun away. She lunged, aiming a karate chop to the jugular.

Blocking, he caught her wrist midair and twisted her arm up her back. Henri fought to unwind, but the man was stronger than an ox. Gnashing her teeth. She ran the heel of her boot down his shin and stomped

on his arch. Grunting with pain, the thug only tightened his grip.

"At last I will watch the life drain from your face,"
he growled in her ear.

Henri's blood ran cold. The accent was Middle
Eastern—but it wasn't his accent that made his words
menacing, it was the pure hatred in his voice. Braving
the pain from her arm being wrenched up her spine,
she twisted and reached for his mask. Stars darted
through her eyes while she ground her teeth against
the agony of stretching sinew. His hand reached for
her neck. She had no choice but to abandon her escape and block the choke hold with her fingers.

Gaining the upper hand, the man tightened his
grip like a boa constrictor as he pressed his lips to her
ear. "I like women with fight."

She gasped for air, her temples pounding. Unwilling
to quit, her gaze shifted side to side as she planted her feet.
Bucking, Henri threw an elbow to his flank, nearly dislo-
cating her arm from her shoulder socket. With his jerk to
the side, she bent her knee and flipped him onto his back.
He released her wrist. From the floor, the bastard threw a
side kick to her knee. Henri jumped away. He sprang to
his feet. Leading with his shoulder, he tackled her. As her
back crashed into the floor, pain didn't register.

Arching her spine, she slammed a heel punch to
his nose. He countered with a jab as he straddled her,
forcing the wind from her chest. Henri parried his
hand away. Again, he caught her wrist. With all her
strength, she levered her arm toward his thumb,
caught the back of his elbow and hyperextended his
arm as she rolled. Straining, he kept the upper hand.
The ass was too damned strong and too damned
stupid as she bent his arm to the point of breaking.

Henri's muscles burned. Fighting with every shred of strength, they struggled in a battle of brutal force and wills while Henri gasped for air under the attacker's crushing weight.

The door swung open.

A new surge of power shot through Henri's limbs as Mike bellowed like a madman, pulling the attacker to his feet and pummeling him with a barrage of fast jabs.

Henri dove for the man's mask and yanked it off.

Shit!

Omar Fadli shot her a look of pure hatred as he broke away from Mike and ran for the window. Glass shattered with a deafening crash.

"We're two stories up!" Henri ran.

Mike reached the window a step behind her.

Down on the sidewalk, Fadli was already up and escaping with a limp. He jumped into the passenger side of a black Mercedes. The car's wheels screeched as the car sped away.

"God damn," Henri hissed still catching her breath. "He's the last person I expected to attack me. I-I'm hunting *him*, not the other way around."

Mike stuck his head out the broken window. "Was that Omar Fadli?"

"Same likeness as his picture."

"I thought it had to be Melvut Amri until you pulled off his mask."

"It's unbelievable." She'd never forget the steely-eyed glare of the man who framed her for murder.

"Now there's no question." Mike pulled his head back in. "Those two must be in cahoots. But how did he ken you were here?"

"Don't know. They might have a feed from the

bank cameras." Rubbing her jaw, Henri shifted her gaze to Mike. "Thanks for the help."

"You okay?" his voice sounded a little choked up. He reached out like he was going to pull her into an embrace, but only placed his hands on her shoulders.

"Yeah, nothing a soak in a tub of ice won't fix." Her gaze trailed aside as she clenched her fists to stop the damned shaking—she wasn't the type to lose it. Ever. And now that she wasn't fighting for her life, it was damned awkward to have Mike Rose, spy extraordinaire, burst into her hotel room and rescue her from her nemesis. She didn't need rescuing. What she needed was to keep it together and act like a Delta Force badass.

Mike gently tilted Henri's chin toward the light and hissed. "We need to get some ice on that."

She looked up and met his gaze and suddenly nothing hurt. Her mind blanked. Jeez, when blue eyes like that were looking at a woman, who needed painkillers?

Then those blues grew dark and dangerous. Mike's jaw twitched. "I could have killed that bastard."

She chuckled. "I tried."

"It's a good thing I came when I did."

"I nearly had him."

"Aye. That's why he was on top of you." The big Scot's jaw twitched as he pulled her into his arms and pressed his lips to her forehead. "I dunna ever want to see that again."

Henri's next breath came with a shiver. Her skin tingled with the feeling of his warm breath on her forehead. All she wanted to do was melt into him, feel those brawny arms surround her, listen to him promise to protect her.

But she forced her muscles to stiffen. God, she was

an idiot. When in her life would she not fall for the wrong guy? Mike was her co-worker. She couldn't melt into his arms and turn gooey.

But she was too spent to push him away. Sighing, she settled for resting her head against his shoulder, a well-muscled, powerful, protective shoulder. The next thing she knew, her arms were around his waist. "We should go," she said, despite her heart demanding the contrary.

"You're right. I need to get you someplace safe, ASAP." He inclined her chin upward with the crook of his finger. Warm lips kissed her ever so softly. Though just a peck, Mike's lips imparted more emotion than a sonnet. Warning lights flashed in the back of her mind as her heart won the battle—*just this once*.

"I missed you, Eagle Eyes."

Shit. She'd missed him, too.

14

Mike took Henri to a safe house in the countryside near Avignon. It was an unassuming stone cottage nestled between vineyards. Quaint with one bedroom, it would do until they got a handle on the extent of the Islamic State's presence in France.

Once he'd ensured the place was safe, Mike had stopped at the local shop to stock the kitchenette, including a few bottles of French wine. After the Fadli attack, they both could use a drink.

He carried the packages inside and set them on the counter. "I'm home, dear," he jested while putting some ice in a plastic bag.

"In the bath," she said as water splashed behind the door of the WC. Mike grinned. The greatest asset of the cottage was the enormous claw-footed bathtub —Henri had spotted it first. Before reaching for the knob, he stood with the bag of ice in his hand and listened for a moment. His biggest dilemma was his head was in sharp disagreement with his cock. He didn't trust himself to go in there at the moment. Bloody hell, he'd already kissed the lass. He'd even told Henri he'd missed her. He couldn't let himself slip again. No matter what his cock might be thinking, they were now on an op together which meant it was no time to strike up a romance. Besides, Mike didn't sleep with co-workers.

"May I come in?" he asked.

Water trickled. "Do you have that ice?" Did her voice have to sound sultry enough to melt butter? He could do with the badass sergeant voice she'd used when they first met.

"Aye."

"Okaaaaay. But in and out. No cheap thrills. We're on assignment, remember?"

The last comment was due to the kiss. Jeez, he shouldn't have let loose with that one. And she was right. This was work. Life threatening, dangerous work. Neither one of them could afford to let down their guard. Steeling his resolve, Mike sucked in a breath and opened the door. He was both disappointed and relieved. Henri had found some bubbles and all he could see was her lovely but bruised face peeking above the foam. "How are you feeling?" he asked.

"Better." She reached up with a slender arm and took the ice. "My body likes the warmth of the water, though I'd probably feel less pain in the morning if I were sitting in a tub of this stuff." She put the cold pack against her chin and hissed.

"Do you have any other bruises...ah...below the water line?"

"Several. But none I'll be showing you." She leaned her head back. "Didn't you say you were going to bring back some wine? We're in *France*, you know."

He held up a finger. "Aye, the perfect medicine after a good thrashing."

"Hey, by the way he was limping I reckon Fadli ended up worse off."

"Whatever you say." Mike left the door open as he headed for the kitchenette.

"That leap two stories down had to hurt," she said, raising her voice. "And I'm pretty sure I broke his nose."

Mike popped the cork on a bottle of Bordeaux. "Good on you. I'm impressed."

"Thanks."

After pouring two glasses, he headed back to the WC, bottle tucked under one arm. "What I dunna understand is what Omar Fadli is doing in France. He's number two on Interpol's most wanted list."

Henri sat forward a bit to take the glass. Mike wasn't sure, but he could have sworn he caught a glimpse of a rose-tipped nipple through the bubbles. His tongue slipped to the corner of his mouth as he stole a second glance. Yep. An honest to God, hard-wired nipple detector, he could spot a rosebud from fifty paces.

"Do you really think he's in cahoots with Amri?" she asked, taking a sip, completely oblivious of the peek she'd just given him. "Mm."

"Either that or he's stalking you."

She set her glass on a table beside the tub—probably not his best idea, but he didn't want to miss watching the bubbles diffuse. "Why? Didn't he do enough? For chrissake, he ruined two years of my life. In fact, worse. He destroyed my entire military career."

Mike sat cross-legged beside the tub. "True, but he might want more."

"Then why didn't he just shoot me when I opened the door to my hotel room?"

"Maybe he thinks a bullet is too easy."

Henri shivered. "God, people like Fadli are sick in the head."

"They are, and that's why we're in a safe house, especially now they've figured out who you are."

"It didn't take them long."

"My hunch is you just might be on their watch list."

"Jeez," she snorted. "There are a lot more interesting people out there for them to watch aside from me. It's insane."

"ISIS is growing stealthier all the time. And the more money they steal, the more high-tech equipment they can afford."

"And they're invading Europe."

"Faster than anybody realizes."

Henri reached for her glass, took a long drink, then held it up. "I think I need more wine." Lord, her skin was like burnished amber.

He poured. "It helps curb the sting."

She dropped the bag of ice and leaned over the edge of the tub. "This is good." A lazy grin spread across her lips, sexy as sin.

Mike cleared his throat and took a long drink. He shouldn't be thinking that anything was sexy. And he shouldn't even be the washroom with her. "It's the volcanic soil." Instead of obeying the voice in his head and leaving, he rested his elbow on the tub right beside hers, so close he could feel the warmth of her skin.

"And the climate." She drank again, then watched the ruby liquid as she swirled it in her glass. "Did you mean what you said?"

"Ah...when?"

"You missed me?"

God, he needed to keep his mouth zipped. "Ah,

well, it was cracking to have you as a sparring partner."

"Sparring was...ah...good practice for me, too."

"You're strong...I mean really strong." Now he was grinning like a maggot while the teenaged appendage below his belt stirred to life.

"Shoveling dirt will do that to a girl." Her gaze slid up and met his. Even with the bruise on the side of her chin, she looked delicious.

"Mm hmm." He leaned closer to get a better look at those eyes. They made him hunger for chocolate. Christ, they made him hunger for a whole lot more than food.

She didn't make it any easier, either, lazily resting her arm on the side of the tub, her mane of wet, sleek, black hair running down into the water. Her lips, moistened by wine, were too enticing to resist. Could he allow one more wee kiss?

Mike's tongue slid along his bottom lip as he continued to near. Rivulets of water tricked along her cheeks making her look tastier than ice cream with a cherry on top.

Her mouth parted with a quick intake of air. Though the sound was hardly noticeable, Mike's cock lengthened with a blast of fire. He shouldn't be doing this, God save him. But the Almighty was nowhere in the loo because as their lips met, Mike's mind sizzled with lust. If only he could pull Henri to her feet and rake his gaze down her wet, naked body. A body toned by hours of exercise. A body he'd admired with her clothes on—every inch of shapely woman, from the smooth and healthy skin on her face to the way her t-shirt molded to her shapely breasts to the way her hips filled out a pair of tight jeans. Henri Soaring-

Eagle Anderson was pure woman. Complete and total hotness.

His tongue plunged into her mouth as his hands slid around her neck and down her slick back. She met him with a clamping of her lips, her fingers threading through his hair. Her lazy, feminine sigh made him leak from the tip of his cock. He wanted her on top of him, naked and straddling him. He wanted a rose-tipped breast in his mouth with his cock plunging deep inside her.

He swirled his tongue with hers in an erotic dance until his phone's ring registered in the back of his mind.

Christ, the damned thing wouldn't stop.

If only Mike could ignore it, but the ringtone was one he'd assigned to Garth. And his damned phone was on the kitchen counter.

Henri's fingers stilled and she pulled away slightly. "You'd better get that."

Mike groaned. "Bloody hell, his timing is for shite."

"PUT IT ON SPEAKER." Henri sank back into the water while Mike went to answer his phone. Her lips tingled and she ran her hand across them to wipe away the sensation. Thank heavens the ring had interrupted them. Jeez, she needed to put on the brakes and fast, or else their working relationship was going to be too awkward to handle.

Once he was gone, she stepped out of the bath and wrapped a towel around her body.

"Hiya, sir," Mike answered from the kitchen.

"You'll never believe who we just spotted in Tanzania." Garth's voice came through clearly from the speaker.

Henri poked her head out of the bathroom. "Tanzania?" she mouthed in disbelief.

Mike shrugged. "Who?"

"Melvut Amri—he was caught by a security camera at the Kilimanjaro International Airport in Arusha."

Henri moved in beside Mike to better hear. "Was he picked up?"

"Slipped through," said Garth. "Damned crooked cops."

Combing his fingers through his hair, Mike glanced out the window. "What in God's name would Amri be doing in Africa?"

"Who knows, but you need to find out. Tanzania's a hub for nasty shit."

"Tell me about it—if it's mined, they're selling it." Mike's gaze meandered down Henri's body. Jeez, the guy needed to get some. Not that she didn't.

"But what about Fadli?" Henri asked.

Mike knitted his brows and looked to the phone. "You think he's still in France?"

Garth cleared his throat. "My guess is he headed straight for the border right after he jumped out of the window."

"Maybe," said Mike. "But not before he ordered a hit on Henri, I'll wager."

Henri lightly touched the bruise on her chin. The damned thing hurt. "Do you think Fadli is connected to the bank heist?"

"He's guilty," said Garth.

"Then why aren't they together? Why is Amri in Africa?"

"That's what I'm paying you to find out. Right

now, nothing makes sense. Sure, they can buy guns in Tanzania, but there are plenty on the black market in the Middle East. My guess is they're brewing up something the world doesn't want to know about."

"And in the meantime, Omar Fadli has Henri's number," said Mike. "I think Agent Anderson ought to fly back to Iceland. I can pick up my team in Kenya— move across the border stealth."

Henri poked him in the shoulder. "No way. That bastard's mine. I'm not going to go into hiding because he threw a few jabs."

"Rose has a point," said Garth.

"With all due respect, sir, I disagree." Henri threw a hand out to her side, glaring at the damned Scot with a look of exasperation. "What good would I be in Iceland when there's a terrorist out there with a million euros in stolen gems?"

"You'll get in the way." Mike knitted his brows and pulled an angry face. "What if Fadli finds you?"

"In Africa?" she demanded. "He thinks I'm in France. And you said yourself we can't be sure where he's headed." She stamped her foot. "Remember your promise!"

Garth started to speak, but Henri wasn't done. "What if you need me for bait?" She thrust her finger at the phone. "Sir, I *am* going to Tanzania. If Fadli wants me, then I want him more. I can draw him in. The jerk ruined two years of my life. He thinks I'm going to pay for his brother's death? Well, what about all the US soldiers Fadli murdered? I'm going with Rose and that's final."

Garth's chuckle cackled through the receiver. "It looks like you found yourself a partner, Rose."

"But, sir. What if—"

"She made the better argument," Garth said. "She's going."

Mike shot Henri a heated glare—his expression a far cry from the way he'd looked at her when she was in a tub of bubbles a few minutes ago. "Roger that, sir." He flicked off his phone.

"No. More. Kissing!" Henri spun and headed for the bathroom. "It's better if we don't make things too complicated, especially if you don't think I'm tough enough to go after a pair of terrorist thugs."

15

Mike and Henri used Canadian passports on the flight to Nairobi. His read Mike Emmerson, but Henrietta's was Annabelle...Emmerson. Yep, according to their paperwork, they were husband and wife. Henri wasn't impressed, but Mike thought it was a wise move. And their cover would be a lot more believable if they were a couple. They were posing as gem scouts, looking for deals on gems to supply to Canadian jewelers. Wearing baseball caps and keeping their heads down, Mike and Henri stepped out of the private Gulfstream and headed across the tarmac to a pair of tan-colored Land Rovers. A tall African man extended his hand to Mike. "Hey, boss. I was wondering when we'd meet again."

It was good to see a familiar and smiling face. He shook the offered hand. "You havena aged a day." Then Mike gestured to Henri. "Hali Obasanjo, meet Annabelle. My...ah...wife."

Hali waggled his eyebrows. "A woman finally pinned you down, yes, boss?"

Mike cleared his throat and threw an apologetic glance to Henri. "Mm hmm."

She smiled pleasantly and shook Hali's hand. "Mike has had nothing but good to say about you."

The Kenyan thumped his chest. "That's because I'm boss' right-hand man. No one keeps him out of trouble like Hali."

"And he'll get us across the border, act as master translator, and take care of our backup." Mike gestured to the front Land Rover with five men, none of whom were smiling. Then he recognized an old friend in the passenger seat of the rear vehicle and waved. "I see Pili's still with you."

"Pili will live forever." Hali opened the rear door for them. "The drive to Arusha should take four hours give or take."

Mike gestured for Henri to climb in, then slid beside her. "With Hali behind the wheel it should be smooth sailing."

Except it wasn't.

A mile before they reached the border town of Namanga, the traffic slowed.

"I dunna like the look of this," said Mike, craning his neck and estimating the number of cars in the queue.

Hali regarded him in the rearview mirror. "It looks worse ahead, boss. Maybe they can tell us what's causing the backup in the shop." He pulled over into a rundown convenience store and opened the Land Rover's sunroof. "You best stay here with the missus."

Mike pulled a few bills from his wallet. "Get us a couple of Cokes and a bag of crisps, would ya."

"Sure thing boss."

"And water," said Henri.

Hali gave her a white-toothed grin as he opened his door. "Water is in the cooler in the back, missus."

After the guide headed for the shop, she reached

over the rear seat and pulled out two bottles, handing one to Mike. "Missus? Why can't he just call me Annie or something equally as irritating?"

Mike cracked open his water and took a long drink. "Missus probably works better than anything. And if the men refer to you that way, it'll be less likely to draw attention where we dunna want it."

Her eyebrows slanted inward with her leery look. "Are you still pissed that I'm here?"

"Pissed means you've had one too many where I'm from."

"You're from Canada, remember? And you're still pissed. I can feel the irritation oozing off you." One thing was for certain, he could count on the lass to speak her mind.

Mike snorted. Perhaps he was a wee bit annoyed. He didn't want Henri there for a boatload of reasons. Aside from the fact that she'd been targeted by Omar Fadli, a man who was rapidly climbing the ISIS chain of command, she was a white woman—well she might be half-Native American but around these parts she was a white bird and no one would give a rat's arse about her heritage. A white woman in Africa always added complexity to any mission. Christ, things were hard enough walking around with a mop of flaming red hair.

"So, are you just going to sit there and pretend I don't exist?"

Mike glanced her way. "Sorry. I've got a lot on my mind at the moment." Yeah, he'd been absorbed in his thoughts, but his mind hadn't been on the op where it bloody should be.

"Like what?"

"Like how we're going to find Melvut Amri once we arrive in Arusha."

"Do you think he's peddling the gems?"

"No doubt."

"So, I was reading on the plane that there's actually an Arab/Tanzanian population in Arusha. That the city is the most cosmopolitan in the western part of the country, and it's a center for trade. Gold, tanzanite, diamonds all trade hands there."

"Tell me something I dunna already ken."

"Yep, still pissed." Henri crossed her arms. "There's got to be an angle for ISIS, otherwise they wouldn't be here."

"Agreed."

"So what do they need?"

"Guns."

"Yes, guns and military equipment, but I'm thinking sophisticated stuff." She drummed her fingers against her lips. "What if they could get their hands on a guided missile system? What about tanks? I wish they were stupid, but they're not. They can't blow us out of the Middle East because they can't come close to matching us in fire power."

"Thank God, and they never will."

"Never?"

Mike rubbed his temples. Jet lag had a way of making him tense. "Not at least while we're alive."

"You might be right, but they still need money. And they need an industry, or some sort of front that'll make it for them."

"So, *missus*, your theory is that al-Umari and his goons don't just want to sell the diamonds they stole from Avignon. They have established a business in Tanzania to launder stolen gems and turn them into cash?"

Henri sat back and grinned. "Something like that."

"Well, if we ever cross the border, you might just discover you're not far off the mark."

She elbowed him in the ribs. "See?"

He gave her a pointed look. "But then you could be dead wrong as well."

She smacked him in the arm. "You're insufferable."

"That's what all the lassies say."

Her gaze shifted his way and drilled into him, charging the air with tension. "What lassies?"

Before Mike thought up an excuse to avoid answering her question, Hali returned and climbed into the driver's seat.

"It's not good news, boss." He handed back the Cokes, two bags of crisps, and some peanuts.

Mike looked out the window. The traffic alongside the shop had come to a standstill. "It rarely is."

"Word is the border's closed. Another trade dispute between Kenya and Tanzania."

"Damn." Mike hit the seat back with his fist. "I knew we should have flown in somewhere else."

Henri snorted, but she kept her mouth shut, which was wise.

"You want I should go bush, boss?"

"Bush? Like through the Serengeti?" asked Henri.

"Didna you see that in your research? The Serengeti is west of us." Mike knew he was being testy, but going bush was always dangerous and now even more so with a woman, even if she was a sharpshooter. Damn, Amri already had too much of a head start. If they didn't move now, they'd have no chance at picking up his trail. He flicked his wrist at Hali. "All right then, go bush. Just stay away from any radical militants."

16

H enri watched the scenery pass as the Land Rover jolted along the pothole-infested dirt road while hot air whipped through the open sunroof. The area was hilly and covered with scrubby trees which made things a bit uncomfortable for a sniper. She preferred to have the best ground advantage with a wide view of the area. She also preferred to have her Win Mag in her hands with a half-dozen spare magazines in her bulletproof vest. Presently, she didn't have a rifle, ammo or vest, which made her all the more on edge.

"I thought you said they have guns?" Henri whispered in Mike's ear.

He pointed downward. "Hidden compartment."

"Caliber?"

"Whatever they got."

"Ammo stores?"

"Hali's instructions were to come prepared. He kens what that means." Mike reached over and patted her thigh. "Relax. Things have settled down in this region."

Right. Settled down with the border closed? Henri might believe him once they were on a plane out of there. In the meantime, she was formulating a plan in her head. Keeping her comrades alive had been her job in the Army. She was hardwired to it. And knowing Mike, he was playing up the relax thing for her benefit, which was stupid. He knew her past.

It was late afternoon when Hali announced they'd crossed the border. Mike blew out a long breath and gave Henri a wink.

She almost shared in his relief until they drove around a hill sloping to a thicket. *Perfect place for a mob of thugs to stage a holdup.*

"Tollbooth," Hali said over his shoulder.

"Pay them off." Mike glanced at Henri and moved his fingers down to the floor mat. He lifted it up, grabbed a Glock and inserted a magazine, hiding the gun in his belt. She did the same, spying an arsenal of M4s and ammo as he replaced the false bottom. "Insurance," Mike said.

Henri nodded. There had been plenty of road patrols in Afghanistan and they all wanted one thing. Money. If you didn't pay up or blew through their barricade, there was certain to be an ambush waiting somewhere down the track.

The guards were all dressed in camo gear and carried AK-47s. "Military?" she asked.

Mike craned his neck. "Probably rebel forces or crooked police."

"I thought you said the civil unrest had settled in these parts."

"I did, but that doesna mean there isna any." He gave her a look. "My guess is these assholes ken the border's closed and there'd be dupes like us who will try another route."

"Great." Henri rubbed her fingertips together,

itching for a chance to put her hands on the cold steel of one of the rifle barrels beneath her feet.

Hali brought the Land Rover to a stop and rolled down the window. "*Hodi.*"

Henri glanced back. A pair of men toting AKs moved to the driver's side of the second Land Rover.

Four men remained by the lead Land Rover, two on the passenger side and two on the left. The man in charge was the largest. He was a mean-looking man with an ugly scar on his cheek. He sauntered back, shouting at Hali in Swahili. Henri couldn't understand a word, but the guys with the guns looked like a mob of angry sons-of-bitches—not much different from Taliban rebels in Afghanistan.

"You ready?" she asked Mike.

"Always ready. But Hali will handle it. He's a pro."

"Good thing, because it's not going to be easy to pull out the M4s without those Rambo wannabes noticing."

"Give them the cash," Mike growled, looking out the window.

The man doing most of the yelling pointed his rifle at Hali's chest. The tall Kenyan held up his hands and backed to the driver's seat door. After popping it open, he ducked his head inside. "Just getting the dough, boss."

"Give it to them and get us the hell out of here!" Mike said through clenched teeth.

The irate guard poked his head inside the SUV, his gaze shooting straight to Henri. The bastard licked his lips and cracked a smile.

She glared back.

Mike made a show of sliding his arm across her shoulders.

Hali blocked the man's view when he straightened and handed over an envelope.

After checking the contents, the asshole launched into another round of shouting, this time pointing to Mike and Henri and carrying on like they were about to cross the border with a boatload of IEDs.

"Blast it. Cover me." Mike stepped out of the car. "What's the problem? Isna there enough cash?" He led the guard to the front of the vehicle.

When all eyes shifted away from the backseat, Henri quickly yanked away the carpet and shifted up the false floor. With no time to examine the equipment, she snatched an M4 and a magazine. Thank God Hali was better equipped than the commandos outside. The only problem was the guns were in the Land Rover. She glanced back to the rear truck—those two guards were standing either side of the Rover, hands on their weapons pointed at the ground, trigger fingers straight. They weren't expecting a fight but, still, she could only pray the men inside the vehicle had enough sense to arm themselves.

"What are they arguing about now?" she asked.

Pili regarded her over his shoulder. "You, missus." Waist high, he slid a Glock into her view. "Bad men."

"Can you handle the two on your side?" she asked.

"Ya, missus."

Sliding across the seat, Henri reached for the latch but it slipped from her grasp as the leader yanked open the door. Yelling something imperceptible, he reached inside, his ugly face contorted by a sneer. In a heartbeat, the predatory glint in his eyes soon turned to wide-eyed terror as she lined up the sights of the M4.

"Now!" she shouted, pulling the trigger and hitting the bastard from point-blank range in the chest with a

45mm bullet. The force of the blast picked him up and catapulted him fifteen feet away.

From the front seat, Pili's Glock fired, but his man was only clipped.

Mike reached for his pistol, but one of the guards swung into motion. The Scot grabbed the AK's muzzle and wrenched it from the man's hands. Bellowing like a madman, the guard tackled Mike to the ground.

Repeating fire erupted around them.

With no cover anywhere, Henri darted up through the sunroof, took out the second guy on right, turned and shot the two standing by the rear Land Rover. Whipping around, she set her sights on Mike's man. The two were rolling on the ground, fists flying. With a pistol in his hands, Hali couldn't get off a shot without risking a hit to the boss.

Mike threw a punch. His opponent's head snapped back as he rolled away and pulled a knife.

Henri didn't wait. She aimed between the eyes and stopped the bastard before he had a chance to lunge.

Silence swarmed through the air as the echo of her last shot faded. Not even a bird chirped. Mike stood and brushed himself off.

"Nice shooting, missus," said Hali.

She looked at Mike. "Are you still pissed that I came?"

"Oh, aye, I'm hotter than a hornet. Once the bastard saw you he reckoned you'd make a fine contribution to the toll." He glanced to the dead man with the knife. "On top of that, I aim to wrap my fingers around a bottle of whisky and get good and *pissed* as soon as we take out the ambush up ahead."

Henri slid through the sunroof and down to the seat. *Jerk.* She'd show him. Eventually. No, the ambush wasn't her fault, but they might have gotten away without a fight if she hadn't been there.

Fuck it.

For now, she had more problems to conquer than proving her worth. Mike was right. These thugs always had friends. She slipped out the door and looked him dead on. "Okay, ace. What's plan B?"

17

M ike and Henri took two of Hali's men and set out on foot. There was absolutely no way he would consider leaving her behind. On top of everything, she was the best damned shot he'd ever seen. Still, since the commando-on-steroids back there had made it clear he wanted a piece of Henri's arse, Mike was even more convinced that she should have gone back to ICE. The problem was he had no way to send her there now.

"You know I can take care of myself," she said as if she could read his mind.

"Aye." *Except not even an ace with a gun could fend off an army.*

"Then why are you walking like you have barbed wire up your ass?"

He increased the pace. "You might have been able to take out a mob of amateur guerrillas, but what would have happened if those guerrillas had been an organized group of radicals? What would have happened if they'd killed everyone but you?"

"I would have been in deep shit."

"You would have been raped a dozen times or more and sold into slavery."

"So, that's why you're pissed? Haven't you worked with women in the field before?"

Mike had and he'd never liked it. For some reason he liked it even less now. Sure, she was unbeatable with a rifle in her hands, she could even give him a good run in the sparring ring, but she was still a god-damned female.

"Well?" she pushed.

"Aye, I've worked with women."

"All right then. You cover my back and I'll cover yours. That's how it rolls," she said as if she'd solved all their problems.

If only it were that easy. Plenty of soldiers had walked into ambushes they hadn't seen coming. Anderson might have keen vison, but she didn't have ESP. Before they marched into an ambush, they needed to spot the culprits first or else they were dead. God knew he wouldn't be able to protect the lass if he ended up shot in the head.

It didn't surprise him when she held up her hand and whispered, "Whoa."

Even after blinking, Mike couldn't see anything. But the hair on the back of his neck stood on end. Gut instincts trumped vision every time. Ahead, the road ran through a gorge with cliffs on either side. A perfect spot for an attack.

She motioned for them to lay low and move behind the scrub. Hali's two men didn't say a word, but they understood Henri's sign language and hid.

"Did you see something?" Mike asked, pulling her behind the brambles.

Thrusting her finger toward the gorge, she gave a sharp nod. "There are shooters up on the cliffs on each side of the road about a mile up."

"You saw them?"

"Movement caught my attention first. As soon as I made out one guy, the others just appeared to me. I saw two on the north side and two across on the south."

"So, the Soaring-Eagle moniker has a deeper meaning?"

"It's not a moniker."

"Right-o." Mike nodded his head in the direction of the gorge. "If you saw them, they most likely spotted us."

"Maybe. If they have scopes trained on the road." She pointed to her eyes. "Twenty/seven vision. Best ever recorded in a human."

"All right then, let's assume they spotted us—or at least saw movement. They'll be watching more closely now."

She nodded.

Mike motioned for the other men to gather in. Hali had picked the pair because they understood a little English. After he explained his plan, they set out through the brush, making a northern arc which enabled them to creep up on the rear of the group on the north side. It was a tougher climb, but the peak was higher on that side which would give them a ground advantage. Mike's seventh rule of war? Never take the easy path. The unexpected route might be grueling and take longer, but the commander who adheres to this rule will be rewarded.

It took an hour to cross the distance and climb up. In the lead, Mike crested the hill first and held up his fist, indicating for the team to stop. The sun had set, but he could still see the ambushers. He crouched down—it looked like the same four guys Henri described as seeing from the road. The perps on the far side were sitting with their legs dangling over the edge of the cliff, though AKs hung from their harnesses. A snap of a twig and those assholes would be up on their feet, chucking bullets.

"You see 'em?" Henri whispered from behind.

He slipped down far enough to hide his head behind the crag and pointed downward, catching the eye of Hali's two men.

Henri pulled back the bolt of her M4. "Cover me. I'll take care of them."

She started off, but Mike grabbed her arm. "Just a minute. I dunna want you in harm's way."

She practically blew snot out of her nose. "Yeah, right. Come on, Rambo. I'm hungry and I want dinner ASAP."

Mike motioned to the guys. "Cover us."

They nodded their understanding. Together, they climbed on their bellies until they were peeking over the top of the crag.

Laying on her stomach, Henri moved her rifle to her shoulder and snapped off the safety. "You ready?"

"You need a scope?" he asked.

"It would be nice, but not necessary from this distance." She glanced at him over the black butt of the gun. "I'll pick off each from nearest to furthest. I need you and the men to provide a smoke screen. Keep firing to keep them guessing."

"Roger that. Wait here." He slid over to the men and relayed the plan, then resumed his spot at Henri's six.

"Three, two, one," she counted down with the concentration of a microsurgeon.

As soon as she fired the first bullet, Mike unloaded a spray of fire across the crag. He couldn't hear much above his rifle, but he sensed everything. Henri immediately took out perp one, adjusted and hit two,

then three, then four. It was over in less than six
seconds.

Mike let up on the trigger. Henri continued working, her cheek glued to the M4's butt as she scanned
the scene for strays.

"Nice shooting," he said.

"Thanks." She stood and shouldered her weapon.
"Now, where's my dinner?"

He couldn't help his chuckle even if he was still
aggro—*pissed* as she liked to call being bloody mad.
But she sure proved her worth in a combat situation—
and with flair. How in God's name a sniper could look
so sexy, Mike had no clue. But there she stood. Proud.
Self-assured. And as gorgeous as a whisky sunset.

IT WAS midnight before Hali dropped Mike and Henri
off at a guesthouse just outside of Arusha. A half-
asleep woman showed them to a dingy room at the
back of a weatherboard house. She dropped a key in
Mike's palm. "Toilet out the back."

Henri closed the door and gave the room the once-
over. There was a double bed and a side table and that
was it. She'd endured rougher accommodations, so
she kept her mouth shut. The problem? She was still
hungry. They had a measly bag of potato chips, a bag
of peanuts and a fifth of whisky that had been hidden
in the Land Rover with the guns. "I'm going to starve
to death."

Mike held up the bottle. "This ought to take your
mind off your stomach."

She grabbed the bag of chips and opened them.
"No drinking on an empty stomach. Neither of us can
afford to have a hangover in the morning."

He plopped down on the bed with his back against the wall like it was no big deal they were in a shoebox with a double bed hardly wide enough for two adults. "Who said anything about a hangover?"

Henri moved to the end of the bed, sizing up the floor—chipped linoleum, not terribly clean. If given the choice, she'd rather sleep under the stars than on that floor. She bit into a chip and arched an eyebrow at Mike. It was either the bed or the floor and, after the overseas flight from France where she hadn't slept, she was exhausted. Reluctantly, she slid beside him and stuffed a few chips in her mouth. "So, Scottish tough guys don't need sustenance?"

"I didna say that." He reached in the bag and pulled out a handful. "We'll have a good breakfast but, until then, these will have to suffice."

Henri took the bottle from him and washed her bite down with a swig of whisky. It burned going down and sloshed in her empty stomach. Squinting, she wiped her mouth with the back of her hand. "Pass over the peanuts. At least they have some protein."

Mike leaned in with the bag and the mattress dipped, making them roll against each other.

Henri shoved him back. "That's a little too close there, soldier." She was sticking to her no kissing rule if it killed her.

He snatched the bottle with a smirk. "Then I need a wee bit more of this sleeping potion."

"Oh?"

He held it up in toast. "Else I might be inclined to ravage you, m'lady," he said with a rolling Scottish burr, sounding lazy and rough as if the potion had already started to kick in.

Unfortunately, the rumble of Mike's voice made an arrow of liquid heat spread through Henri's limbs and didn't end there. Intense desire coiled between her legs. The swig of whisky didn't help. It made her head swim with a melty all over feeling.

She pushed against her eyes. *Would you stop?* It had taken a will of iron to pull away from their last kiss. She absolutely must not allow the brawny Scot to affect her.

Damn.

If only there was a curtain or a partition or *something* between them.

She glanced from wall to wall while every hormone in her body sizzled. This night was going to be even more torturous than she thought. Even if the guesthouse had an extra room, it would ruin their cover to sleep apart. The only solution? Find out what ISIS was doing in Tanzania as soon as possible. She'd just have to hang tough for a couple of days and then they'd be out of there and, hopefully, assigned to separate missions.

While she stuffed her face with peanuts, Henri tried to lean away from Mike. But the more she fought it, the more the mattress curled toward the center making her leg grind against his. Giving up, she reached for the whisky and took a couple of healthy swigs.

"What was that you said about a hangover?" he asked.

She handed it back. "Shut up."

"No more bloody kissing, remember?" He chucked as he took a drink then swiped his hand across his mouth. "Och, lass. That which doesna kill us makes us stronger."

18

Through the vague blur when consciousness
returns after a night's sleep, Mike sensed
light streaming in from the window. In truth,
he sensed a great deal more than that. His cock was
harder than a steel gun barrel, and the intoxicating
scent of woman swirled around him. He felt too good
to open his eyes. All he needed to do was slide his fingers across the mattress and pull Henri flush against
his body. Och aye, with a few clothing adjustments, he
could slip between those shapely thighs she'd
wrapped around him a time or two in the sparring
ring.

God. He wanted to spar right now. The kind of
sparring that's done between the sheets.

With a deep moan, he slid his hand over and met
with nothing but cool cotton. Then he moved his
palm up and down. Come to think of it, the length of
Henri's body had been pressed against him all night.
The pillowy soft crack of her bum had cradled his
cock, and there had been nothing Mike could do
about it. The mattress dipped to the center and
nothing he tried to shift away had worked. In the end,
the whisky did its job and they'd both fallen asleep

with Henri spooned against him as if they were really man and wife.

Disappointed, Mike opened his eyes and pushed himself up, his head full of cobwebs. While he stretched, Henri walked in carrying a tray of food. Mm, it smelled good, especially the coffee. "A woman after my own heart."

Henri stopped. "Do you think I got this for you?"

The vixen had tempted him all night and now she wasn't about to stop. "Bloody hell," he groaned and leaned down to pull a couple of aspirin out of his pack.

"Just kidding." She put the tray on the bed, then slid in with her back against the wall.

Mike popped the aspirin and reached for a cuppa. "What's on the menu?"

"Scrambled eggs, beans and fried bananas."

"And toast," he said, snatching a piece.

She picked up her coffee while her gaze trailed downward.

Mike usually slept in the nude, but last night he'd kept his jocks on. The only problem was the bed-clothes had shifted and his hard-on was practically wrapped around his hip. He stuffed the toast in his mouth and tugged a blanket over his crotch.

Henri's gaze flickered away as her tongue tapped the corner of her mouth.

Trying not to groan, Mike leaned against the wall and took a long sip of coffee. The caffeine may have begun to clear his mind, but that only sent his libido into overdrive. Again. Her hair was wet and loose rather than in its usual braid. He took a long drink as he watched her eat. She might act like a tough bird at times, but she ate like a duchess. She even used a serviette to dab the corners of her mouth.

She glanced up. "What?"

He pinched a lock of her hair between his fingers and brought it to his nose. *Jasmine*. God save him, he loved the fragrance of jasmine. "Where did you find a shower?"

"It's out the back by the head."

"You showered outside?"

"There's a curtain." She shrugged. "I've endured worse."

That's right, she had, and he needed to keep reminding himself of the fact.

She nudged the plate of food toward him, her gaze shifting to his crotch. "The water's cold but it might be just what you need."

"Bloody temptress you are."

She laughed. "The same could be said for you—oh Mr. Ripped Abs staring me in the face."

No matter how much Henri would have liked to stay in their ramshackle room and test the endurance of those ripped abs, they had a job to do. They both knew it. She'd made the mistake of dating a guy in her squadron once and, after working with him day and night for a few months, the relationship fizzled. Then it became unbearably awkward—almost got her shipped stateside.

Never again.

Henri was a big girl now and tougher than she'd ever been. Jail had a way of turning a woman to ice. The sooner they exposed the ISIS operation in Tanzania, the sooner she could go home—or move on to the next assignment. Mike said he usually worked alone. She liked that idea. In fact, she might push the issue with Garth once she chalked up a few wins against her name.

After breakfast, Hali took them to Tengeru, east of the city. A dirt road cut through the center of town, festooned with vendor's stalls like an old-time market. Henri and Mike dressed their parts and the game was on. She wore an orange sundress with her voluminous hair tucked up in an enormous straw hat. Mike complemented her ensemble with a loud Hawaiian shirt, sunglasses and a Panama hat. Their getups were ridiculous, but that's what made them not look like themselves.

By mid-afternoon they'd browsed through most of the stalls, here and there using cash and gold coins to buy uncut gems and, hopefully, spreading the word that a pair of Canadians with deep pockets was in town. If their hunch was right, Amri and his friends were laundering the gems by selling them to unsuspecting overseas buyers.

It wasn't until they stopped for a Coke that they found their first break. A man from one of the shops where they'd purchased some uncut tanzanite slid into a seat at their table. "Have you found all that you're looking for?" he asked in English, giving them a leery smile.

"Not yet," Mike said, sounding distinctly Canadian. He was good.

The man glanced over his shoulder, then leaned in. "I have been given approval to show you the first-quality gems—those we only present to serious buyers like yourselves."

Mike arched his eyebrows in question. "Why didn't you say something when we were in your shop?" he asked, affecting the accent.

Henri sipped her Coke, keeping her face impassive but taking in every word.

The man chuckled nervously. "Sorry, boss, but I'm not allowed to mention our highest quality gems until I am given approval from my superiors."

"I see. And for this transaction, will I be bartering with you or with your superiors?"

The man sat back and thumped his chest with a grin. "You will deal with me, of course."

"Hmm." Mike looked to Henri. "I think not. I am no dupe, sir. When I make an offer, I want an answer. I do not want to wait while an agent moves back and forth as a middleman to the negotiation."

Beads of sweat peppered the man's brow. "I assure you, I am able to transact business on his behalf."

"Tell you what. Introduce me to your boss. If we like what he has to show us, we'll make it worth his while."

Then man pulled out a kerchief and wiped his forehead. "That can be arranged. But first I'll need more to give him." He rubbed his fingers together. "What kind of investment do you have in mind?"

"Seven figures." Mike picked up his Coke. "For starters."

"I see. Where are you staying? I'll send a boy for you when it is arranged."

Mike hesitated.

"The Arusha Hotel. Under Emmerson," Henri said with a pleasant smile directed at her work-husband.

"I would have thought no less," said the man. "I am Mr. Kisongo. I shall be in touch."

Mike waited until Kisongo left the café, then gave her a look. "The Arusha Hotel?"

She shrugged. "It was the nicest place we passed on the way out here."

He snorted. "Hali will be crushed. That was his auntie's bed and breakfast."

"I'm sure he'll understand—and so will my aching back."

"What? The wee dip in the mattress didna form to those shapely hips, madam?" Mike shook his head with a laugh.

"I'd rather get a good night's sleep than appease Hali who, by the way, nearly got us killed yesterday regardless if I was there or not."

19

After entering the honeymoon suite, Henri dropped her duffle on the ottoman and turned full circle. There was still only one bed, but it was a king and it had a silk mosquito net. There was also a desk, a television and a refrigerator, even a bathroom. Better yet, the room had plenty of space to move around. "Now this is more like it."

Mike set the room key on the dresser. "I thought you didna mind roughing it. If you prefer luxury, what were you doing at the mine?"

"It's not roughing it that matters, it's our MO. We're posing as wealthy gem buyers. If we stayed in the cockroach motel back there, our ruse wouldn't be very convincing."

He tossed his gear on the bed. "You're right."

"Wait." She held out her arms and inhaled deeply. "I want to revel in this for a moment."

Cocking his head to the side, Mike knit his eyebrows.

She grinned. "I actually was right about something."

"Bloody hell, you've been right plenty." He spread a map out on the desk.

"Paper?"

"Nothing beats it."

"Okay, what are you thinking?"

She bent forward and leaned on her elbows while Mike pointed out the location of Mr. Kisongo's Jawhira shop.

"Hey, isn't Jawhira Arabic for jewel?"

"It is, and that's another reason why I think we're on to something." He used his pin to point to the location on the map. "It's in the middle of the market. We were right here, but my guess is the shop on the marketplace is a front."

"There's more in the back, then?"

"I'd bet a quid that's where the shady deals go down."

Henri pulled out her laptop. "If that's so, we need to look at it on Google maps."

He gave her a thin-lipped nod. She knew he didn't like to use electronics in the field, but ICE went to great lengths to ensure their devices couldn't be tracked. The encryption code changed constantly.

She sat in a chair and he moved in behind her, leaning over to look at the screen. He was so close, if she shifted to the side a fraction of an inch, her shoulder would touch his arm. Her skin tingled with the unseen current pulsing between them like an irresistible magnetic pull. But his closeness was soothing. He imparted a sense of confidence she liked. It made her feel energized.

Henri made herself focus on the computer.

Together, they analyzed the topography, establishing five different ways of escape, what to do if they were separated, and Hali and his men's roles. Another important rule of war that spilled into the spy game? Go over the plan until it was like reciting poetry.

All the while, she stole glimpses at Mike, studying his profile. His primal masculinity, the thick hair, closely cropped on the sides but wild and wavy on top. His nose was prominent but not too big for his face. He kept his dark-auburn beard trimmed short, but it wasn't prickly. Her tongue tapped the corner of her lips while she reached up and smoothed her fingers along his jaw—oh yes, smooth as velvet.

He glanced her way and grinned, crinkling the corner of his eye.

A flutter spread through her stomach.

"Envious of me whiskers, are you, lassie?" God, he was sexy when he poured on the brogue.

She shrugged. "Just surprised at how soft they are. Your beard's not wiry at all."

"Glad it passed your inspection." He cleared his throat and returned his gaze to the monitor. "I dunna like the location. There are too many crevices for perps to hide."

She zoomed out the satellite image, broadening the view of the marketplace. "There's a two-story building here. Maybe I should set up a rifle on the roof to cover your back."

"Aye, that would solve all our problems. Pick off the ISIS members one by one."

"You don't like it?" she asked.

He shrugged with a wink. "Unless they're waving an ISIS flag, it'll be difficult to peg them."

"You're right. And I'm the last person who needs to have innocent blood on her hands."

He straightened and gave her shoulders a squeeze. "I'm sorry about Fadli. He really messed with your life —but remember, he's the one with innocent blood on his hands, not you."

A lump swelled in her throat. "I know."

Straightening, he gave her arm a pat. "Why don't I go fetch us something to eat?"

"Sounds great." She scooted away a little, swallowing down the damned lump. "I'm starving."

She watched him saunter out the door with an aura of wildness about him. It could have been the way his muscular physique filled out his jeans, or the way his shoulders stretched his t-shirt so it clung to his back, tapering to a tight waist. Whatever the reason, Mike Rose was way too sweet on the eyes.

But still off limits.

Henri let out a long sigh. After the cold shower this morning, she was ready to bathe in luxury. She pulled her toiletries out of her bag and a pair of bike shorts and a shirt to change in to, then headed for the bathroom, shutting the door behind her.

At least she *thought* the door was shut.

~

THEY COULD HAVE ORDERED room service but, aside from needing a breather, he wanted to buy a couple of bottles of good wine. Hali had also told him where to find the best fried chicken in town. The guide might live in Kenya, but his mother was from Tanzania, and Hali was familiar with just about everything in eastern Africa. He earned a good living as an African mercenary and hired trustworthy men who had military backgrounds. Having been a spy for nearly a decade, Mike had colleagues like Hali all over the world. Men and women who could be trusted to help him quickly work through the maze of local neighborhoods and customs.

Once he found the wine and the restaurant, it

didn't take him long to order take away and head back to the hotel and up to their suite.

He could hear the shower running as he unlocked the door, stepped inside and put the food on the table. Henri had to be the cleanest Native American in Africa. The outer door closed behind him with a whoosh.

What he didn't expect was the door to the WC to swing open right behind it.

Mike stood stunned. There he was, a big Scot, trained to kill with his bare hands and his tongue went completely dry. His heart raced and blood rushed to the place where blood always rushed when a man gazed upon a stunningly beautiful, naked woman. Just not this particular stunning woman.

Lord save him, Henri's body surpassed all his imaginings. With her back to him, her black hair cascaded down to her hips, tapering to a point right above a pair of heart-shaped buttocks. They weren't just any buttocks. Honed by muscle, they had dimples on the sides and curved into the shapeliest, longest legs he'd ever seen. Slender legs he'd dreamed about having wrapped around him more than once.

Henri reached for the shampoo—no it had to be conditioner because she ran it through her hair and fingered it into the ends.

If only Mike could strip bare and step into the shower stall with her. Cup those delectable bum cheeks in his palms and squeeze. The mere thought made him so hard, the torture was about to drive him to the brink of insanity. He braced his hand on the door knob as Henri turned around.

"Ack!" she squealed, but not before he caught a glimpse of a goddess from heaven through the clear glass of the shower. Breasts like hers should never be

covered. No. Breasts like that *should* be covered unless
they were alone with him. His fingers flexed. He'd
wanted to fill his palms with her shapely bum cheeks?
Christ, he'd pay an entire month's salary just to fondle
those breasts, to smooth his fingers across them and
tease those rosy nipples into hard pebbles he could
suckle while he slid between her shapely thighs.

With his next blink, Henri crossed her legs and
arms and crouched. "What the hell are you doing?
Close the fucking door!"

Thrown off balance, Mike squeezed the knob.
"Why the hell did you leave it open if you're so goddamned modest? If you hadna noticed, there are two
people staying in this room," he barked. Closing the
door, he shook himself. *Jesus, what just happened?*

He'd walked in, set the food down and, when he
turned around, he saw her. Any red-blooded man
who'd ever walked the face of the earth would have
looked. Aye, women would have looked, children,
dogs, cats. Hell, civilization would have erected a mon-
ument to the glory of goddess Henrietta Anderson
and her shapely buttocks.

The shower shut off.

Still annoyed, Mike faced the WC door. Being a
spy, someone who was keenly trained to notice everything, he retraced his steps. When he had entered the
room, he'd gone straight to the sideboard and set
down the bags. But first he had to walk past the bathroom door. If it had been ajar, he would have noticed
for certain. He was a true-blue homing beacon when it
came to spotting wet, naked women. So, the slight
vacuum created by the whoosh from the closing of the
outer door must have been enough to make the other
one swing open.

But now, Henri thought he was a bloody perv. He

snorted. Just as well, because he was still hard. If she so much as raked her gaze down his body, she'd be on her back before she could utter a word.

If only.

By the time she came out wearing a pair of shorts and a t-shirt that looked like they had been painted on, Mike had the food laid out. He'd used two hotel tumbler glasses for the wine. They'd do in a pinch.

"Sorry," he said. Before he passed away, his father once told him life was a lot easier if a man apologized first. No use making excuses when there's a misunderstanding, just ask for forgiveness and move on. "It was the vacuum from the outer door closing."

"Whatever." She pushed her wet hair behind her back, which only made matters worse because there was a wet spot right over her boob.

Mike swiped a hand across his eyes. "You dunna believe me?"

She sat and reached for a chicken leg. "Sure."

Groaning, he crossed the floor, opened the outer door and let it slam just as he'd done when he'd entered. The bathroom door opened, thank God for small mercies.

Henri gaped. "Holy shit."

"I might have opted for something a little deeper, like, gee-whiz, Mike, I'm sorry I didna believe you."

She coughed out a chuckle and washed her bite down with a sip of wine. "Gee-whiz? Do people still say that in Scotland?"

He returned to his seat. "Not really."

"Well, then, gee-whiz, the door really did pop open on its own."

"Thank you."

"But you were ogling me."

He grinned and raised his glass. "I won't deny it,

lass. You should be proud. There was plenty to ogle. In fact, I doubt I will soon forget the exquisite beauty I beheld this evening."

Her face turned bright red. Letting out a nervous laugh, she drank more wine. "You're full of shit."

Mike opted to not respond and focused on eating. Just as Hali had said, the food was good—a little on the greasy side, but delicious. The difficult part about not talking? Henri's t-shirt. Aside from being skin-tight and wet over one boob, it had a scooped neck and showed off her cleavage. If he wasn't already walking on thin ice with the woman, he might ask what prompted her to wear it.

But the food did its trick. Tension in the air ebbed —at least Mike felt better. Henri appeared to relax a bit as well, until she grimaced and rubbed her neck. Then she moaned and rolled her head.

"You have a sore back?" he asked.

"Mm. Compliments of last night's saggy bed."

Mike glanced to the king-sized bed to his right. It looked plush like it was top shelf. He hadn't tested it yet, but this hotel had been full of pleasant surprises thus far. "You want a massage?"

Henri's gaze flickered to the bed and back as her lips parted. "Ah…"

Making a grand gesture, he stood. "Go on. We havena much else to do until we meet with Mr. Kisongo in the morning."

He could tell she was tempted by the way she licked her lips. "We shouldn't."

"It's up to you, but if I canna rub your shoulders, maybe we should rethink training together, too. I mean, what are people going to think when you have me in a leg lock?"

"That's different." She shifted her gaze to the bed

again. "All right. If you do me, then I do you. It's only fair."

Mike liked that even better. "Good food, good wine and a massage. Sounds like a recipe for a relaxing evening."

Except it wasn't relaxing.

"Turn away," she said over her shoulder.

Gulping, he did as she asked.

Clothing rustled. The bed creaked.

"Okay."

Mike turned back to find her face down on the bed, her bra and shirt on the nightstand.

If he didn't have an erection while he tried not to look at her boobs, he had one now. And as soon as he made the mistake of straddling her, his balls tightened to the point of agony. Bloody Christmas, if he didn't get laid soon, he'd have to resort to a hand job in the shower. Jesus, Mike didn't know how Logan Rodgers did it. His partner, Olivia, was almost as beautiful as Henri—though she didn't have Soaring-Eagle's voluptuous hips.

As soon as Mike sank his powerful fingers into her shoulders and began to rub, Henri floated into bliss. She couldn't remember the last time anyone had given her a decent rubdown. All she knew was it had been years and she'd never allow so much time to pass before she signed up for another.

When it came to massages, the big Scot certainly was gifted. Maybe he'd even missed his calling. Every time he found a knot, he worked it with long, languid strokes until it eased enough for him to work deep.

God, the man could dig deep and manipulate each

strand of sinew with those talented fingers. Drill deep and brutalize those knots until they had no choice but to release every iota of tension.

She moaned out loud when he got down and dirty between her shoulder blades.

And he didn't stop there. Those magic hands continued along her spine, kneading, brushing, swirling. Henri could lie there and take this kind of magical torture forever. His fingers got a little frisky, brushing the outside of her breasts when his palms spread across her back—not too bold and easy to ignore on the promise of more deep tissue massage. Mm hmm—those strong, colossal hands.

Her breath caught when those same hands sank into her butt, demanding she go limp for him. The problem? She felt so good, she was on fire. Relaxed and hotter than a filly having her first season. As soon as he touched her ass, her legs slipped open a little wider as if they'd grown minds of their own.

When he swirled his thumbs in the muscles just below her crotch, Henri released a languid sigh. It was as if her sound gave Mike a cue to delve deeper as his fingers pushed up her short legs and lightly brushed over sensitive skin—the one place where she desperately needed to be touched.

Ah, hell.

She arched her back and gasped with a shudder while his finger teased. Then he slid it inside—where it shouldn't be—where it felt too damned good. Henri's dug her knuckles into the pillow, forcing the warning lights in her head at bay until the only thing her mind focused on was how good her body felt. In and out, Mike's fingers moved inside her slick core, ratcheting up her desire.

Dear Lord, she shouldn't have agreed to the massage, but now he'd rendered her powerless, swirling her hips with his wicked caresses.

He chuckled, his shirt hitting the floor...followed by his pants.

Jesus.

"Ah..." Her mind was too awash with desire to form words.

Before she could summon her willpower, warm kisses trailed up her spine. "I canna resist you." His deep burr sounded way too sexy, way too alluring.

Henri closed her eyes and hugged the pillow. How could she resist *him*? Mr. Hotshot. Hell on wheels? The bad boy spy?

When his lips touched her ear, he enticed her with a swirl of warm breath. "You had *the shot* at ICE, yes?"

"Yes." All female operatives were given a birth control shot to prevent any unwanted pregnancies should they be captured and...

"Then let me make love to you."

Unable to refuse, she nodded.

Mike moved to her back again, his mouth making her tingle all over. Her hips rocked with his motion. God, she needed this. It had been so freaking long since a man had touched her intimately.

When he reached the small of her back, his fingers gripped her bike shorts and tugged.

Henri rose up just enough for him to pull them off. Cool air whooshed around her tingling skin taking her anticipation higher.

He adjusted his knees between her legs and spread them wide. She could come right there, vulnerable and prone to him.

Dying to see him naked, she glanced back. Henri's breath caught in her throat. Oh yeah, if there was a heaven, this had to be it. His long cock was standing at attention with a bead of cum dripping from its tip. She licked her lips. "I want it."

Chuckling, he rubbed himself between her legs while his hand slipped around her front and teased her clit. Henri bucked against him, rising to her knees and arching her back. "Now, damn you."

Mike's voice rumbled with a deep chuckle while he smoothed his hands over her ass. "You're like a prized thoroughbred, born for pleasure." Ever so slowly, he slipped inside, the walls of her vagina stretching like never before.

Again, she gasped.

He froze. "Am I hurting you?"

"No." She wouldn't admit that he was. Good Lord, it had been so long, she felt as small as a virgin. Hot, driving need trumped the pain of stretching and she pushed back, forcing herself to take the length of him all the way.

Behind her, Mike growled as his fingers continued their treachery.

"Thrust," she demanded, her peak on the ragged edge. "Faster!"

"You're so freaking tight," he moaned, his hips giving her everything she'd asked for.

Henri could take no more. With a deep inhale, she shattered, the power of her orgasm making stars fill her vision. Behind her, Mike rode her like a bronc, bellowing with his release. Together, they collapsed to the mattress. "Good God, you've got to be the hottest woman alive."

20

H enri awoke naked and curled against Mike's powerful frame. Last night had been mind-blowing, though the new day brought the hollowness of guilt spreading through her chest like a giant chasm. She glanced over her shoulder while she scraped her teeth across her bottom lip. They'd made love five times in five different positions as if their sexual hunger was insatiable. No denying it, the night had been the most erotic of her life.

But stupid.

She had to work with Mike and see this op through. And she couldn't let feelings get in the way. How could she have been so stupid to let a night of hot passion ruin things? Now what was she going to do? Pretend it never happened? From now on, every time she looked at him she'd remember...*way too much*.

Rolling away, she pulled the sheet around her body, picked up her bag and headed to the bathroom.

Mike moved, but she didn't look at him. "Gonna work out?" he asked, his voice deep and gravelly.

"Yeah."

"I'll go with you."

Those words were all they said from there to the
workout room. After all, what should they talk about?
Last night was awesome, but it could never happen
again. Henri had been adamant about not kissing and
look how effective her insistence had been. She wasn't
a weakling. The Army saw to it "hard as nails" was her
middle name. She'd just been too long without a man.
Now that she'd gotten sex out of her system, she'd be
fine. Heck, for anyone who'd gone over two years
without a good toss in the hay, one night of hot passion ought to last a helluva long time.

Mike pumped the free weights while Henri
worked the all-around. When he moved to the stair
stepper, Henri cranked up the gym's sound system and
hit the treadmill. She caught him stealing glances, not
that she wasn't watching him out of the corner of
her eye.

Yeah, this is going to be as awkward as fuck.

And it continued. No talking. Steamy glances. And
sweaty bodies.

Fortunately, by the time they had breakfast and
coffee, they'd moved on to talking about the op
without a word mentioned about the blistering night
of intense passion. Thank God. Right now, the op was
all that mattered. Henri's focus homed in on finding
Melvut Amri and the thief would lead her to Omar
Fadli's door. Now she had all that pent-up sexual desire out of her system, she'd strap on her weapons and
concentrate on the job.

Hooah.

She wore the big, orange hat with her transition
sunglass lenses. Indoors, they didn't clear all the way
and in the upper right corner was a camera that sent a
live feed to ICE. Mike wore his ball cap and had applied another temporary color to his beard. He looked

mysteriously sexy with dark brown stubble on his face, though Henri preferred the auburn.

Now I know I've lost my mind.

Mr. Kisongo met them outside the jewelry shop in the center of the market. It was the ideal front for a jeweler who traded in blood diamonds and gems. Inside, the stall looked like it catered to tourists with cheap necklaces made from semi-precious stones and dirty, uncut stones like garnets that were hardly recognizable. As a prospector herself, Henri had pegged the stones as too worthless to bother trying to do anything with them.

Mr. Kisongo ushered them to the rear of the shop and pulled aside a curtain. "This way. Out the back is where we keep the inventory for serious buyers." As they'd seen on the satellite images, there was a run-down adobe building just across from the rear of the market stalls. There was one window and it had iron bars. As they slipped inside, Henri took note of the infrared lights lining each side of the door.

Inside, the décor was Middle Eastern, not African. In contrast to the exterior, it exuded wealth from the polished marble floors to the rich royal blue and gold trim. The showroom was small, and a man of Middle Eastern descent stood behind a glass display case with a licentious smile plastered on his face.

Mr. Kisongo gestured to the man with a slight bow. "May I introduce Mr. Arni Bashir." He shifted his palm to Henri and Mike. "Mr. and Mrs. Emmerson from Canada."

"Pleased to make your acquaintance," Mr. Bashir said in accented English as he held out his palm. "Passports please."

It was common practice for gems dealers to verify genuine buyers through a quick background search.

As always, ICE had developed extensive histories of
data for each of them. But still, Henri hesitated before
she pulled hers from her purse. The man's shifty eyes
were about as trustworthy as a snake's. Mike fished in
his top pocket, then took hers and handed both passports to Bashir, but Kisongo grabbed them.

"If you haven't already, please check out our web-
site, Emmerson Associates," Mike said. "We deal only
with the most elite jewelers in Canada."

"It is good to hear." Bashir gestured to the uncut
jewels in the display, though he looked directly at
Mike. In fact, he hadn't even glanced at Henri. "What
particularly interests you, Mr. Emmerson?"

Mike leaned down, giving the stones a good look.
"Everything, but our clients cannot seem to find
enough tanzanite..."

Being gender-snubbed gave Henri an opportunity
to use the camera in her glasses to slowly scan the
room. Behind Bashir were a computer, desk and a
walk-in safe much like a bank's. Beside that was another door. In the back corners, security cameras with
infrareds were pointed directly at them. Henri glanced
over her shoulder. Two more infrared sensors were
mounted above—as well as another two in the center
of each of the sidewalls. Jawhira was seriously
guarded, but not impenetrable. "Do you live here with
your family?" she asked innocently, focusing on
Bashir, insuring she was getting a good facial profile
for Asa.

"I do," he said, pulling out a tray of purple stones
and placing it in front of Mike.

"Mm. Impressive," said the Scot, using a pair of
tweezers to pick up a stone and examine it beneath an
illuminated magnifier.

Henri leaned in to her partner, straining to see the

stone. "I'll bet they get customers from all over the world here." She pulled out a set of jewelers' glasses and handed them to Mike. "What do you think, dear?"

He grinned and subtly arched his brows at her. "I think we're on to something." He shifted his attention to Bashir. "We are also interested in diamonds, but it is of utmost importance to our clients that they're clean, if you get my meaning."

"Of course. I assure you, we do not associate with the thugs who deal in conflict diamonds."

Bullshit.

Mike picked up another stone and examined it. "I thought as much. We're looking for large gems—anything over a karat."

Bashir grinned. "You're in luck. We've recently received in a shipment from the Mwadui mine."

"You deal with Mwadui?" Henri asked. "I'm impressed."

Bashir looked at her for the first time since they'd entered the shop. "I assure you, Mrs. Emmerson, once your husband has a look at these stones he will not entertain buying from another supplier."

She bit her tongue as the man brought out a tray of sizeable, uncut diamonds. Making sure to get a good shot of them, she again leaned into Mike. "Impressive. I've never seen so many gems of that size in one cache."

After examining the stones, they made an initial purchase of $200,000. Mike made a call to "his banker" who happened to be at ICE, and a quarter of the funds were transferred to Bashir's Swiss account with an agreement to pay another quarter when the gems were delivered to the transport to Canada, and the remaining half when Emmerson Enterprises took

possession of them on the tarmac in Toronto, or so
was the plan.

NOT SURPRISINGLY, before they made it back to the hotel, Asa reported that Bashir had been photographed
in Baghdad with al-Umari—five years ago, but still,
the Jawhira shop's ties with the Islamic State were
confirmed. And the jeweler's name wasn't Bashir. It
was Hazma Mahmoud and he'd done some nasty stuff
—had been one of bin Laden's cronies as well.

They needed to move fast. If Bashir was part of the
ISIS regime, no doubt they'd be running film on Mike
and Henri as well. Their disguises were decent, but
someone as skilled as Asa or the cyber recruits at ICE
would eventually be able to drill down and connect
the dots.

With no time to waste, they decided their next visit
to Jawhira had to be that night.

They dressed in black, including balaclavas and
night vision goggles. It was July and they were hotter
than hell, but it was worth it to get inside and begin
their attack on terrorist funding.

Mike carried the duffle with his tools. They were
armed to the teeth and had choreographed their every
moment. They each had their tasks and it was well
after midnight.

Taking on the grunt work, Mike disabled the security system by unscrewing the keypad and using the
ICE decoding program on his watch. It took 1.5
minutes.

Weapon balanced against her shoulder, Henri entered first. Mike had the barrel of his M4 pointed over
her shoulder as she moved. Once she verified the in-

frared was down, she stood against the wall while Mike slipped razor blades into the camera cables to create static. If he completely sliced through the cables, ISIS would know they'd been hit but if he pushed the blade in until it connected with wire, the cameras would only record static, then would be back up as soon as the blades were removed. They were also banking on the fact that in this part of the world, it was common for there to be interruptions in the electric grid.

Once security had been shut down, Henri made a beeline for the computer. Her job? Copy the contents onto a thumb drive which they would upload to ICE as soon as they got back to the hotel. They didn't care about the safe or its contents. Right now, they needed intel. And a "robbery" would only make the rats scatter. Even if the Avignon diamonds were in there, once confirmed, Interpol would be all too accommodating to seize and arrest.

It was best if they slipped in and out stealthily with ISIS none the wiser.

Mike stood guard while Henri worked her magic, her fingers flying over the keys and clicking the mouse.

"Holy shit," she whisper-shouted.

"What?" He moved in beside her and pushed up his NV goggles.

"Bank transactions—big ones, to a mine in Ruhuhu."

"Buying gems?"

"Can't tell." Her fingers typed rapidly. "I'll download it all. Checking the e-mails now."

Mike looked over her shoulder. One word caught his eye, *nuclear*. "What's that?" He pointed.

"Jeez, let me start the download first."

Mike kept his eye on the subject line. "Tell me when."

"Right." She glanced his way. "What did you see?"

He pointed, the tip of his glove touching the screen. "Fifth e-mail down. Open it."

Henri clicked and read aloud. "Doctor Thomas Flynn from MIT flying into Ruhuhu on July 16th to lecture about mining uranium."

"That's tomorrow."

She snorted. "You mean today."

Mike's jaw twitched as looked at the green bar indicating the progress of the download. "How much longer?"

"Less than a minute."

21

W ith their rifles hidden inside a duffle, Henri followed Mike out of the elevator, itching to hook up to her laptop.

At the door he swiped his key card. "How'd you get so computer savvy? You're almost as good as Asa."

"It pays to go through ICE training with a bunch of cyber nerds." Her mouth dropped when he flicked on the light.

The entire place had been ransacked. Clothes strewn everywhere. Dresser drawers discarded and strewn across the floor, the contents of the bar fridge scattered.

She drew her Glock from the small of her back. Mike already had a pistol in his hand. It only took a glance between them and they fell in step, taking opposite sides of the wall. Mike went first and scanned the bathroom. "Clear."

Henri slid past and swept her gun to the blind corner before she peeked around it. "Clear."

Mike ran to the bed and dropped to the floor while Henri made a sweep behind the drapes. "They're gone."

Jesus, even the trash had been tossed across the floor.

"They didna find your computer. Thank God." He pulled it out from where she'd taped it. "This is exactly why I dunna take computers into the field."

"Even if they'd found it, they never would have cracked it."

"So you say."

"So says ICE." She tucked her Glock back into her rear holster. "You know they change the encryption daily. That's why they need so many cyber nerds."

"Yeah, well, I like paper maps and paper notebooks."

"Notebooks can be stolen, too."

He pulled his out of his back pocket. "Only if they go through me first."

"Anything can happen." Henri picked up the duffle and tossed it on the bed. "I need to upload this stuff to ICE."

"Not here. I'll call Hali and have him meet us."

"Roger that." Snorting, she shook her head. Mike wasn't so old fashioned he didn't travel without his phone—it was a minicomputer, too.

After they'd packed their gear, Mike pulled his Glock and headed for the door. "You ready?"

"You think someone's out there?"

"Dunno. Probably not. But they ken who we are, lass. That's for certain."

Mike led with his gun and Henri followed. Together, they dashed for the stairwell. The elevator dinged as they passed.

The doors opened as the hairs on the back of Henri's neck pricked.

All it took was a peep over her shoulder. "G-e-t. D-o-w-n!" she hollered as if in slow motion.

Flinging her body into Mike, she tackled the enormous man to the ground. Something seared her bicep as she rolled and fired at the gunmen. Her hand became an extension of the pistol, squeezing the trigger. It took three bullets to nail three attackers. Without suppressors, the shots were loud enough to wake the dead.

Henri sat up, watching for any flicker of movement, her gun ready.

Mike was already on his feet, throwing her over his shoulder.

"Put me down," she growled.

"You're hit."

The searing pain started again—right where she'd felt it the first time.

Bouncing, she glanced to her arm as he ran into the stairwell. His feet barely touched the steps as he flew down them like she weighed nothing. But she'd been shot all right. A trail of blood followed them. Henri's head swam and her eyes rolled back.

"Stay with me, lass," he said as if he could sense her going limp.

He burst out the hotel's side door and ran for the curb.

A Land Rover sped beside them and screeched to a halt.

Mike opened the passenger door and shoved Henri inside, then slipped in beside her. "Head south out of town! Punch it!"

22

"Set your GPS for the Ruhuhu Basin," Mike said as he used his hunting knife to cut off Henri's sleeve to the shoulder.

"Ruhuhu, boss?" asked Hali. "It's a big place. It's like asking me to head for the Serengeti."

"Just drive." Mike pulled a first aid kit from his duffle, ripped open a roll of gauze with his teeth and jammed it against her arm.

"Ssss," she said, her face ashen.

"Sorry, love, but I need to have a look at the damages." He knew it would hurt, but he pressed hard enough to feel for a bullet.

She winced. "I think the shot just grazed me."

"I dunna feel anything in there." When he pulled away the gauze, blood gushed, but he'd seen enough. The bullet caused a jagged wound that was surrounded by purple flesh. She'd be sore for a good while.

Henri closed her eyes and rested her head back. The woman was tough. He knew men who would be whinging and carrying on with the pain, but not her. He fished in the kit for a shot. Special ICE issue—antibiotic combined with a local painkiller that worked in seconds. All he had to do was punch it against her skin. "I'm jabbing you now."

Grunting, she jolted as the needle pierced her skin. "Damn, that hurt."

"You got the worst of it." After holding the compress in place for a minute, he doused the wound with an iodine solution, then tore open a field dressing and wrapped it around her arm. "This baby will stanch the bleeding."

She looked at him with half-cast eyes. "Thanks."

"How're you feeling?"

"Like I've been shot—a little woozy. Don't worry. I'll be fine."

"You cold?"

"A little."

Mike pulled a Mylar blanket out of the kit and draped it over her. "This'll help." He looked to Hali. "Take us to a hospital."

Henri sat forward, pushing the blanket away. "Are you crazy? Someone's got our number. There's no fucking way we're going to stop anywhere to treat a freaking flesh wound."

"But—"

"I said *no*. I'm tired because it's nearly four in the morning—and we didn't get much sleep the night before. I need a few winks and then I'll be fighting fit. You got it?"

Mike gave her a narrow-eyed glare while he shook his finger under her badass nose. "If you grow any worse, I'm taking you in."

"I said I'd be fine." She flicked her fingers toward the windscreen. "Now just get us the hell out of Arusha."

"You heard her, Hali. Let's make tracks." Mike sat back, his head pounding. The older he got, the harder it was to go without sleep. But right now, too many things swarmed through his mind. Who ransacked their hotel room and what did they know? They must have been made at the Jawhira shop. Had their passports given them away? If so, the Islamic State was growing more high-tech by the day.

Still. They made us damned fast. Almost ICE fast.

And it was clear that whoever ransacked the suite expected to find them there—otherwise why would they have sent the hitmen back? And who knew they'd slipped to Jawhira to do a little snooping of their own? Or did they?

Most likely not, else they would have jumped us there.

Henri opened her eyes. "We still need to upload the files to ICE."

Mike pulled out his phone. "I'll call in. Let them know about Thomas Flynn. Tell Asa to expect the upload."

She grabbed his wrist before he punched the speed dial. "Don't tell them I've been shot."

He gave her a look. "You'd be better off in Iceland."

"I'll be better off when Fadli has daises growing over his coffin."

Pressing the speed dial for ICE, he said, "I reckon only thorns will sprout on that bastard's grave."

~

"THEY'RE ALL DEAD," said Melvut Amri from the other end of the phone.

Omar Fadli could have spit out his teeth. "I knew it was Anderson."

"You should have let me kill them when they were in the shop."

"You know we couldn't risk it until we were sure. Killing a pair of Canadians would have exposed the cover we took years to create." But Fadli had known it was her beneath that ugly hat and glasses. And the passport check had confirmed it—not a standard passport check that would lead them through the backgrounds of a pair of fictitious Canadians, but high-tech facial scans run on their photographs without hats and glasses had revealed it all.

Anderson's traveling companion was Mike Rose—a Scot and former officer with the SAS. The only problem was that's as far as his background went. The man was a ghost. Who they were working for was a mystery. Worse, the assholes were getting too close. Omar could have put a bullet in his chief information officer's brain—if he didn't need the man's computer genius for other, more important things. That's right. He must remind himself that there were things far more important than Henrietta Anderson.

But he'd get her, too.

"Where are you now?" he asked.

"The plane just landed."

"You need to move swiftly. Hours. That's all you have."

"Yes, sir. Peace be unto you."

"And unto you, peace." Omar clicked the red phone icon and tossed his cell on the desk.

So far, Amri had managed to stay two steps ahead, but ISIS needed Anderson and Rose off their trail for good, and preferably dead. Nothing could get in the way of their plans. Too many hours of careful preparation had gone into this mission. It was both brilliant and divine. Omar was so close he could taste the glory that would be his. Once he ensured all the world knew who possessed totalitarian rule, he would become the true caliph. It was time for al-Umari to step aside. Omar Fadli would bring all Muslims together and unite Earth under one true faith.

And those who dare to defy me will die.

23

H enri felt like her head had been bludgeoned
and her arm cleaved. Nothing like trying to
sleep in the back of a Land Rover with a
gunshot wound to put a girl in a foul mood. Thank
God the day had come and gone.

She and Mike were holed up in a private reading
space in the Dodoma Library, which would close in an
hour. It was stealthier than booking a room, and they
both doubted ISIS would have spies watching for
them there. In fact, Henri could bet any bad guys were
either ahead of them or behind.

They'd put two chairs together on the far side of
the desk so the laptop faced the wall. They also had a
clean line of sight through the glass office windows. At
ICE, Garth had summoned Asa to the sit room as soon
as they'd dialed in.

"The feed just indicated it's complete," Henri said,
clicking the "finish" button on the screen.

"Got it," Asa said, her fingers already tapping the
keys in Iceland.

Mike sat back and folded his arms. "I want to
know who this Thomas Flynn is and what's going on

in Ruhuhu—Hali tells me it's an area the size of the Serengeti."

The monitor shifted to Garth. "The Grand Canyon is more like it." More clicking came over the speakers. "Here it is. Top secret shit. There's a summit at the Nelson Uranium Mine."

"Nelson?" asked Henri. "US owned?"

"Affirmative." Garth squinted like he was reading something. "Only top brass will be there. US, UK, Canada, Germany, Australia and France."

"Weapons? Bombs?" Mike probed.

"The brief says nuclear power summit." Garth looked up. "Probably is."

Henri reached for Mike's pen and started clicking it—this whole thing stank of a terrorist orgy. "But we can't discount weapons."

"You can't discount anything." The boss shook his finger. "Especially since you pulled this intel off a suspect's computer."

The screen split so Asa's face appeared next to Garth's. "Thomas Flynn works for Nelson, but he's based in the US."

"And?" asked Mike.

"This says he's the top nuclear physicist in the world. Earns seven figures. Lives in Cape Cod."

"Can he make a bomb?" asked Henri, clicking the pen faster.

"Affirmative," said Garth, the angry crease forming between his brows.

Mike elbowed Henri's clicking arm. "Who does Nelson supply?"

Asa tapped the keys, her eyes scanning. "Everyone. They're the world's second largest supplier of uranium."

"Military?" asked Garth.

"Of course."

"Shite." Mike snatched the pen from Henri's grasp and slapped it on the desk, holding his palm over it. "We need a plane. The summit has already started and there's no way we can drive there fast enough."

"That's right," Asa agreed. "It would take you a week to go bush."

Garth grabbed the red phone—the one with the direct link to NATO. "I need a jet. Ten minutes. Dodoma, private airfield." He hung up. "Mark me, they'll be watching for you. Go in stealth. Report back when you can."

"Thank you, sir," they said in unison.

"And guys?"

Mike leaned forward. "Yeah?"

"If ISIS gets their hands on a nuke, you'll both be calling Antarctica home."

THE GULFSTREAM PILOT introduced himself as Luke Fox from Australia. He was tall, blond and lean, worked for NATO and said he liked flying at night. The guy looked like Val Kilmer from Grandfather's favorite movie, *Top Gun*—an 80s flick filled with testosterone-touting fighter flyboys.

Right. All Henri needed was to be surrounded by hot-looking alpha males.

No distractions.

She took the first seat and sank into luxury as it molded to her curves like a recliner. She almost sighed aloud. "How long will it take to get to the Ruhuhu Basin?"

"About an hour and a half," said Fox. "The airfield

is crude—just a dirt landing strip. Might take some crafty maneuvers, especially in the dark."

"How long do we have you for?" asked Mike.

"As long as you need."

"Do you have military experience?"

"Flew jets in the RAAF before this gig—did three tours in Iraq."

Mike nodded. "Good to know. Any guns aboard?"

He patted his sidearm. "I carry a pistol."

"And?" asked Henri, eyeing Fox critically. He might be easy on the eyes, but she was wary. Being framed for a crime she didn't commit did that do a girl.

"There's a Springfield Saint behind the pilot seat."

"Scope?"

"Yes, ma'am. Mark 6."

"Forty-four millimeter?"

"Yes, ma'am."

Henri made a mental note about the rifle. A Saint was certainly superior to the M4 she'd been hauling around.

"So what's your story?" asked Fox. "You must be pretty important to take me off the Rwandan relief project."

Mike shrugged. "We're chasing bad guys."

"Well then, I'd better get you there. Buckle up." The pilot stepped through the cabin door into the cockpit. "We'll be aloft in five. Once we hit altitude, help yourself to the tucker and drinks in the galley."

"Thanks."

Henri rested her head against the backrest and closed her eyes. "I could sleep for a week."

"We can sleep after the op." Mike walked aft. "There's a bed back here."

"We only have an hour."

"Damn my rotten luck."

Henri chuckled, a shot of heat blasting between her thighs. Though neither of them had mentioned the passion they'd shared, every time she glanced at Mike, he aroused the lioness lurking deep inside.

A lioness that needed to be caged.

He slid into the seat opposite and grinned. Straight, white teeth, eyes like the desert sky and sexy as sin. "I want to change your field dressing once we're aloft."

Nothing like a bit of medical talk to take her hots down a notch. She shifted her gaze toward the rear. "An hour, huh?"

He waggled his eyebrows. "I like how you think."

But once Luke announced they'd reached cruising altitude, Mike pulled another field dressing out of his bag. "Let's have a look at your arm."

"It feels better already."

"Yeah, but once the painkillers wear off, it'll hurt like a son-of-a-bitch." He unrolled the bandage

Henri didn't doubt it. Looking at the wound made her hiss. It was uglier than it felt—jagged and puckered purple skin, and the bandage had sopped up a shit-ton of blood. And it was still oozing.

"You could use some stitches."

"I'll be fine."

"Sure, it'll heal, but I dunna like seeing such a delicate arm mangled like this." His concern was adorable, but unnecessary.

"I'm not as delicate as I look." Still, Henri couldn't remember the last time someone doted on her—or cared for that matter. "Got any super glue?"

He fished in his pack and pulled out a tube. "Yep, but let me wash the cut with some more iodine solution first."

She watched as he carefully doctored the wound

with a look of concern on his face. "I should have been the one to take the bullet, not you."

"You tried. We weren't expecting an attack from behind."

He pulled off the glue cap with his teeth then spread a thin line around the mangled flesh. "You're gonna have a scar."

"Ooo, another scar? I'll impress all the boys back home." She pointed downward.

Chuckling, he pinched the wound together and blew on it. "The only boy I want you impressing is me."

A swarm of butterflies attacked her stomach. *Shit*.

Mike looked up and met her gaze, his eyes dark. Intense.

"Ah…" Henri scraped her teeth over her bottom lip. It was time to have "the talk". She took a deep breath. "What are we doing here?"

He grinned, looking way too sexy. "I'm applying a field dressing, m'lady."

She cleared her throat and watched him wrap her arm. Then she reached for his hand and squeezed. "You know that's not what I'm talking about."

"I ken." He chewed the corner of his mouth. "Sex was…" He cupped her cheek and leaned in, his breath caressing her lips. "Och, it was off the charts."

"Mm hmm." God, the only time Henri hadn't thought about their night of steamy passion was when they'd been under fire. *Dammit, I knew things would be awkward*. She took another deep breath and forced herself to look him in the eye. "But?"

Before she could arch away, he pecked her mouth with a soft kiss. "Our dilemma is we both have the same boss."

She cringed. "Garth can't *ever* find out."

"Agreed, no one at ICE can know." He tapped his forehead to hers, his eyes looking ginormous.

"We kinda crossed the line." Lightheaded, Henri ran her finger over his bottom lip. "But we shouldn't let it get too serious."

"You're right." He grasped her braid and slowly ran it along his hand. But when he held it to his nose and inhaled, the look in his eye told her exactly what he had on his mind.

She placed her hands on his shoulders. They had a job to do, and the plane would be landing soon. "So how about some food?"

Mike sat back and groaned. "Dammit, woman, now you're acting like a tease."

"We need to eat more than we need..." Groaning, she pushed herself to her feet. "I'll get it."

No matter how much she wanted to drag him to the bed and enjoy a quickie, she had enough field experience to know that as soon as the wheels touched the ground, they'd both need to be at the top of their game.

24

M elvut Amri had chosen his men carefully. They were elite ISIS fighters. Each man would give his life to further the cause. Amri himself would be the first to take a bullet if anything went wrong. He'd rather die a hero than face shame. If he failed, Omar Fadli wouldn't hesitate to parade him through the streets of Mosul. In a public demonstration, Fadli would use a machete to sever Amri's head and proclaim him a coward. That's how ISIS punished failures. But if he succeeded, he would be given accolades, power and wealth. He would report directly to the caliph, al-Umari. Yes, Amri would earn his place and become an equal to Fadli and then he'd prove to the world he was the tougher soldier and the more loyal servant of God.

Under cover of darkness, he led his men from the African bush. Fanning out, each man carried an AK-47 with a silencer. The Nelson employed a handful of security guards with little to no training who were no more than bushmen given meager pay to patrol the compound. Amri's inside man had watched for weeks, and the guards' routine never changed. Stationed at the four corners, the bushmen were doomed. Amri and his men cut them down like chaff, then rendezvoused beyond the gatehouse.

Their inside man had given Amri the room assignments, yet no one on his team knew who the target would be. No one except Amri himself.

At the gatehouse, he shot the first guard in the face, then took out the second. In less than five minutes, Nelson's entire security team had been dispatched.

Amri pointed to his lieutenant. "Cut the power."

"Straight away, boss."

Then Amri took one of the dead guards' keycard and headed for the bunkhouse at a crouch, his men falling in behind. As expected, the outdoor lights shut off, casting the compound into darkness. He pulled down his night vision goggles. No one would stop him this time.

They all knew the drill. They'd practiced a thousand times.

After using the keycard to access the side door, he led them to room 123, fired a suppressed shot at the lock and pushed inside.

The sleeping man stirred awake and pushed up. "What—?"

"Thomas Flynn?" Amri asked.

"Yeah, but—"

His lieutenant slapped duct tape across the man's mouth.

Though the scientist wasn't given a chance to utter another word, the surprise in his eyes gave him away. And time was everything. One misstep and they could lead the superpowers of the world to their hiding place—to the place where they would plot to raise al-Umari to ultimate power. A place where no one would think to find them.

Amri stood back while two of his men held guns to Flynn's head while his lieutenant finished the job, making sure the duct tape held fast on Flynn's mouth and wrists. In thirty seconds they were outside the bunkhouse. And in three minutes they were climbing the steps of the waiting Gulfstream.

Amri's breast filled with pride. His op had run flawlessly. Come morning, Amri would be heralded as a hero throughout the Islamic State.

~

THE PLANE JOLTED sideways and free-fell, making Mike's Coke crash to the floor. Once the plane stabilized, Mike released his vise-grip on the armrests and shot Henri a look as he released his seatbelt. Jerking open the cockpit door, he shouted, "What the hell was that?"

Fox glanced back from the console, his eye wide. "A frigging plane. Came out of nowhere and buzzed. Crikey, they practically sent us into a tailspin."

Mike squinted through the windscreen into total darkness. "What the hell? This isna exactly high traffic airspace."

"Too right," said Luke. "I didn't expect to see anything. There's nothing here."

"Aside from a gathering of energy moguls," said Henri, careful to leave the word "nuclear" out of the conversation.

Mike leaned against the door jamb and crossed his arms. "Who all probably arrived by private jet."

She nodded. "Maybe."

"What the?" asked Luke, leaning forward.

Mike again peered out the window. "What is it?"

"The airfield is supposed to be down below but there aren't any lights."

Henri climbed into the co-pilot seat, scanning out the window. "There's the compound."

"Huh?" Mike squinted and finally made out a black box-like structure. He pointed. "There?"

"Yes, can't you see anything?"

"Pardon me, Eagle Eyes."

"We've flown past the airstrip." She ran back and got her laptop and brought up the satellite image of the compound, shoving it in front of Luke. "See?"

"Got it. I'll double back. One fly over ought to give me the lay of the land."

The problem?

Why were the lights out? All of them.

"We'd better buckle in." Mike threw his thumb over his shoulder, pointing to their seats. "The place probably runs on a generator, but I dunna think it's a coincidence that the power's down."

"Hooah, it's time to dance." Henri grabbed the Saint and ammo vest on the way aft.

"Seatbelts," Luke said over his shoulder. "I mean it."

And he did. Aside from a nasty crosswind, the plane hit hard, jerking and shuddering as if the airfield were infested with potholes. But the Australian proved his skill, pulling the plane to a stop and cutting the engine. "Welcome to the edge of the earth, ladies and gentlemen. Land of coal and oil, there's nothing but bush for miles no matter which direction you go."

Mike checked his Glock's magazine, then looked at the pilot. "Stay with the plane. You got that sidearm loaded?"

"Yes, sir." Luke saluted.

"Good. Be ready...for anything."

"Roger that, mate. At least they didn't open fire on the plane—that's a good sign."

"We'll see." Lowering his NV goggles, Mike exited first. The last thing he wanted was for Henri to take another bullet—not on his bloody watch. *Never again.* He leapt over the handrail and used the stairs as cover as he panned his gun across the airfield. "Clear."

Henri slipped down the steps as silently as a cat. She carried an M4 strapped over one shoulder, a Glock in her back holster and the Saint supported by a lanyard in front of her body with her fingers wrapped around the handle. She looked like a female version of Rambo. Hot, gorgeous and ready to kill. "Lead on, Bubba."

"Bubba?" he asked in a whisper as they dashed for the safety of the scrub at the edge of the airstrip.

Henri crouched beside him, scanning everywhere through her NV goggles. "It's just a pet name I like to use."

"For friends?"

"Specifically reserved for good guys."

"All right then. You got it, Eagle Eyes."

"Soaring-Eagle," she said over her shoulder.

Mike chuckled to himself. They might be walking into a shit storm, but he was learning quickly it was a very good thing to have Henri on his side. And they worked well together—could practically read each other's minds.

She moved like a panther through the dirt path that led to the compound. Still shrouded in darkness, the place loomed like a green ghost town. It was too quiet—no crickets, nothing. It didn't take long for them to discover why. Two guards at the gatehouse had been shot at point-blank range.

"Looks like a professional hit," Henri said. She

stepped over one of the dead men and examined the compound diagram. "Generator's located to the left."

"Let's sweep the perimeter first before we light the place up."

Their tour around the grounds turned up four more dead guards, and it was a big place—complete with bunkhouse, command center and mess, not all that different from a military operation, except fancier —more resort-like. From the satellite images, the quarry was about a quarter-mile south.

As soon as they reached the generator, Henri went to work while Mike stood guard. Five minutes and the thing roared to life. Lights went on in all corners. Talk about a resort. The walks were lined with palm trees and grass as green as Scotland's hills.

Henri brushed off her hands and picked up the Saint. "Ready to go in?"

"What canna you fix?"

"I'm hopeless with forty-year-old Ford trucks."

By the time they hit the bunkhouse, Mike was convinced the plane that had nearly sent them into a tailspin was their target. Still, they took the building as if there were enemy suspects inside. Once they ensured the common areas were clear, they started pounding on doors.

"What the hell is going on?" barked a bald man tying a sash around his bathrobe. "I'm Caleb Gruber, Head of Security."

"You tell me," said Mike. "Your power was cut and you've got six dead guards out there."

"We what?"

Henri gestured with her Saint. "You can help us by assembling everyone in the mess hall including employees. We also need a manifest of each person attending this summit."

Gruber didn't budge. "And who the hell are you? This convention is top secret."

"Aye," said Mike flashing the appropriate credentials. "We have NATO clearance. You were just hit by terrorists. If you dunna cooperate, I'll assume you are one of them."

"Jesus." The man looked stunned.

"No one makes any calls, texts or e-mails until otherwise authorized," said Henri. "Move!"

25

Henri wasn't surprised to discover that Thomas Flynn was the only person attending the summit who'd turned up missing. And she knew Omar Fadli and his lackey, Melvut Amri, were behind the kidnapping—*suspected kidnapping*. She'd requested a download detailing every Nelson bill of lading for the past year. Her computer was running a database query to separate each one by its final destination. There was an outside chance at best but, maybe, just maybe a customer or shipment could be suspicious enough to lead them to Flynn.

Tedious work while operating on too little sleep and too much pain wasn't a good combination for maintaining a calm exterior. Though she tried. Internally was a different matter. She felt like someone had taken her into the ring and beat the crap out of her. Someone who was as sadistic as Fadli. The bastard was probably hiding somewhere protected by radical militants while he laughed his murderous head off.

But Henri vowed she'd have the last laugh. She didn't take kindly to being shot just as she didn't take kindly to spending two years in the pen for a crime she didn't commit. Exhausted beyond caring, she promised herself not to stop until that man was six feet under. And if Garth wanted to take her off the case, she'd quit.

After establishing an encrypted connection with ICE, she sat beside Mike and faced Asa on the screen. "There was a plane that blew past us. Our pilot said he came out of nowhere. Fox checked it out, but found no flight plan on record—no one should have been within three hundred miles. They were heading due north. See if you can pick anything up on radar, say, six hundred miles out or so."

"Roger that. Scanning for noncommercial pigeons now—including north, northeast and northwest."

"How the hell could they have gotten in and out so fast," Garth asked, the screen filled with his angry face.

Mike shook his head. "If it was the same guys from Arusha, they could have flown in whilst we were driving to Dodoma."

"The reason doesn't matter. Flynn is gone and we have to find him." Henri winced at a jabbing pain in her arm.

"Are you hurt?" Garth demanded like he was about to reach through the screen and strangle her.

"No, sir."

Mike gave her a look, but said nothing, thank God.

"I want hourly updates until you figure out where they have taken Flynn. Christ, if this gets to the media before we find him, we'll be facing World War Three."

"We're in lockdown here, sir. No cells, no internet."

"Work fast. We have no time to lose. Over and out."

"Wait," said Asa. "Satellites show there are three northbound planes flying noncommercial routes in Eastern Africa."

Garth grinned. "There you are, Rose. You see why I like technology so much?"

"I never said I didna like it, sir. I just prefer to not to use it in the field."

"I want to know the destination of each of those flights ASAP," said Henri clicking on the results of her database search. "Over and out."

Mike leaned over her shoulder. "What have you got?"

She scrolled. "This is a listing of all ports Nelson has shipped into. Every location on the list should have a representative here—at least someone from their country."

He scratched his head. "That sounds like a long shot."

"Have you got a better idea?"

"I'm going to question the rest of the staff. There might be a leak."

"You going to use profiling?"

"For starters."

"Hey, ace." She gave a cheeky wink. "That's a long shot."

"Touché."

~

AFTER QUESTIONING Nelson mine's Head of Security, Mike was confident the man knew nothing about the disappearance of Thomas Flynn. Gruber brought all the employees who worked in the compound together —a total of twenty-four, including the kitchen staff, the cleaning staff, an IT guy, an activity director and four remaining security guards.

His racial profiling idea fizzled before it started. Thumbing through their paperwork, everyone was a native Tanzanian. Good for Nelson for hiring local. Bad for Mike's op.

Of course, no one had seen anything or knew anything. They all looked scared.

He'd need to try a different tack. Something that wouldn't be too obvious and alert a mole to what he was digging for.

He made a quick trip to the business office and printed out assorted pictures from the internet—an American flag, a man and a woman holding hands by a public fountain, a cross, a baby, a red sports car, the Star of David and a clock. They were random but there were a couple that might elicit the emotional response Mike was looking for.

Once ready, he had Gruber bring in each person individually.

Mike watched their eyes and asked them three questions: *did you know the compound would be attacked?; has anyone in the past asked you about the security at the compound?; did you tell anyone there would be a summit including high-ranking international dignitaries?*

Next, he took the pictures he'd printed and asked them to say the first thing that came to mind when he showed them each one. Mike had Gruber write down their answers in a tabular form.

Everyone said they didn't know the compound would be attacked. No one admitted to giving out information on compound security, though there were a few eye shifts that Mike noted, and most everyone had told their families about the high-ranking dignitaries.

The interesting part was the pictures. Most associated Jesus with the cross and New York with the American flag. But there were two outliers. One gave mostly negative responses to all the pictures, but when he saw the Star of David, his eyes narrowed and he said, "Infidel". The second man used the word "war".

Those two gentlemen were escorted into separate rooms and secured to chairs with duct tape while Henri ran background checks.

Mike didn't enjoy interrogation, but he was good at it. His particular method of martial arts had taught him how to inflict pain with little effort. And through the years, Mike had invented a few techniques of his own. Give him an exposed neck and his victim would be begging for mercy.

The first man, one of the off-duty security guards, admitted to being a former member of the Rwandan Patriotic Front. He was a militant with some radical anti-Semitic ideals. He was one twisted son-of-a-bitch. But by the time Mike was finished with the militant, he was convinced the man had nothing to do with the murders of the guards and the suspected abduction of a nuclear scientist.

The next guy proved much more difficult to crack and he was a bloody groundskeeper. His name was Dia Turay and he swept the compound's footpaths for a living. Sweat bled from the man's every pore as Mike drilled his fingers into the points on either side of the man's head where the jaw and skull meet.

"I am a soldier of God!" Turay shouted. "I have nothing to say to you."

"You would die to protect terrorists?"

"You will not kill me." The man cackled in a high pitch. "You are an American."

"That's where you're wrong, mate." Mike twisted his fingers, pushing harder and the damned toad passed out just as Henri walked in the door.

She crossed her arms. "Wonderful. It looks like he's full of valuable intel."

"Wheesht. He'll come around in a minute." Mike took her into the corridor. "What have you dredged up on your end?"

"Nelson's shipping to three locations not represented by diplomats attending the summit—China, Greece and Israel."

Mike smirked. "I think we can count out Israel." He scratched his head. "China?"

"I found it odd, too. It's not like them to climb in bed with a terrorist organization, but stranger things have happened." She clasped her hands behind her neck. "All three countries are members of NATO."

"So, that doesna rule anything out, then." *Maybe her shipment idea is off.* "Have you heard back from Asa?"

As if on cue, Henri's phone buzzed. "Hopefully, she's got the info now." She moved back to the office she'd been using and scratched the information down on a pad. After she hung up, she looked at him and smacked the paper with her pen. "The northbound planes landed in Rhodes, Saudi Arabia and Cairo."

"That narrows it down considerably."

"Rhodes is part of Greece."

"Yeah, but Greece? That doesna make any sense. They're fast allies with the EU and the US."

"We're talking terrorists, not countries. For that matter, Syria is a fast ally with the US and they harbor a lot of terrorists."

"Not to mention Saudi Arabia."

"True, but Nelson Mines hasn't shipped uranium to the Saudis or the Egyptians."

"But according to your manifest, they've shipped to Greece. Where? Rhodes?"

"Athens. But that doesn't mean the uranium wasn't offloaded onto another boat. As a matter of fact, if it was, it would have been easier to avoid a customs inspection."

"Shite."

Henri inclined her head toward the makeshift interrogation rooms. "So what does Mr. Turay have to say?"

"He's not talking. But he kens something." Mike held up a finger. "I'll need your help."

She blew out a sigh and nodded. "Let's hop to it before I fall asleep on my feet."

"We can sleep after the op." He led her back across the hall and prepared for another round with Dia Turay who had regained consciousness.

Mike placed the man's hand on a cutting board, splaying his fingers and applying enough pressure to the ulna nerve to cause excruciating pain. He inclined his head to Henri who was holding a hunting knife with a shiny new blade. "This here's my partner. She's not as kindhearted as I am."

Henri scowled. Jesus, she was perfect for the part. Her mean face even made Mike's spine snap to attention.

He took a Sharpie and wrote China, Greece, Israel, Saudi Arabia and Egypt on Turay's five fingers. "See, I'm making it easy. I'm not even asking for cities. I'm asking for entire countries and it will take us days if not months to drill down from there, but all you have to do is give me a country."

"Fuck you."

"Sorry, mate, that's not one of the options I've given you." He motioned to Henri. "Let's eliminate China."

A low chuckle rumbled from her throat as she slowly drew the blade over Turay's pinky—not hard enough to sever the finger, but a warning that told the asshole they were serious. Blood seeped through the slit and pooled under his hand.

The man jolted, trying to tug his hand away, his feet thrashing. "Damn you to hell! They went to Greece. That's all I know. Fuck you!"

After giving Mr. Gruber orders to hold Dia Turay until he could be picked up and convicted by Interpol, Henri and Mike headed for the Gulfstream.

26

"**S**even hours to Rhodes," Luke announced before he closed the door to the cockpit.

After they were airborne, Henri looked to Mike while she unbuckled her seatbelt. "I'm heading aft." She didn't invite him to follow, but there was no need to turn around to know he had.

"Seven hours to sleep," he said, his voice close enough to send a thrill down her spine.

"I'm ready to drop." She was...aside from the tingling all over her body. He was driving her insane. She had to get a grip on her feelings, compartmentalize and shut them down before she ended up in so deep, she'd be hurt. They'd agreed not to get serious. Hell, Henri hadn't been serious about anyone since her first tour in Afghanistan and that hadn't ended well. And she reminded herself for the umpteenth time the affair had practically ended her career with Delta Force before it started.

Pure and simple: continuing the romance with Rose was a bad idea.

After being dragged through the gutter and enduring the hell of prison, her self-esteem was still too

fragile. Not that she'd ever let anyone know how much
she doubted herself. Henri had spent so much of her
life being rejected she'd built up an external wall that
people couldn't penetrate easily. Hell, she'd been rejected by her father. Her people looked at her as a
half-breed freak, and then to have her military career
crash and burn while she endured the humiliation of
a court martial, it was no wonder her psyche roiled in
the depths of hell. No, she couldn't handle a relationship letdown right now. And that's where this thing
was headed. There was no other place it could head.
Sooner or later, Garth would find out and that would
be the end of it. Just like her CO had given her an ulti-
matum to end the affair with her heartthrob or quit
Delta Force. Why did work always get in the way?
Why was the op always more important than
happiness?

Exhausted beyond rational thought, she headed
for the shower. A quick duck under a spray of warm
water ought to clear her mind as well as her unwel-
come female urges. She didn't say anything, just
slipped into the miniature bathroom and locked the
door.

It had been two days since she'd been shot. She'd
slept a little in the car on the way to Dodoma but that
didn't count much. Combine that with their late-night
intel gathering in Arusha and she hadn't had a decent
night's sleep in seventy-two hours. No wonder she was
a wreck.

Henri peeled off her clothes and the field dressing
and examined her wound in the mirror. She'd done a
good job of ignoring it, but the sight of her bruised
and swollen flesh brought on throbbing pain. When
she stepped under the shower, she cried out with the
toe-curling sting.

The sound must have been loud because in two seconds, Mike burst through the door. "You all right?"

The problem aside from the fact he'd ignored her privacy even though she'd engaged the lock? He'd stripped down to his boxers.

God save her, the man should be a fitness model, not a spy. His shoulders barely fit through the doorway. His chest put GI Joe to shame. And his abs? A six-pack of growler-sized pure steel.

"Fine." Henri braced herself against the wall as he strode toward her with his mammoth thighs flexing with each step. God, her knees turned to mush along with her resolve.

"Mind if I join you?"

She shook her head and blinked. "The door was locked."

"That's the thing about airline lavs. They're all fitted with external unlocking devices."

Yeah, she knew it. But she could still say no. Until he dropped his shorts.

A rush of scorching need gushed to her vagina. Her clit felt like it would shatter with a single swipe of that thick shaft when he slid it between her legs. By the time he stepped inside, his cock was standing at attention and was the first thing to touch her.

Henri licked her lips, forcing her gaze to meet his eyes—eyes filled with the same ravenous hunger that thrummed through her breasts, her heart, her crotch. His breath caught as he pulled her against his naked body while hot water cascaded around them.

His lips plundered hers with hot, tonsil-probing passion. She met him with equal vigor, unapologetic and seductive. Every thought of trepidation melted from her mind as she gave in to the intensity caused by the frenzy of emotion pooling between her legs.

"You clean enough?" He asked, lifting her up and urging her to wrap her legs around him.

"Mm hmm," she managed to sigh into his shoulder.

HER BREATHS CAME in ragged gasps, making him wild. They'd both been pushed to the edge of their endurance. Working beside her and not being able to have her had amped up the predator deep inside—aroused the woman-seeking beacon always on full alert just below his belt. Soaking wet, he lowered her to the bed and climbed between her thighs. Taking his weight onto his elbows, he stared into those liquid chocolate eyes. "I need you, lass."

She sank her fingers into his ass with a quick nod, her lips parted just enough to look like sex served up on a platter. He watched her as he slid his cock up and down through the slick cradle between her thighs.

Gasping, Henri arched and swirled her hips, capturing the tip of his cock with the hottest, tightest pussy on Earth—or above Earth. Christ, in the entire freaking universe. Moaning, she sunk her fingers into his glutes and guided him deeper. Throwing his head back, he filled her with his length only stopping when he hit her wall. Tight, ribbed muscles clenched around him, milking him as he forced the frenzy to ebb and reveled in the turn-on of being buried inside the only woman who had ever made him want to possess her. That's right. *Possess*.

"Faster," she sighed into his ear as her hands dictated the tempo.

He wasn't going to last long with her in control. His cum boiled in his balls, demanding release. "I want you to come first."

"I want..." With a deep gasp, she rolled him to his back, working her hips in a fierce rhythm. God, she was on fire.

Mike nearly lost it when she threw her head back with a rush of erratic tremors squeezing him, begging for his release. But he'd found his second wind. With a growl, he the reversed rolls and took control, shifting her legs over his shoulders and pushing inside to his root. Lowering his head, he joined his mouth with hers dancing with her tongue while he slammed his cock in and out, deeper and deeper. The pressure mounted. He clenched his bum cheeks to make himself last. He arched and bellowed, too damned close... Yes! Yes! Oh, God, yes! His mind exploded with the power of his orgasm.

HENRI BARELY HELD on for dear life as she peaked in tandem with Mike's shattering orgasm—her own body coming with a detonation to rival a dirty bomb. Sex was off the charts, but they connected on a level she'd never been before. She couldn't pull her gaze from his if someone came into the room with a loaded gun. The electricity between them was fierce. Frightening.

You can't get too serious. Those words echoed in her head. She tensed for a moment until he captured her lips in a whisper of a kiss. Henri closed her eyes and reveled in the softness of it and the sweetness of those gentle lips. He pulled out of her gently while he trailed feathery kisses down her neck...all the way to her breasts. He cupped them like he was holding a bird while his tongue brushed her nipple.

She stretched against the want starting to recoil

between her legs. "If you keep that up, we'll never sleep."

Grinning, he slid alongside her and pulled up the covers. "Watch me."

27

"Wakie, wakie, sleepyheads," Luke's Australian-accented English came over the intercom. "You pair have a call from HDQ."

Mike opened his eyes and buried his nose in Henri's hair. *Jasmine. Good God, this woman will be the death of me.* Her body shifted against him bringing on a new rush of anything but the desire to head for the cockpit. He chuckled. The only cockpit he wanted to visit was lying right beside him.

But Henri moved first, bless her. "Let's go before Garth suspects something."

While Mike pulled on his pants, he watched Henri don a pair of leopard panties. She was a total cat woman who made him want to roar. Her curvy arse could fill out a pair of bikinis like no one else. Then she caught his eye with an expression that said a million words. At the top of the list were, I want you, I don't want to get hurt and WTF are we doing—all things going through Mike's head as well.

Keep it simple? Hell, simple was thrown out the window in Arusha. And "complicated" just ratcheted up thirty-thousand notches in the back of this Gulfstream.

He tugged his shirt over his head. "I'm ready."

Luke patched the call through to a flat-screen computer attached to the bulkhead.

"What the hell took you so long?" Garth never beat around the bush.

Mike rubbed the back of his neck. "Catching a few winks, boss. Seventy-two hours on the go even taxes me."

"Likely story." Garth snorted. "While you've been in lala land, our new techies have been studying the satellite images on Rhodes—mind you, it's a Greek island where nothing ever happens, so we don't have a ton of film, but we did find an abandoned World War II airfield."

"Can we land there?" asked Henri.

"Nada. I've given Fox orders to land at the private airfield, *Aerolimenas*. You pair rent a car. Go to the Temple of Apollo. There's a cache of guns under a slab in the southeast corner. You'll need a crowbar. Fox will be your backup."

"Luke?" Mike glanced toward the closed cockpit door. "You sure about that?"

"I'm giving him an unawares audition." Garth arched his eyebrows. "After you're armed, pick up Luke and then set your ICE GPS for Kalathos—it's not going to show up on Google or any other non-military device. There's nothing there but the airstrip and a decrepit concrete bunker. Word is there's some underground space that survived the World War II bombings."

"You said you've picked up some activity?" asked Mike.

"Might be a red herring, but satellites show vehicles coming and going, which is unusual. We're trying to find more intel—though a quick search says the property hasn't been sold. All we know at this point is it was used by the Italians in the war and fell into the hands of the South Africans who abandoned the post in 1947."

Henri pulled a bottle of water out of the galley and cracked it open. "At least we have some sort of lead. That's a hell of a lot more than we knew five minutes ago."

"Where did the plane land that was headed to Rhodes from Tanzania?" asked Mike.

"Same private airfield where you're landing. Anyone who tries to land at Kalathos Airfield without clearance is likely to have the Greek military breathing down their necks and that's the last thing we need."

"Right, and if ISIS is there making nukes, you can bet they're equipped with some sort of antiaircraft weapons."

To pass through security, Henri wore a makeshift hijab and Mike wore a turban with a black beard gummed in place. They proceeded to the private airfield's customs using the aliases of Mr. and Mrs. Assad from Malaysia. Another boon, customs procedures for those who could afford to land at private airfields was minimal and they passed inspection without incident.

Luke also cleared customs, but separately and on the pretense of a pilot stopping over and spending a few days on R & R while his wealthy boss enjoyed a vacation.

Mike drove the rental car to the Temple of Apollo

which gave Henri an opportunity to glimpse the island paradise. The city of Rhodes was lined with cobblestoned roads and the remnants of medieval architecture with the centerpiece being the renovated Grand Master's Palace of the Knights Hospitallers.

The ancient architecture dominated the modern, giving the feel of a trip back in the time of gallant knights riding armor-laden horses.

Along the drive, the view was remarkable. It took about five minutes to go from the bustle of traffic in the city to the sparsely populated countryside. Cute, white-washed, flat-topped houses sprawled up the hills in tiers. The cobalt blue Mediterranean stretched forever. Palm trees swayed in the gentle breeze as if in complete unity with the fiber of the universe. The car ambled along until they reached the end of the road and found the Temple of Apollo ruins standing alone without a soul in sight.

Henri sat in awe for moment. To think this was a mecca where ancients came to worship—and it was abandoned, sitting alone on the hilltop, dominating the sea. "Wow."

"You don't see stuff like this in America."

"Nope, only petroglyphs and pueblos. You know, Native American ruins."

"That's right. Sorry if I downplayed the importance of your people's history. It's just the Romans were such..."

"Expansive and conquering tyrants?" she finished.

Mike opened the car door. "Aye."

As promised, they found their cache of guns exactly where Garth said they'd be. Henri was happy because she found an AR-15 Featherlight with a Leupold scope. They took what they needed and left the rest.

"You never know what will happen. It's best to

have a cache of weapons, food and money in every corner of the world," said Mike.

"It's a good thing ICE has had our backs through everything."

"Sweetheart, lesson number one of espionage is to look out for yourself. What happens when you have no access to a phone and you're running for your life? Sometimes you have to go silent."

"I know."

"Remind me next time we're in Europe—you need to establish safe deposit boxes."

"I opened one in Avignon."

"That's a start."

Henri slung the rifle over her shoulder. "All right then. Are you ready to find this airfield?"

Mike drove back the way they had come and Luke met them at the rendezvous point outside the city of Rhodes or Rodos as the signs indicated.

"Where are we headed?" asked the Aussie from the backseat. He had a casual drawl and a cocky grin and it made Henri's gut clench. The reason ICE was so effective was because no one knew of its existence. Luke might be a NATO pilot, but he wasn't an insider and, in her mind, the less he knew the safer they were.

"Doing some reconnaissance on a lead," said Mike, looking in the rearview mirror.

"Those guys back in Tanzania have anything to do with it?" Luke persisted.

"They do, and that's about all we can tell you, mate."

Luke gave a thin-lipped nod and looked out the window. "I can help."

Henri decided it was her turn to speak up. "We're counting on it."

"So, what branch of NATO are you working for?"

Mike met Henri's gaze. "That's classified." Though he was wearing black aviators, she could still see him squinting by the pinch to his brow.

But Luke didn't get the hint. "Where's your headquarters? Your boss sounded American."

Henri had enough. She rose on her knee and faced the backseat. "Look, we're not here to play nice and answer thirty questions. We brought you along to cover our backs and, since you were in Iraq, I have no doubt you know what that means. Following fucking orders and not asking questions. You got it?"

Luke met her gaze. "Yes, ma'am. *Crikey.*" Then he narrowed those sharp, blue eyes. "Just one more question."

She leaned in without blinking. "It better be a good one."

"What's our objective?"

Henri shook her finger. "I think—"

"Pull in your daggers, Eagle Eyes." Mike reached over and slapped her seat. "Look, Fox, I ken you're NATO, mate, and so far you've done a good job getting us where we need to go. These guys we're tracking are ISIS thugs. They've kidnapped a nuclear scientist. Need I say more?"

Luke raked his fingers through his hair. "Holy shit."

"That's right," Henri agreed. "Holy shit."

"Eagle Eyes here is our Delta Force sharpshooter. I'm ex-SAS. We need to play this cool and, right now, we dunna ken for certain if our scientist is even in Rhodes. Worse, if news gets out that ISIS has captured someone like this guy, the whole world will erupt in anarchy." Mike glanced over his shoulder. "And it's our job to see to it that doesna happen."

Henri turned to the back seat. "You breathe a word

about this to anyone and I'll make sure you don't ever speak again."

Mike chuckled. "The lass is the deadliest woman on the planet."

"Whoa." Luke held up his palms. "Hey, I want in on what you guys got. You won't hear a peep coming from me. Check with NATO. I'm their most trusted pilot—get all the tough assignments."

"Good to hear," said Mike.

"So, my job is to watch your backs? That's all?" asked Luke

"You got it."

"Understood." The Aussie leaned forward and rested his elbows on the front seat backrests. "If I prove myself here will you put in a good word with your boss? I'm sick of bloody Africa. I want to be in the middle of the action like you pair."

"One thing at a time, mate. If you prove yourself here, we'll talk." Mike pointed toward the window with his thumb. "In the meantime, have a gander at the view. You dunna see ocean as blue as the Mediterranean every day."

They skirted around the mountains by traveling south on the eastern coastal road. It took about an hour for them to wind their way to the unmarked turn to Kalathos. Mike stopped the car at a lookout point and Henri brought up the satellite map on her laptop.

"I dunna like it." Mike scratched his chin. "There aren't any trees and the ground's flat. It's worse than Aleppo."

"Not many shadows to hide in either." Henri traced her finger west. "There's an outcropping here— that would give us some cover."

"Yeah, but we'll have to crawl—there's nothing but scrub for cover."

Luke shook his head. "You guys are insane."

"Have you got any better ideas, flyboy?" asked Henri.

"You could go in by sea—the tower looks to be about a hundred meters from the shore."

"Nah." Henri shook her head. "There's even less coverage."

"You're both right. The sea would work for a night op, but not for surveillance. Let's overshoot it and head up the beach." Mike used a pen to trace along the southern road. "Cut in here and climb the back-side of the outcropping."

"I think that'll work." Henri closed her laptop.

"Am I going with you, or what?" asked Luke.

"Drop us off about a half-mile past the airstrip. Then go into Lindos and rent a room—say it's for one. If they ask, give them the same cover as before; you're a commercial pilot waiting for your boss and his wife to enjoy their holiday in the city and you decided to head for the tranquility of the south shore." Mike gave a thumbs up. "I'd even buy it."

Once they'd concealed their arms in a duffle and set out on foot, Henri fell into step alongside Mike. "I don't have a warm feeling about Luke. He's too nosy."

"Know what I think?" He adjusted the strap on his shoulder, wearing the duffle like a backpack, but it contained the Win Mag and extra rounds.

"What?" she asked.

"He's bored to death flying NATO execs around Africa and he senses we're seeing a lot more action."

"So that gives him the go-ahead to pry?"

"He has a right to know what he's risking and why." Mike stopped and grabbed Henri by the shoulders. "There's nothing wrong with giving him enough info to enable him to make smart decisions. He doesna have a clue about ICE."

"But he suspects were not above board." She wrenched from his grasp. "Are you always so friendly?"

"Aye. At least until someone crosses me."

"I wish I could be so trusting."

"I can understand why you're not. You just need to ken how far you can depend on someone like Fox. In this game being too trusting will get you killed, but so can ostracizing someone who's been sent in to help."

She huffed. "It has never been easy for me to open up to anyone. A person has to earn my loyalty first."

"I've noticed that about you."

Tension clamped between her shoulders. "Do you think it's a bad thing?" she asked a little too defensively.

He stopped again but, this time, he cupped her face between his palms. "As long as you dunna doubt my loyalty, I have no problems whatsoever."

She moved a bit closer and regarded his lips, nearing by the millisecond. "We're on assignment."

"Yeeeeee-ah, but two lovers would be a fair bit less suspicious than a pair of undercover spies marching in a direct line toward an abandoned airfield suspected of being used by a mob of terrorists intent on blowing up the western world."

"Well, if you put it that way..." Henri slid her hands around Mike's waist and kissed those scrumptious lips slowly, savoring every swirl, every crackle of energy that flowed from the tips of her breasts right down to where she wanted him most. With another step, their bodies fused, Mike's fingers treaded into the hair right above her braid. No matter how much she wanted to convince herself this kiss was for the job, the emotion coursing through her body made her heart squeeze with longing.

If only she could let down her guard and allow herself to fall in love. Mike wasn't even an all-out bad boy. Yeah, he flew by the seat of his pants, but having someone like him in a meaningful relationship would certainly make things so much...so much...*happier*.

He glanced to the side and arched his eyebrows. "The sand looks soft."

"And we could be standing about a quarter-mile from the free world's greatest enemy." She chewed her lip, wishing those words hadn't slipped out.

"Och, that only adds to the rush, lass."

Her libido went on overdrive as Henri stared at him. Tingles fired across her skin. Moisture soaked through her panties and it was all she could do to force herself to blink. She tugged Mike by the hand before he convinced her to drop her drawers and enjoy a quickie in hostile territory. "Come on, before we fall too deep into our cover and forget the mission."

"Bloody terrorists always interfering with my fun."

She marched ahead while breathing deeply. The man was dangerous for her heath. Not because he was joking around, but because she'd actually considered it.

And she couldn't allow herself to get serious. Not now. Not ever.

They both grew quiet as they began the ascent up the crag. It wasn't an overly large outcropping and when they crested the top, they were about 600 to 700 meters from the old control tower. Sure enough, it looked like someone had set up some sort of operation. A white truck with a covered van and a car were parked near the building with the tower. The roof had caved in on one side and the windows were gone. A shooter walked in a circle around the tower, shaded by the flat-topped roof, making it impossible to see anything but shadow.

Henri signaled with her fingers. "Give me my gun. I want to have a peek through the scope."

Mike dug in the duffle. "You see the guard?"

"Sure do. Keep your head down."

"I wonder what's in the back of the lorry." He handed her the rifle.

"That's the golden question." Placing the butt against her shoulder, she kept both eyes open and focused the scope on the man in the tower. "Middle Eastern. Wearing all black—just like an ISIS uniform."

"Balaclava?"

"Nope. Guess he doesn't think he's going to be photographed out here."

"Or he mightn't be ISIS."

"My gut tells me he is."

"The only way to find out is to slip inside and check it out." Mike crawled sideways.

"What are you doing?"

"If I can find enough cover, I'm going down there."

"Are you insane?" Henri gestured to the stretch of barren, sandy land between them and the tower. "There's nothing between us but tufts of sea grass."

He pointed. "There's a couple ridges—those could be ruins—and that looks like a trench over there."

"All right. Let's just say you make it to the trench without being seen. You still have at least two hundred yards to cross, and my eyesight is better than yours. There's no way in hell you'll make it across without being seen."

"But..." Mike took in a sharp inhale. "Shite. We need to get in there."

"The only way we'll pull it off is at night."

"Bloody hell."

Movement from the building drew Henri's focus to her scope. "Two perps heading for the car."

"You recognize anyone?"

She adjusted the sights slightly and her heart rate sped. "Shit."

"What?"

Calming her breath, Henri pulled back the charging handle. The sound of the bullet entering the chamber made a sense of calm flow through her veins.

"What is it?" Mike grew more insistent.

"Fadli." She moved her finger to the trigger.

"Stop."

"I have a shot!"

"No, goddammit." Mike placed his palm on her shoulder.

She whipped her head around and whisper-shouted, "Fuck you! That man's responsible for ruining my life."

"Yeah, well, you take him out now and, one; you expose our cover and, two; you ruin any chance of finding Thomas Flynn."

"Fuck it." She ejected the bullet, but gave Mike an angry glare. "I want that asshole so bad I would risk everything for a shot at him."

"Everything?"

"My life, anyway." Inside, Henri's gut churned while she watched the man responsible for unquantified death and destruction saunter to the car. Her every muscle stiffened when he stopped and turned, as if scanning the horizon for a threat. Then he shifted his gaze to the outcropping. He stopped panning, his eyes lingering there while she watched him, frozen—not even breathing. Rubbing the back of his neck, Fadli got in the car. The slamming of the door echoed above the sound of the surf.

Mike shifted ever so slightly, snapping pictures with his ICE phone. "So, ISIS brass is in town."

28

After studying the map and pictures of the site, Mike and Henri opted to go in by sea just as Luke had suggested. On the north side, opposite the outcropping, there was an old stone wall leading from the shore that would give them enough cover to move within twenty feet of the old control tower. They couldn't get half that close by any land approach. Garth had a satellite pointed at the airfield, but with the night op and cloud cover combined, the folks at ICE wouldn't be much help.

They'd spent the rest of the day getting their gear organized. Luke hired a small boat and Mike acquired diving gear while Henri worked with Asa analyzing the data from the satellite feed. Once night fell, they climbed into the dinghy and motored out of the marina.

"Are you sure you don't want me to cover you?" asked Luke while Mike helped Henri strap an oxygen tank to her back.

"I dunna want anything to make them suspicious."

After securing her belt, Henri picked up Mike's tank. "Cast in a fishing line and make sure the boat is out of sight, hidden behind the outcropping."

"Yeah." Mike slid his arms through and took the tank's weight. "And if anything goes wrong, you're a tourist. Just a pilot from Australia. Got it?"

"Anything else?"

Mike slapped Luke's shoulder. "That's it, mate. If we dunna make contact within four hours, call Garth." He pulled down his facemask and looked at Henri. "You ready?"

"Locked and loaded." She gave him a cheeky grin before slipping the regulator into her mouth and rolling into the swells backward.

"See you on the other side." Mike gave Luke a thumbs up and followed Henri into the Mediterranean.

The cloud cover made visibility bad, but they had darkness on their side. Sitting alone at the end of the airstrip, the white control tower stuck out even in the dark. Otherwise, the place looked abandoned. No surprises there. The site was ideal for a mob of militant radicals. Since NATO had been scouring Iraq for weapons of mass destruction, it made perfect sense. Keep the bomb development offshore. And the isle of Rhodes was only a stone's throw from Turkey, as well as a half-day's sailing from Syria. Nothing like hiding in plain sight. If they weren't terrorists, Mike might give them credit for brilliance, but he couldn't do that.

He swam alongside Henri as they let the tide push them toward the shore. When Mike's feet hit sand, he grabbed her hand and pulled her to a halt. "What do you see?" he asked.

She nodded toward the compound. "It looks like both the truck and the car are gone."

"That's not what I expected."

"Me neither." Henri leaned into him. "Do you think they've abandoned the place?"

"The only way to find out is to have a look-see."

They hid their tanks, masks and flippers in the brush at the edge of the beach. Mike had used a dry pack to stow two pairs of black boots, NV goggles and suppressors. He carried a Glock, and an M16, had a knife up each sleeve as well as one hidden in the inside of his boot. He'd seen Henri do the same. Funny, though. He never thought he'd see the day when he was glad to have a woman partner undercover on a covert mission but, after his trepidation in Africa, he was glad to have Henri there. He'd worked with a lot of other soldiers who didn't have half of Soaring-Eagle's talent. Sure, he might tease her about having eagle eyes, but he admired her skill. He figured she knew it, too.

"Do you see anyone in the tower?" he asked.

She put on her night vision goggles. "Oh yeah. There's a spook at ten o'clock."

"Just one?"

"Don't see any others. Ten o'clock isn't moving, either. Looks like he's having a smoke."

"Then let's roll."

They crept along the old stone wall which had nearly been buried after years of sand blowing over it, but it provided the best cover given the flat and treeless terrain. When they reached the far end, Mike stopped and gave the building a good once-over. Their reconnaissance mission earlier in the day had been on the south end. This side of the building had more windows—something he hadn't expected.

Mike panned his gaze up to the tower. The sentry was on the move again and looking straight toward them. Stopping in his tracks, Mike dropped and held up his fist to tell Henri to lay low.

The sentry was joined by another. The tone of

their voices carried on the wind over the sound of the surf though their conversation was indecipherable. Again, Mike rose high enough to peer above the wall. The pair shifted away from the north side, still talking. Seizing the opportunity to slip in unawares, he gave the signal to move.

Time to see what Fadli is up to.

Mike kept an eye on the control tower as they ran. Neither guard looked back as the sand absorbed the sound of their footsteps. In seconds, they pressed their backs against the wall, listening for movement inside.

A conversation sounded like it came from an echo chamber just inside the window. Henri motioned forward with her hand, then crouched and took the lead. On the west side of the building, they found a tractor concealed under a canopy.

"It looks like they've been busy," Mike whispered as he tried to push through the door. But it was locked.

Henri pulled her ICE fob from the watertight pocket on the front of her wetsuit. The gizmo was designed to unlock anything. Definitely state-of-the-art, but useless in the hands of anyone untrained. It looked like a button with a laser pointer, but hold it to a keyed lock and push the button. The thing used laser technology to shift every cog to the open position and worked like magic every time.

The lock clicked and Henri turned the knob. Mike stood aside the jamb, his M16 at the ready. She gave a silent count—Three, two, one—and pulled the door wide.

Mike shouldered in, his gaze flashing across the dimly lit hall.

Nothing moved.

The conversation came from a room up ahead and now the men were laughing.

Definitely not an interrogation happening in there.

To his right, a stairwell led downward. He motioned to it with a slice of his hand.

Together they descended, their toes lightly taping the steel steps. Safely at the bottom, they crept toward the lower passageway. Mike led with his gun and peeked into the hall. As they expected, the underground bunker was still intact.

A door opened down the hall.

Mike snapped his head in and nudged Henri under the staircase just as two men entered. "I will make him talk, mark me," a man said in Arabic.

Another man snorted. "You always do."

They started up. The men's footsteps boomed through the small space. Simultaneously, Mike could have sworn he heard a vehicle approach.

He held his breath. One glance down and the two ICE assets would be seen as they crouched in their hiding place. But the men continued on as if they were wearing blinders.

Once clear, Mike let out a breath. Turning to Henri, he whispered, "Let's go."

Entering the passageway was like stepping back in time. Crumbling sea salt encrusted cement walls. A lone lightbulb swung from a rusted metal fixture. Sweeping their weapons into the first doorway they secured room one. Inside, dim light shone in from the hallway, illuminating old wooden workbenches covered with tools, wire, and plate metal. In the center was a crate about the size of a coffin.

Mike shouldered his weapon. Henri stood guard as he opened the lid. "Holy shit," he whispered.

She glanced inside as well, taking in a sharp breath.

It was a warhead—or at least a housing for one.

What he didn't expect was to see a World War II German swastika on the side. The metal was in decent condition with very little rust.

Mike used his ICE watch to snap a few pictures, praying they'd be discernable without a flash.

"This place is like a war museum," Henri whispered.

"It's like a sleeping dragon." Mike unshouldered his weapon and moved toward the door. "Let's find Flynn and get the hell out of here."

The passageway had to be as long as a rugby field, lined with decrepit and empty chambers. But Mike knew they were getting close when he spotted a tiny infrared beam shining across the hall about knee height. Just beyond it was a bend leading to the right. Halting in his tracks, he held up his hand.

Henri stopped across from him, pressing her back against the wall. She shifted the muzzle of her rifle indicating she was ready to provide cover.

Time to party.

Mike gave a nod, then stepped over the beam and led with the point of his rifle.

A metal chair clattered over backward as, down the corridor, a man sprang to his feet and fumbled for the bolt on his AK-47. "A—!"

He didn't get the word out as Henri's bullet shot through the center of his forehead. Mike hit the floor as a black muzzle appeared from behind the wall.

"Down!" he hissed when Henri didn't follow. But she stood her ground, gun poised. As soon as the shooter's face cleared the corner, she squeezed the trigger of her Win Mag. The man crashed backward while a spray of bullets from his rifle pummeled the wall.

Mike ran ahead. "Our cover's blown. Move fast!"

Stepping over the bodies, he kicked in the door. A man sat duct taped to a chair, his face looking like mincemeat. "Jesus Christ."

Henri darted past him. "Are you Thomas Flynn?"

The man was too beat up to speak. He raised his head and gave a single nod while Mike cut the duct tape binding his legs and arms to the chair.

"H-how...?"

"Save your breath," Mike said.

Henri moved to the doorway. "Footsteps approaching."

"Can you hold them?"

"On it."

Gunfire erupted from the corridor while Henri held back, pressing her body against the cement wall. When the bullets finally stopped hammering the corridor, she dove into the opening, shooting from her back with a burst of rapid fire. "Three down!"

Holy hell, she acted as if her shoulder injury didn't bother her a bit, but Mike knew differently. He'd seen the damage. The woman was just that tough.

"Whoa," Dr. Flynn grunted, his eyes wide.

Mike pulled the middle-aged scientist to his feet. "Are you able to walk?"

"Damn right." But Flynn only managed a few steps before he stumbled.

Mike pulled the man's arm across his shoulders and levered up his M16 with his opposite hand. "We're heading out of here fast. Use the doorways for cover."

One corner of Henri's mouth turned up. "Shoot first?"

"Och aye, lassie."

She winked. "No wonder we work so well together." Moving like a panther, she weaved through the corridor ready to kill anyone who stepped in her path. No wonder she'd survived six tours in Afghanistan.

Thomas Flynn moaned and grunted, trying to move quickly as Mike practically dragged him toward the exit. "We're nearly there, mate."

At the stairs, Henri stopped and waited for them to catch up. "Five down, but I haven't seen Fadli or Amri yet."

Mike took in a deep breath. "They might not be here—the car's still gone."

She looked to Flynn. "Do you know how many men we're dealing with?"

The PhD shook his head. "They brought me in blindfolded."

"Count on more. And they're probably waiting for us at the top of the stairs." Mike turned to Flynn. "I'm going up first. We'll clear a path. You strong enough to follow?"

The scientist nodded. Mike wasn't sure if Flynn would make it, but he had a fighting chance if he used the rail for support. And there was no way he was about to let Henri run roughshod into an ambush. She might move like a panther but, aside from her Kevlar vest, she wasn't bulletproof.

Together, they ascended the stairs stopping at the 180 degree bend.

Mike pointed to himself, then up the stairs, indicating he'd go first. Henri was too much of a pro to disagree in the midst of an op, but her lips thinned.

Without hesitating, Mike led with his rifle. Determining the coast was clear, he motioned to Flynn and waited long enough for him to climb to the first landing.

Henri moved to point and proceeded forward. Mike stayed on her flank and nudged her when they reached the top. She caught his eye and indicated she'd go first, then made a beeline for the door. She glanced back, bared her teeth in a cringe and thrust her finger at Flynn. The man needed help—bloody hell, he was clinging to the rail like a ninety-five-year-old heart-transplant patient. Mike hesitated. Damn it all, Henri was a better shot and Mike was stronger. It was the only option that made any sense.

Mike ran back and slung the man's arm across his shoulder. "Be ready to run," he whispered, hefting the man up the stairs purely by brute force.

With a burst of speed, Henri sprinted to the outer door. She turned and covered herself with a sweep of her rifle. As Mike followed with Flynn, she crept outside, panning her gun across the blackness. She motioned with her hand, leading them to the corner of the building. Mike tightened his grip around the scientist, making him speed his pace. All they needed to do was make it fifty more yards and they'd be behind the shelter of the stone wall.

Mike closed the distance as Henri waited for them to catch up. Her white teeth flashed with a grin before she stepped around the corner.

All hell broke loose.

Her weapon discharged as she was tackled to the ground with a thud. Bellowing like a madman, Mike lunged from beneath Flynn's arm and dragged the attacker off her. The bastard slashed with a blade that flickered through the dim light. Mike hopped aside, caught the bastard's wrist and flipped him to his back, forcing the knife toward the man's jugular.

But this thug was tough as steel. He fought with raw strength and the blade shook as Mike used leverage to overpower him in a battle of muscle.

Another thud slammed the ground. And another.

Mike looked up. His opponent reversed and rolled to the top.

Henri shrieked.

His heart lurched as he focused on the blade. One slip and he'd have a razor-sharp knife slice across his jugular.

With his next surge of power, Mike flipped the opponent on his back, gaining the upper hand—until the cold steel of a pistol pressed against his temple.

"Give it up," a man said in heavily-accented English.

Mike froze while the beefcake beneath him skittered away and wrenched the knife from Mike's fingers. Henri lay on the ground face-first with her hands zip-tied. Two men grabbed Flynn under the arms and headed back inside.

"Move out!" the gunman bellowed in Arabic, slapping a pair of zip cuffs on Mike.

"Where are you taking us?" he asked.

"Someplace where you'll never be found," he said in English.

"Oh? Why not kill us now?"

The bastard smirked. "Your death will be too entertaining not to broadcast to the world."

29

Cloud bursts deluged rain as Henri and Mike were forced at gunpoint to strip down to their t-shirts and shorts for a search. Their hidden weapons were removed, their wetsuits cast aside. Even their ICE watches were ripped off and stomped on with the heel of a thug's boot. Thugs brandished AK-47s while they marshaled the ICE assets to the beach where they were forced into the cargo hull of a boat—a boat that hadn't been there before.

They'd failed on every front. They'd found Dr. Flynn, but couldn't manage to rescue him. They'd seen the warhead, but no one knew about it. And their only backup, Luke Fox, was fishing behind the outcropping where he couldn't see a damned thing happening at the airfield.

Wet and miserable, Henri sat beside Mike with her back against the wall. The hold was blacker than coal. She hated not being able to see, cramped in a tiny space. Engines roared to life making the boat shudder. The water had turned choppy with the storm and the boat crashed through the surf, jolting and groaning as if it were sure to sink with the next lightning strike.

Henri raised her cuffed hands to her chest and

used her fingertips to rub her angry gunshot wound now punishing her for the exertion of the op—*the failed op*. Grunting, she hadn't expected it to sear with pain.

"You okay?" Mike asked.

"I'd be a helluva lot better if I weren't sitting on a boat in zip cuffs, sailing away from the scientist we were supposed to rescue." She pounded her fists on the floor. "Damn it!"

"Tell me about it. And no one kens he's there."

"How about you, hotshot? You threw some pretty mean punches. Did you come out of it unscathed?"

"A couple bruises. Nothing serious."

"Thank God." Henri stared at the blackness while her blood boiled. "Fadli *knew* we were there. We played right into his hands."

Mike drew in a deep breath. "I should have guessed. We got in too easy."

"But we were so careful—flying in to the private airfield. For crying out loud, I wore a hijab through customs." She wracked her mind. Had someone informed on them? Was there a bad egg at ICE? Everywhere they went, Fadli and his thugs were a step ahead. In France, then in Arusha. They'd already struck only minutes before they arrived at Nelson's mine, and now Rhodes.

Could it be Luke?

She shook her head. The pilot had only come on the scene in Dodoma—after Arusha.

"Facial recognition," said Mike. "Gotta be."

"Even in Rhodes?"

"Even there—or they had eyes on the plane. Somehow Fadli's got your number—probably mine, too."

About an hour later, the boat slowed, rocking in

the water. Men yelled on the deck above while the gears ground.

Mike grasped her arm with his cuffed hands. "We need to stay together."

She leaned into him. "Do you think they'll execute us right away?" Henri had never feared death, but she'd never been captured, either.

"They've brought us this far, I doubt Fadli will kill us without having some fun first."

"Interrogation?"

"Doubtless—including some sort of propaganda farce."

She looked upwards even though there was nothing to see above them. "Do you think the satellites stayed with us?"

"No chance. Not in this weather. The good news is it's still night. I doubt they'll try to film our torture until daylight."

"Charming—but why's that good?"

"Time."

The door burst open and someone shone a blinding flashlight straight in Henri's eyes. "Come," he said.

If anything, the rain had grown worse and visibility sucked. They were marshaled off the boat and onto a stone platform at the bottom of a sheer rock face. Through the rain, nothing looked familiar.

The guards pushed them single-file up a ledge, made slippery by rainwater streaming over her feet. Up and up they climbed while the surf crashed against the rocks below. A fall would be deadly. One slip and *splat*. When they reached about two hundred feet above the sea, the guard led them through an archway that looked medieval.

The man in front opened an iron gate. Henri hesitated, but the thug behind jabbed her in the back with the muzzle of his gun. The door creaked and boomed shut behind them.

Mike shoved his arms through the bars. "Come on, cut these zip cuffs."

The guard moved his hand to the hilt of his knife, but shook his head.

"We're not going anywhere." Henri stuck her wrists through as well. "Please?"

Pursing his lips, the guard unsheathed his knife and cut both sets of cuffs.

"*Sukran,*" she thanked him as he walked away.

"Thank you?" Mike asked, rubbing his wrists.

"Might as well. Who knows, he might be a terrorist with a compassionate streak."

"I doubt it."

Henri rubbed her neck and looked from wall to wall. "Where the hell are we?"

Mike turned in a circle, gingerly tapping a gash on his head. "Ruins of some sort." It was still night and raining. The inside of the chamber was dim at best. "Probably Turkey."

Henri leaned against the cold, stone wall and crossed her arms to ward off the chill of the cold, wet clothing clinging to her body. "Tell me you have a plan for escape."

"Working on it," said Mike, moving to the only window recessed in an embrasure at the back. It was barred and had no glass.

She pushed off the wall and joined him. Rain splattered her face as she wrapped her fingers around the bars and peered out. Straight down, the white-capped Mediterranean roared with the motion of the tide, spanning as far as she could see. She strength-ened her grip and twisted. "These are loose. We could probably work them free."

"Aye, if we have a week. Not to mention, there's nothing but a sheer wall out there. We'd plunge to our deaths on the rocks below."

"That might be preferable to what Fadli has in store for us."

He smoothed his hand over her shoulder.

Henri hissed with the sting.

Knitting his brows, he bent down to examine her arm. "You're bleeding again."

Sure enough, blood had soaked through her sleeve. The wound throbbed like a bitch, but there was nothing they could do about it. "It'll be all right."

Mike pulled her into his arms. "I'm sorry I got you in this mess."

As the comfort of his warmth surrounded her, Henri chuckled. "I think I can take responsibility for my own actions. Remember? You tried to make me go back to Iceland when we were in France."

He pressed his lips against her temple. "I should have been more insistent."

She closed her eyes and allowed herself to melt into him. By now, Mike had to realize once she had her mind set on something, it wasn't easy to convince her to change. But his tenderness was heartwarming. Never in her life had another human being shown so much concern for her. Well, maybe Grandfather in his own way. But there was something special about Mike Rose, something Henri never wanted to lose. She slid her hands around his waist and held on for dear life while tears stung the back of her eyes. "What if they kill us?"

He crushed his body against her even tighter. "Dunna say it. Dunna ever say it."

"But this is *ISIS*." She whispered the acronym as if it were a curse.

"Shhhhh." He cradled her head and held it to his chest. "Believe in yourself. Believe in us."

"But what if—"

"No, lass. You must keep your mind positive. We are a team—an undefeatable team. Where is my tough Paiute warrior? You have the heart of the eagle and you have never needed to soar as high as you do right now."

Releasing a stuttered breath, she nodded. *Yes!* His words made new strength pulse through her blood. She *was* a warrior. A sniper. A member of the Paiute Tribe, and she was no coward. "I am Soaring-Eagle."

"You are. And always remember: In war your foe is never perfect. They will drop their guards and make mistakes. Our job is to be daring. To watch and wait for our chance and then act swiftly."

"You have the heart of a Paiute." She smoothed her hand along his jaw. "You are my spirit warrior with the courage of a lion."

"That's right, lass. I will never bend to their will."

"Come." Henri pulled Mike to the center of the chamber and, together, they sat cross-legged opposite each other. She took both of his hands in hers. "In this moment, our souls unite. Together, we are more powerful than we are apart. Together, we can conquer all in this life or the next."

Mike opened his mouth, but she shook her head. "In this circle, we make a bond and our souls are joined forever. We are proud warriors of the Paiute Tribe. We are warriors of the universe and we will *not* fail."

Closing her eyes, she took in a deep breath and released it slowly. Mike did the same until their breathing became one, until the heartbeat thrumming through their connected palms beat as one. The power between them grew and swelled throughout the cell.

She would not think of what might come tomorrow. But right now, in this hour, no Earthly being could sever the strength of their bond.

30

M ike stirred when something buzzed outside the window.

Beside him, Henri sat up, alarm written across her features. "That's a plane."

"You're right." Mike pushed to his feet, peeled off his t-shirt, and darted to the window. Waving the shirt like a madman, he searched the sky for the plane.

Henri stepped beside him and squinted upward.

"Do you see it?" Mike waved harder.

"Ten o'clock." She pointed.

"Damn. It might be too high to see us."

"You never know. Just keep shaking that thing." Henri pushed closer, craning her neck. "The plane's right above us now—looks like a small jet."

"A Gulfstream?"

"Maybe."

Mike kept it up until the noise disappeared and was replaced by the surf thundering against the cliffs below and gulls squawking around them.

He pulled on his shirt. "When they come for us, focus on last night," Mike said. "Time is our friend. The longer we are able to stay alive, the greater our chance of rescue."

Henri nodded, but before she had a chance to reply, guards came through the archway, brandishing their AK-47s.

Mike and Henri's wrists were again restrained with zip cuffs and they were led at gunpoint up higher to another chamber in the labyrinth of ruins.

Mike turned on his internal camera, plotting their escape. This chamber was much the same as the one they'd been locked in and he had no doubt there was a sheer drop to the water below. In fact, the roar of the sea swirled through the room with a ghostly echo.

The guards made them sit facing each other and duct taped them to the chairs—a typical interrogation move. A skinny guy came in with a video cam and set it up to record. Great, their interrogation would be broadcast to jihadists, maybe to the whole world.

Mike gave Henri a hard stare. If only she didn't have to go through this. If only she was back at her mine or anyplace but there.

He shifted his gaze to the pair of thugs guarding the door. They were both armed with AKs, but their posture gave away their lack of skill. Shoulders drooping and looking straight ahead, they weren't ready for a shit storm. Sure, he was bound to a chair and so was Soaring-Eagle over there, but anything could happen.

Damn right.

Henri drew in the slightest of gasps when two men entered—Mike recognized Amri right away, but the second's face was blocked from his sight.

Henri confirmed the other's identity. "Omar Fadli. I was wondering when our paths would cross again."

So, it was the assassin. Convenient to have both wanted terrorists in the same place at once—inconvenient to be unable to do anything about it.

"I should have killed you in Avignon." Fadli sauntered toward her.

"No. I should have killed you," she seethed.

The bastard backhanded her across the face.

Mike bucked so hard his chair lurched off the ground. "Leave her alone!" Shite, he'd just broken the first rule of interrogation by showing his hand. Now they knew he cared.

Fadli whipped around with a sneer. "So, Anderson, who is your boyfriend?"

She didn't say a word. Hate filled her eyes as a trickle of blood ran from her cheek. But her silence earned her another slap.

Mike gritted his teeth and made his face impassive. The only reason they were still alive was because Fadli wanted something. It didn't take a genius to know a sensational death on film would make the world sit up and take note. Oh yeah, that's Omar Fadli, the most feared terrorist in the world.

"Mike Rose—you're a slippery snake. And yes, I know who you are." A reedy chuckle rasped through his nose as he wrapped a leather strip around his knuckles. "I didn't think you'd talk easily. Besides, that would ruin my fun."

Mike steeled himself to watch Fadli strike her again but, instead, the bastard lunged and landed a fist in Mike's gut.

Doubling over with the impact, he made a show of grunting loudly—drawing the attention away from Henri. If Fadli thought he could get to Mike faster, it might just take the brunt of the punishment away from her.

She kept her lips pursed, though her eyes narrowed.

"Who are you working for?" Fadli slammed his fist

across Mike's jaw. Jesus, that one hurt. He stretched his chin to the side to make sure it still worked. Aside from pain and clicking, he'd live. The guy grabbed Mike's hair and yanked his head back. "You recruited her, didn't you?"

"Wouldna you?" Mike asked, buying some time. "She's a bonny lassie—and unsurpassed with a rifle in her hands. But then you ken that, do you not?"

"Shut up!" He threw a jab across Mike's jaw, but this one was wild and filled with emotion. "Henrietta represents evil. She embodies everything that is wrong with western civilization."

Henri twisted her shoulders as if she could free herself from the duct tape. "I served time for you, ass-hole. And I was *innocent!*"

"You're a trained killer." Lunging across the floor, Fadli smacked her with a backhand across her face. "You murdered my brother in cold blood."

She shook her head and glared at him. "Your brother was about to chuck a grenade at a dozen peacekeeping soldiers."

"Lie!"

"I fucking saw him!"

Fadli struck her again and again.

Mike was about to explode. God damn, it hurt him far more to see Henri hit. He'd take a hundred jabs to the face if only they'd leave her alone. "Over here ass-hole," he seethed. "Unless you're proud of beating women when their hands are tied—you fucking coward."

The assassin spun on his heel and aimed a round-house kick at Mike' head. The chair teetered but stayed upright. Stars crossed his vision as he blinked in succession, Henri's face going in and out of focus.

"Who's looking for you?" Fadli demanded.

"No one," Henri said. "We teamed up to find you, you bastard. You ruined my life!"

That stopped him. Fadli even grinned. "And you played right into my hands." He gave Mike another slap. "But something's telling me you're lying."

"Why would I lie, Omar? Or is it that you've lied so much you don't recognize the truth when you hear it?" God, she was convincing.

But that didn't stop Fadli from using Mike's face as a punching bag. When the bastard stopped, the only thing keeping Mike upright was the duct tape securing him to the chair.

"Damn you! Stop you sick freak!" she shrieked. "It's me you want. I'm the one who pulled the trigger and stopped your brother from killing Americans."

Fadli slammed an uppercut to Mike's chin and the world turned black.

HENRI FOUGHT BACK her rage as Mike's head lolled forward. He was out cold. Just as well. If Fadli kept wailing on him, he'd kill the poor man. God, she couldn't take any more. And Fadli knew it. Hell, there was a good chance Mike had internal injuries inside that hard head of his. She twisted her arms against the duct tape, futilely spending her strength. Christ, even if she could break free, she might get in one vicious kick before one of the guards shot her.

The hate roiling in her gut made her venomous. She memorized Fadli's every feature—from his pockmarked face to his 5'8" height, his stockiness, the way he placed his feet when he walked. She busied her mind by learning his every nuance because she vowed she would not check out of this life until she killed him.

"What are you going to do with Flynn?" she asked.

"Exactly what you think." Fadli motioned to Rose. "Cut him loose and haul this worthless piece of trash back to the cell and dump a bucket of water on his face."

She took in a long breath, trying not to let the relief show on her face. If she showed any sign of softening, Fadli just might pull his sidearm and shoot Mike in the head—or worse. Their cameras were rolling and the showboat loved to air his assassinations on film. But Fadli must have something sinister planned, a grandiose murder. Whatever. Henri was grateful for a reprieve even if it was temporary. They were taking Mike back to the cell where he could recover. She hoped.

After they dragged his limp body away, the guard cut the duct tape with a four-inch blade that nicked the back of her arm. Henri didn't even wince. Once they zip-cuffed her wrists, Fadli grabbed her elbow and hauled her up a ramp until they reached the edge of the cliff. She didn't try to resist until he shoved her backwards out over the sea. The ground beneath her feet started to crumble as Fadli hung on to the spindly, plastic cuffs cutting into her wrists.

"This is your fate. Turn your head and look down," he said with sick pride in his voice. "You will die on those rocks and your soul will burn in hell."

Out of the corner of her eye, she watched the waves crash against the base of the bluff. The water didn't just slide in gracefully. It smacked the cliff and sprayed white foam in a violent torrent. And straight down below, jagged rocks pointed upward like the teeth of a ravenous sea monster.

"All of Islam will watch you and your accomplice plunge to your deaths. And I will be revered as a hero in their eyes." Fadli shook her by the wrists, laughing out loud. "Scream for me! I can smell your fear."

Henri swallowed back the thick, pulsating lump in her throat and forced herself to close her eyes and summon a sense of calm before she looked Fadli dead on. "You'll never have the satisfaction of hearing me scream, asshole."

And suddenly she felt weightless, suspended two hundred feet above a deadly fall, her life held in the grip of a madman.

In a moment of pure terror, the makings of plan took root in her mind.

31

M ike's face felt pulverized. Worse, the jackhammer thundering in the back of his head was about to explode. His throat rasped with his grunt.

"Mike?" Henri's voice rattled in his brain.

He winced. "Not so loud."

"Huh? I'm whispering." She smoothed cool fingers over his forehead. "Can you open your eyes?"

Mike wanted to open them, but the slightest movement made that jackhammer pummel his skull harder. "Perhaps after a bit more caressing."

Henri's chuckle was almost indiscernible—a good sign that he was coming around. He couldn't help his moan when she swirled her fingers at his temples. It hurt so good. There wasn't much real estate on his face that hadn't been pulverized. He ran his tongue along his cracked bottom lip. "We survived that one, lass."

"Are you going to make it?"

"Och aye, embrace the pain. It is our best friend. It tells us we're still alive." Opening one eye, he reached up and grasped her hand. "You okay?"

She gingerly tapped a bruise at the side of her chin. "Never better, but..."

He managed to open both eyes. "What?"

"You're not going to like it."

Gnashing his teeth, he pushed himself up and shoved the heels of his hands against his aching temples. "What happened after I passed out?"

"Fadli took me to the top of the cliff—held me over the edge like he was going push me off."

Mike's gut twisted. "Christ."

"It gets worse."

"And it has something to do with death-defying heights?"

She nodded.

Mike raked his fingers through his hair and took in a deep breath—commenced combat breathing. Though he could jump out of a plane if he was in charge of packing his parachute, heights weren't his forte. "Tell me you have a plan."

"I do but, like I said, you're really, really not going to like it."

"I've done plenty of things I've no' been thrilled about. Come on, I havena all day."

"That's truer than you think. And there's no way to sugarcoat it." She took his hand between her palms and looked him in the eye. "They're going to push us off the cliff."

He pointed upwards. "You mean a two-hundred-foot drop? Ah...to the rocks?"

"Mm hmm. And they're going to film our deaths for Uncle Sam's viewing pleasure."

"And that's your plan? Our bodies obliterated?"

"No." She squared her shoulders. "I am Soaring-Eagle—"

"Dunna tell me, you're going to miraculously grow

wings, set to flight and swoop down and nab me in your talons afore I splatter across the cliffs."

She cracked a smile and chuckled. "I wish, but it's not quite that easy." She drew an arc on the dirty floor. "If we fall straight down, we'll be dead, no question. But when Fadli suspended me out over the rocks, I took a good look, and the water gets deep fast. If we spring away from the cliff—I mean really jump, we just might live."

"Might?"

"It's a freaking long way down. If the wind's against us, the odds are slim."

"Fuck!"

She cringed. "It's a risk, but it's the best we've got."

"And when's this leap of faith happening?"

"As soon as you regain consciousness." She lightly brushed her fingers around his palm, immediately bringing a sense of peace. "I know you can do it," she said in a soft tone that also, somehow, packed a punch. A tone that refused to be questioned.

He looked to the barred window. "Our only other option is to make a run for it."

"Against fifty men with AKs?"

"Fifty?"

She nodded. "That's my estimate, anyway."

"So...a giant leap and a prayer?"

"You *must* believe we can do it."

"Do you believe?" He met her gaze and took a sharp breath. She did believe and her conviction transferred to him with the jolt of an electric current. He held her hands while his heart squeezed into a tight knot. Sure, he'd been in situations as bad—situations that looked hopeless, death imminent. But in this moment, all pain subsided—all doubt melted. Only Henri existed, staring at him with those dark-chocolate eyes filled with determination. He pulled her onto his lap and grazed his lips along her ear while a low growl rumbled from his throat. "I feel your strength in my every pore, my every nerve and every pulse of blood thrumming through my veins."

She cupped his cheeks between her palms. "No matter what happens, we are connected through the bond of our souls. We must fight them because if we fail, they will win. Hundreds—thousands of lives depend on *us*."

Mike closed his eyes and nuzzled into her neck while black, silken locks swept across his face. "We will not let them succeed."

"If my strength flows through your blood, your thirst for life infuses mine."

The words no sooner escaped her lips when the outer door creaked.

Staring into her eyes as if nothing else in the world mattered, he clutched her palm over his heart. "Show no fear."

"I wouldn't give them the satisfaction."

"That's my girl."

They both stood and faced the door as two guards walked through, wielding their AKs. Mike refused to give them the gratification of knowing how much pain he was in. In all likelihood, he'd be in a hell of a lot more pain by the end of the day.

If he survived.

If they both survived.

He'd give his life ten times over if it meant saving Henri. Bless it, God would never forgive him for leading her into this mess.

Why did he do it time after time? Run into the mayhem and risk his neck? Time and time again, he'd asked himself that very question and every time he'd end up with the same answer. Who else would? True, he lived off the rush. He liked staring death in the face and telling the Grim Reaper to bite his bum—even when facing death from atop a 200-foot, stony cliff.

But that was him.

It was fine for Mike Rose to put his life on the line, but he had no business asking Henri to run full-tilt into harm's way.

After their wrists were bound, Mike kept Henri behind him as they followed the guard up the pathway carved out of the rock face. He refused to look down. Showing any sign of fear right now would mean the end. If the terrorists picked up the scent of his fear, things could turn out even worse.

He looked down.

Fuck.

His heart rate spiked. Taking a dive for the white-capped sea below might be the most insane thing he'd ever done. But if Henri wasn't afraid, he'd be equally courageous. Soaring-Eagle could fly? Well then, so could he—he had the courage of a lion. He was Mike Rose, a Highlander descended from Viking stock. He was a warrior and he would protect his woman. They would survive this day, and he would not allow himself another errant thought.

The gunman jabbed with the muzzle of his rifle, pushing them toward the edge of the cliff. Just as Henri expected, Omar Fadli stood in front of a camera ready to make a mockery out of their deaths. Also standing well back from the cliff, Melvut Amri crossed his arms with a smug grin. Mike clenched his fists, desperately needing to bury his knuckles in that ugly smirk.

One day, mate.

Fadli flashed a hateful glare over his shoulder and

pointed to the guards. "If they try to move, shoot them." Then he faced the camera and puffed his chest out with self-importance. "Today is a great day for Islam! Today, I have captured American murderers Henrietta Anderson and her accomplice, Michael Rose. She killed my brother and returned to murder me, but I caught her red-handed and she will slay our sisters and brothers no more."

"I'm not an American you fool," Mike growled under his breath.

A gunman struck him in the shoulder with the butt of his rifle. Mike teetered. Gasping, Henri grabbed his elbow. "Not yet," she whispered.

Mike gave her a wink.

Fadli gestured toward them. "This woman murdered my brother in cold blood."

"Yeah, right," Henri balked. The butt of the rifle moved her way, but Mike thrust out his bound hands and stopped it from hitting her. The man with the gun tried to force it, growing red in the face. No way would Mike give in, even if it meant an early leap.

"And I will make an example of them today," Fadli continued while the gunman yanked the butt of his rifle away. "Anyone who dares to defy the Islamic State will be punished severely. These two? Their bodies will be crushed on the jagged rocks below and the gulls will feast on their entrails while we celebrate our victory!"

"You ready?" Henri asked, looking like an Amazon preparing to lead her clan into battle.

"Always ready," Mike replied.

But Fadli wasn't finished. "Beware America, we are coming. We are finished with small attacks. We will face you with the might of a thousand dragons. Our ancestors will rise to squash the infidel and all will bow to me!"

"I knew he was radical, but insane is more apt," Mike whispered.

Henri drew her zip-cuffed hands to her nose and stifled a snort.

"Laughing in the face of death?" asked Amri as he sauntered forward. "You are greater fools than I imagined."

She squared her shoulders. "I am Soaring-Eagle and you cannot kill my spirit."

"Enough!" shouted Fadli, motioning to the camera. "Make sure you get this on film. I want to witness the western world's outrage as our work is aired throughout the internet, on every news broadcast, in every paper."

Mike planted his feet, bending deeply at the knees as the gunmen shifted behind them.

"I wish I could hold your hands," he said.

She grinned. "Believe it. Together we fly!"

The gunmen pulled back the bolts on their AKs. Shit, they weren't going to leave anything to chance. He thought it was a bloody push with the butt of a gun, not a twenty-one-gun sendoff. If they didn't leap now, they'd end up full of lead. Mike's heart lurched as he caught Henri's eye.

"N-o-w!"

Gunfire rang in his ears as he leapt out as far as his thighs could push. His gut lurched up to his throat with the momentum of his fall. In his peripheral vision, Henri soared with him. Time slowed. If only he'd told her he loved her. Told her how much he'd learned from her in the short time they'd spent together. If only he'd told her how much he admired her, her strength, her tenacity, her beauty.

With his next blink, his feet hit the water like slamming onto concrete. His balls slapped the water so hard they felt like they'd been shoved up to his kidneys. Downward he plunged as water engulfed him. Foam filled his nose and the open wounds on his face seared while sea salt lashed across them.

But Mike feared for Henri.

Keeping his eyes open, he peered through the foam for any sign of her. And when his body finally slowed, he spun in a circle. Movement above him caught his eye. She was already swimming for the surface. His lungs began to burn as he raced to catch her before she broke through.

He yanked her leg.

She fought but he caught her eye and thrust his finger toward the rocks.

Giving a nod, she changed course and swam with the current. Waves crashed over them as they surfaced against the rock wall where it would be impossible for the gunmen to see them.

When his head finally broke the surface, Mike sucked in air while grabbing on to Henri's shirt and holding her up. "You—" He gulped in a breath. "All right?"

"Uh..." She swiped her face while catching her breath.

Mike looked up. They were too close to the cliff to see the top. "You're amazing."

"I knew it would work, but I've got enough water up my ass to fill a swimming pool." She laughed. With her wrists still bound, she grabbed his t-shirt in her fists and wrapped her legs around his waist. "We did it!"

"Aye, but were not out of the woods yet." He gave her a quick kiss. "We need to dive deep. Swim along the rocks until we're out of the cove. Can you do that?"

"Let's go."

"Only come up for air when you're on the verge of passing out."

"Then where?" she asked, clinging to him.

"Anywhere there are people."

She winked. "Who aren't terrorists."

C ommanding the last glimmer of daylight, the sun kissed the western horizon glowing like an enormous ball of fire. Hungry and cold, Henri guessed they'd been in the water at least four hours. Every muscle in her body ached as if she'd been running a day-long marathon. After clearing the cove, they swam on their backs, keeping close to the shore. Saltwater continually slapped her face as Henri's teeth chattered.

A small jet passed overhead. Henri's gut roiled as she watched it. "He's up there."

"Fadli?" asked Mike.

"Yeah."

"If that's him, he's heading back to Rhodes."

"And so should we." Just as the words slipped through her lips, the low sound of an outboard motor hummed through the air. Treading water, Henri fought the waves, searching for a boat. "Look!"

Beside her, Mike waved his bound wrists over his head. "Hey! Over here."

"Help!" With a rush of energy, Henri shouted at the top of her lungs, kicking her legs to lift her torso out of the water.

The boat changed direction, heading straight for them.

Thank God.

"It sees us!" Mike grasped her arm and squeezed. He grinned, making the bruising under his eye look even darker.

"Thank God." Henri laughed out loud. "I hope they have food." A wave lifted her up high enough to see the speedboat clearly—and its captain. "I'll be damned."

Mike pulled her behind him, treading water like Aquaman. "What?" he asked, his voice filled with alarm.

She looped her wrists around his neck and gave him a peck on the cheek. "It's Luke, silly."

Fox throttled back as he neared, then dropped the anchor and tossed out an orange life ring. "Bloody hell, Rose, your face looks like you lost a fight with a croc." He pulled them to the boat's ladder. "How'd you pair end up here?"

Mike helped Henri climb up first. "Question is what the hell are you doing here?"

"I was watching when you were taken from the airfield. I noted the direction they were sailing, then hightailed it for my plane."

"Did you see me waving my shirt out the window of the cliff ruins?" Mike asked, pulling himself up the ladder.

"What window?" Luke produced a pocket knife and cut their zip cuffs.

Henri rolled onto a seat. "If you didn't see him waving, how'd you find us?"

"When I flew over, the same boat that left Rhodes was tied up alongside the ruins."

Mike collapsed beside her. "You recognized it?"

"Took pictures as they left the airfield—infrared camera. It was a little blurry because of the rain, but I nailed it."

"Where's the Gulfstream now?" she asked.

"A hangar not far from here." Luke moved to the wheel and started the motor up. "Did you get anything on Flynn?"

"He's still in Rhodes," said Mike.

"I don't think so." Luke shook his head. "The US Navy sent in a team of SEALs. Found nothing, mate."

Henri looked in the direction she'd seen Fadli's plane heading. Her tried and true rule of war? Always trust your gut instincts. "Maybe they thought they found nothing. My guess is Fadli had the underground op walled up so no one would find it." She grasped Mike's arm. "We have to stop them."

ONCE THEY MADE it to the Gulfstream, it took far too much time to convince Garth that Thomas Flynn was still in Rhodes. Bloody hell, the boss even had trouble believing that Mike and Henri had seen a WWII warhead. But neither one of them let up.

Garth finally agreed.

Mike had also insisted on returning completely, utterly and unquestionably stealth. Henri had been identified too many times for it to be a coincidence. That meant landing anywhere other than Rhodes with Henri completely covered by a burka. Mike shaved his beard and wore a turban with robes to match. He even put in brown contact lenses. Then they landed on Halki, an island 20 kilometers off the east coast of Rhodes. They'd have to sail across to the larger island, then around to the Kalathos Airfield on the west side, but the added travel was worth it. Garth arranged for the use of a small patrol boat with two outboard engines. Mike didn't ask, he just did a weapons check after they climbed aboard. Garth never let him down when it came to fire power—ammo, rifles, grenades, scopes, silencers, NV, two infrared borescope cameras—even two brand new ICE watches.

The boss' only caveat?

"Don't fail."

Because the Navy had come up with zilch, there was no chance Garth could call in the fleet. And if they were wrong, he would have looked like an idiot for the second time. But at least the CO sent them the ammunition they needed—including a Win Mag with Leupold sights. Hell, Mike couldn't bet his life that Flynn was still being held at the airfield, but he'd bet everything he owned. And Henri was damned positive. If ever there was a human being with a sixth sense, Eagle Eyes would be that person.

For additional security, they didn't cast off from the Halki marina until after midnight. It was just the three of them but, this time, they knew what to expect. They'd spent the entire day going over the plan. It consisted of two goals: Rescue Thomas Flynn and put an end to Omar Fadli's reign of terror.

Anything could go wrong. In fact, mistakes were a surety. That's why all three of them could recite the plan backwards and forwards—any variation, any setback would be handled and bring the team back to the goal. That's why planning was so important in this business.

Better yet? It was raining. Not just a wee sprinkle, the skies opened with a torrent powerful enough to wash away the dunes of the Sahara. And Mike aimed to use the weather to his advantage all the way.

They dropped anchor just off the shore where they were still hidden by the outcropping. Before they transferred to a Special Forces inflatable boat, Mike grasped Henri by the shoulders. Even in the dark with rain pouring in her face, she looked like an Amazon ready to take on the world. "No matter what happens, I want you to know you've come to mean more to me than anything." The words I love you refused to form on his lips. Not yet. Not when there was so much a stake. He wanted to save those words for after...when they'd both have time to savor them.

She slid her hands around his waist. "You're not going soft on me, are you soldier?"

He gave her a wink. "I'm never soft, lass."

"Hey." Luke bumped Mike's arm. "Are we heading into battle or are you pair too busy playing googly eyes?"

Henri arched an eyebrow. "I think he'll fit right in."

"Aye, and there's no time like the present to put him to the test." Ignoring Luke, Mike wrapped her tighter in his arms, his heart stretching in his chest. He hated to see her face danger and, yet, he never wanted anyone else covering his back. "I'm counting on you, lass."

"You'd better be." She stretched up and kissed him on the lips, then pulled away and glanced at Luke. "You too, flyboy. If I say drop over the comm, you drop. Got it?"

The pilot grinned and shifted his gaze to Mike. "Is this sheila always so bossy?"

"You dunna ken the half of it, mate."

"Beauty," said Luke. "Top dogs from the US, the

UK and Down Under. We'd better not fail, else we'll let down our countries."

"We'll let down the world." Mike shouldered his rifle and stepped into the inflatable. "Let's roll before we end up with another Hiroshima."

"What?" Luke practically spat out his teeth.

Mike gave the Aussie a wink. "You wouldna think we'd be giving you an initiation to wage war against the king of the fairies, would you?"

Henri handed Mike her rifle then slid down into the boat. "We exist to take on things no one else can."

"And no one else kens about." Mike returned her weapon. "If the media catches wind of this, we'll be facing World War III afore dawn."

"Right-o, then." Luke fired up the motor. "At least I'm not wasting my time."

"Hooah," said Henri as she took a seat. The leader of this op, she turned on her mic. "This is Eagle Eyes, check. Sound off."

"Lionheart, check."

"Wombat, check."

The boat skidded through the shallows and up the beach. "Follow me," she said before heading for the crag.

The rain made the footing slick and NV worthless. Henri planted her boot, thinking she had a good foothold, but the rock rolled and threw her off balance. Her hip slammed into the stone wall as she flung out her hands to stop her fall.

"You okay?" Mike's voice came through her earpiece.

Her hip throbbed like a son-of-a-bitch. "Fine." She kept going and ignored the burn. She was a warrior, not a princess and she'd endured a hell of a lot more pain than a bruise on the hip. Hell, her shoulder hadn't completely healed yet.

They climbed on their bellies to the crest of the hill. The light in the control tower was like a beacon making their target shine. Interesting, both the truck and the car had returned.

Chalk up another one to gut instincts.

Mike scooted beside her. "You going to be able to take them out in this weather?"

"Whoa, mate," said Luke. "From here?"

Henri gave them both a look. "*Men*...they always underestimate women." She charged her weapon and flipped up a rubber stopper that covered her sights, using it as a rain guard. True, the deluge distorted things, but with the right focus, Henri's mind could adjust. Wind was blowing a gale from the west at least thirty miles per hour. The guards in the tower were sitting—probably bored out of their minds and, without windows, they were every bit as cold, wet and miserable as she was.

"Take your time, sweetheart," Mike's deep voice rumbled through her earpiece.

"Silence," she hissed as she trained the scope on her first target. She had to be perfect. A fraction off and everyone in the compound would know they were there. If she made a mistake now, they'd have no choice but to run for the boat.

Henri focused on her breathing, becoming one with her Win Mag. She homed in on the target, seeing the first shot hitting its mark and the fraction of an adjustment she'd need to take out the second.

In one fluid motion, she fired off two suppressed shots—the sound of the rifle completely muffled by the silencer and the rain. The targets dropped. The second one didn't even flinch when the first shot hit. Bless the weather.

"Holy shit," said Luke, the awe in his voice unmistakable.

Henri looked to Mike. "Ready for phase two?"

"Born—"

"Ready," she finished. "You're so predictable, dude."

"It works for me." In a crouch, he led the team down the crag and across the open land. Rain splattered her face, but she embraced it. That very rain was providing them with a modicum of cover.

Once they reached the building, voices came from inside.

"Cover." Henri and Luke pressed their backs against the wall and covered their ears while Mike threw a flash-bang to blind anyone lurking inside. "Let's go."

He took point. A spray of bullets erupted from the darkness.

Grunting, Mike dove for cover. Henri saw blood. "You're hit."

"Just nicked," he said, pulling the pin from a grenade with his teeth. "This one will mess 'em up good."

Luke covered his head while Mike crouched over Henri, shielding her with his body.

Boom!

By the force of the blast funneling out the door, no one on the first floor could have survived.

Mike signaled for the all clear and headed inside without facing more enemy fire. At least until they hit the stairs.

Another volley of bullets echoed through the stairwell, sounding like thunder.

Mike pulled out another flash-bang and tossed it down. "Cover!" The thing burst with a boom and blinding light, but didn't have enough fire power to destroy the steps. Burying the bastards alive wouldn't be an option until they got Flynn out. Afterwards, turning the bunker into a grave might just be the trick.

Mike led with guns blazing, taking out two gunmen at the base of the stairwell.

They used a triangular formation to make their way through the corridor, kicking in doors along the way. At the corner, Mike slowed, inching forward with the muzzle of his M16. Rapid fire erupted from the hallway where they'd been keeping Flynn.

"The SEALs couldn't find this guy?" asked Luke, his voice cracking.

"Remember the hunt for weapons of mass destruction in Iraq?" asked Henri, whispering into her mic. "It's not so hard to move stuff."

Mike motioned with his fingers, indicating Henri would go low, Luke above. Once they started firing, he slid into the open on his butt and swept a spray of bullets across the hallway, cutting down two more terrorists.

"Clear," he said.

Henri sprang to her feet and took the lead, stepping over the two guards.

In the same interrogation room where they'd found him before, Flynn hung in a chair, looking dead. Luke raced to him and pressed his fingers to the scientist's carotid. "He's alive."

Above, the truck's engine started. Henri's heart lurched. "Fadli!"

"The bomb's live," Flynn rasped, opening his bloodshot eyes. "They threatened to torture and murder my kids...my wife. P-pictures..."

Her gut turned over. "We can't let the bastard fly the coop. Not this time."

"Go!" Mike raced down the corridor with Henri on his heels. They flew up the stairs taking three at a time. Tearing around the corner, Mike ran into fire. He leapt back, patting his Kevlar vest, searching for holes.

Henri fired around the edge of the door. "You gonna live, Lionheart?"

"I'm fighting fit." He clambered to his feet.

Henri took the lead, shooting rapid fire around the corner.

The truck's engine revved.

Over her shoulder, she snatched a glimpse at Mike. "I'm making a run for it."

"Got you covered."

Bullets erupted from the Scot's rifle as Henri dashed from the safety of the stairwell and raced for the door. Out of the corner of her eye, she saw movement. "Guard at ten!" she shouted, darting outside as a burst of rapid fire drilled behind her. She could only pray the bullets had come from the Scot's rifle.

The rain had eased, but the truck was going nowhere, spinning its wheels in the sandy mud. When she caught Omar Fadli's attention, his eyes bugged wide as if he'd seen a ghost. She squeezed the trigger just as the thug ducked beneath the dash. The windscreen shattered.

Henri ran for cover behind the blade of the tractor, skidding to her butt. "You come out now and you'll live!" she shouted, the words tasting like bile on her tongue. She wanted nothing more than to kill the bastard. End it now. Without a trial, without wasting thousands of taxpayer dollars to keep him fed in prison.

No sound came from the truck's cabin.

But Henri new better than to step into the open.

She shifted her gaze for a split second as grunting and thuds came from inside the building. That was long enough for Fadli to fire a shot at the tractor aimed exactly where Henri was hiding. If she raised her head, he'd nail her between the eyes. That's how it rolled. The more patient assassin won in the end. And she was too goddamned close to make a mistake. There had to be an angle. She looked upward. The tractor's scoop had a six-inch notch—one cut for using a chain.

Silently, she rose to her knee and slid the muzzle of the Win Mag through the notch, keeping it steady so it didn't even scrape the sides. After taking a deep breath, she inched up high enough to peer through the scope. The edge of the tractor's scoop partially blocked her vision, but she could see the open door of the cab well enough.

The problem?

Fadli wasn't there.

But then she saw it. The black muzzle of a rifle pointed at the tractor. *Where is Fadli? Hidden under the wheel?*

Unsure, her only option was to wait it out.

Henri used shallow breathing and waited. Her thighs started burning from holding herself up an inch higher than her knee could reach the ground. Her arms tortured her from holding the Win Mag off the metal. A bead of sweat slipped into her eye. Blinking, she steeled her mind to her own pain.

Something moved—something black. Then a face inched up. Henri took the shot, but her hand tremored ever so slightly.

Fadli grunted, then his gun fired on automatic. Henri dropped and crouched into a ball while bullets pummeled the scoop. When his rifle clicked twice she knew she had seconds to move in while he reloaded. Pushing up, she went on the offensive. With blood streaming down his face, Fadli rose to his knees with a pistol in his hand. Before he shifted the muzzle her way, Henri shot the hand. Moving in, she laid waste to his body, shooting with rapid fire until he collapsed on his face.

She stopped a foot away from the truck's door.

Dropping her arms, numbness filled her. She'd lost two years of her life because of this man. An innocent ambassador had been cut down. Countless other Syrian citizens had been murdered by this man. That's right. Fadli had proven time and time again nothing would ever stop him from his madness. Henri hated killing. But she hated tyrants more. Any man who craved power through the destruction of others deserved Fadli's fate.

The rain had completely stopped.

But a chill coursed up the back of Henri's neck when no sound came from the building.

33

There could only be two reasons for the silence. Either everyone was down or there was a standoff. And Henri wasn't about to consider the first. Reloading her Win Mag, she whispered into her mic. "Lionheart?" When there was no response, she tried Luke. "Wombat?"

Nothing.

Crouching, she moved in beside the door of the building. She froze as a volley of gunfire erupted—the shooter was on the first floor and it was darker than midnight inside.

No question. The perp wasn't a good guy.

She'd learned Mike's first rule of war in boot camp years ago: Strategy. And that meant the warrior who chose the easiest, most direct path should expect to be destroyed.

The Native American in her heart took over. Like Grandfather had taught, Soaring-Eagle didn't make a sound as she slipped around to the south side and shouldered up beside a paneless window. She slipped the wire of an infrared borescope camera onto the sill and slowly swept it across the room until she found the shooter.

The perp had his back to her, standing at the entrance to a stairwell, rifle in hand. He had black hair and was tall and thin. Not Mike, not Luke and definitely not Thomas Flynn. Fear oozed off this man. He knew his minutes were numbered. Henri made a quick adjustment and the camera zoomed to his wrist as he lifted his rifle to his shoulder. A tattoo of an ISIS flag told her who he was. Melvut Amri's hand slid down the barrel while he took a step as if he were going to move into the stairwell and go in for the kill.

Wrong.

Henri dropped the camera and slipped the Win Mag through the gaping hole. "Hey!" she yelled, barely able to see his outline without the infrared.

The shooter spun but before his rifle shifted around, Henri squeezed her trigger. For the first time in her career, she couldn't be sure where she'd hit him but Melvut Amri dropped to his back, his weapon inches away from his fingers.

Henri raced around to the door. "Mike! Where are you?"

"Stairwell," a strained voice came over the comm.

Before charging through the door, she had enough sense to slide her hand around and flip on the light. A single lightbulb came to life as Amri reached for his gun. Henri shot the man's fingers first, then lodged a bullet between the bastard's eyes.

She panned her Win Mag across the room, doing a 360 before she moved to the stairwell. As soon as she determined it was clear, she tore down to the landing and dropped to her knees beside Mike.

Blood was everywhere.

"Where are you hit?" she asked, checking arms, legs, hands. There was just too much blood to see where it was coming from.

He grinned, blood between his teeth. "No vitals hit. Got about fifty flesh wounds."

"Fifty?" Tears stung her eyes as she gently held his cheeks between her palms.

"That's what it feels like."

"I'm going to get you out of here." Steeling her nerves, she kissed his lips.

"Mm," he growled like he wasn't hurt. "I'm counting on it, lass."

She looked to the basement doorway. "What about Fox and Flynn?"

Mike threw a thumb over his shoulder. "They're back there someplace."

"Any more shooters?"

"I think we got 'em all."

"I'll be back."

He winked. "I'll be here."

Henri rushed down the steps as she shoved up her sleeve and pushed the call button on her ICE watch.

"Report," Garth's voice came immediately.

"We need an ambulance."

"Who?"

"Mike's nicked."

"And he needs an ambulance?" Garth's voice shot up.

"There's a lot of blood..." She found Luke and Thomas Flynn propped against the wall, alive, but barely conscious. "Make it three ambulances."

"Holy Christ."

"You got the holy part right."

"What about you, Anderson?"

"Fighting fit, sir."

"And Fadli?"

"Deader than roadkill. So are his men including Melvut Amri. On top of that, after you call the medics, call in the bomb squad. There's a hot nuke in the back of a truck that needs to be defused."

"Holy shit."

"Yeah? You might try 'thanks' next time, sir."

~

MIKE'S MOUTH felt like goo. Machines beeped in the background. Machines that could only mean one thing. He was on his back in a bloody hospital. That's right. He'd been shot in the line of duty. Thanks to Eagle Eyes, they'd completed their mission.

God, that woman was amazing.

But now the relentless beeps refused to stop. Couldn't hospital equipment come up with a more pleasant tone about three octaves lower? Gulping down the goo in his mouth, Mike opened his eyes. Clothing rustled before Henri's smile came into view. "Hey you. They tell me you're gonna live."

She had the most dynamite smile. His heart squeezed and as she grasped his hand, he gripped her fingers tightly. Jeez, they were so soft and cool against his overwarm flesh. Heaven help him, he didn't want to let go. "What are the damages?" he asked.

"Bullet removed from your thigh—you'll need some R&R and rehab for that. Everything else was superficial but the Doc said he'd never seen so much shrapnel in his life."

Mike swallowed again, too proud to ask for water. "What about Fox and Flynn?"

"Luke has a concussion—got knocked out after a doorframe fell on his head. He'll be fine."

"And the scientist?"

"He's still hooked up to an IV. Aside from a broken arm and bruises, he was dehydrated. Another day in the airfield basement and he probably would have been dead." She reached for a pitcher of water and poured a glass. "You thirsty?"

She could read his mind. "Parched."

After taking a long drink, Mike's head cleared a bit more. That's when he noticed a butterfly bandage just below Henri's hairline. "That looks bad."

"It's just a nick." She ran her smooth fingers along his cheek. "I...ah...well..." Her eyes trailed aside.

Mike chuckled, which caused pain in too many places to name. "You were worried about me?"

She nodded. "Yeah."

He squeezed her fingers and drew them to his lips. With his kiss, his heart started thumping again—that kind of thumping a person experiences when they realize how close they came to losing someone special. "You'll never ken how worried I was when you were out there facing Fadli alone. I couldn't get past Amri."

Her eyes glistened as she cupped his cheek. "You'll never know the terror I felt when I realized you were still in that building. And then no one replied back to me."

"Sorry. I was a little preoccupied trying not to die."

She kissed him gently, then smiled. "Likely excuse."

He took another drink and straightened. "When are they planning to unhook me? I've already had enough of this place."

She tsked her tongue. "Awake for two minutes and already asking for leave."

"I'm not a fan of hospital."

"I figured the same." Henri ran her fingers through his hair. "You want to go through rehab in Saint George, or wherever it is you live in Scotland?"

"Oban..." Mike closed his eyes and inhaled—fresh

air, the scent of the sea. He could already feel home. "What I wouldna do for home's hearth."

Scraping her teeth across her bottom lip, Henri's gaze trailed aside. "I kinda thought you'd say that."

"But you're going with me, right?" He laced his fingers behind her neck and pulled her lips down to meet his. "Och, lass. I'll need moral support."

"I'm not much of a cook."

He kissed her again. "Who said anything about cooking?"

34

Transferring the Chinese food to her left hand, Henri used Mike's key to open the door to his house. Jeez, if she had a place this nice, she'd talk about it all the time, but Mike had never said much about his home or his past. Henri needed to rectify that now he was on the mend and growing more cantankerous by the day. Men rarely made good patients, especially the gun-wielding alpha types like Mike Rose.

Henri to admired his place, though. The exterior it looked like a stately old, stone building—almost castle-like as if a land baron had built it, or at least someone very important.

On the inside, the home was nothing short of gorgeous. Most of the big windows faced west with a stunning view of Oban Bay. She'd spent an afternoon beside the fireplace watching the Caledonia ferries going to and from the Isle of Mull and beyond. It was like something from a storybook.

She would have expected Mike to have ultra-modern furniture, but his house was bright and cheery and full of antiques. However, his kitchen was renovated with the most contemporary equipment including marble countertops with a well-lit island in the center.

The door closed behind her as she moved into the kitchen. Odd. Thumping noises were coming from the basement. When Henri left to pick up the food, Mike had been by the fire in an easy chair with a Tom Clancy novel and a blanket tucked around his lap.

Hmm.

Leaving nothing to chance, she pulled her Glock from its holster and tiptoed for the stairs. A bit of deep grunting came along with the thumping. Either Mike was working out, or he had a visitor. And she knew it wasn't the latter.

After she reached the bottom of the steps, she chuckled. The workout room was also state-of-the art with an all-around gym, free weights, treadmill, stepper and elliptical. She holstered her weapon and moved her fists to her hips. "What happened to a week's rest, hotshot?"

After looking up with the guilty expression of a kid caught stealing a dollop of cookie dough, Mike slapped the stop button on the treadmill and grabbed a towel. "Och, you werena supposed to be back yet.

"I called ahead. The food was ready when I arrived."

He wiped the sweat off his forehead. "Bloody foiled."

Sauntering toward him, she tried not to smile, but it was really hard. More and more Henri realized they were both hewn from the same cloth. Given the circumstances, she'd be the same, pushing herself to get back on her feet as fast as possible, no matter that they'd both negotiated three weeks off. And as far as Garth knew, Henri was going to help Mike get settled, then head to Utah for her R & R.

She slowly drew the towel from his grasp, making a show of raking her gaze down his body. "All right, stud. If you're well enough for a workout, then meet me upstairs in ten."

His eyes popped with his grin. "Oh?"

She glanced to his injured leg, the dressing covered by his shorts. "That is if you can manage to climb the stairs on your own."

He snatched the towel. "I'll beat you to the top."

"No you won't." She headed off. "And you're not allowed up there for ten more minutes."

In the kitchen she grabbed the food, a bottle of wine and two glasses, then headed up to the top floor. Mike had turned the entire area into an enormous bedroom with a whirlpool bath in the bay window overlooking the water. The place was more romantic than a five-star hotel. After turning on the water, she lit candles in crystal orbs around the tub, then turned off the lights. She pulled over an end table from the bed, set out the food and chopsticks, then poured two glasses of chardonnay.

She swirled the wine first, then tasted.

Delicious.

When the tub was about half-full, she disrobed, stepped in and turned on the bubbles.

Heaven.

The sun had set on the western horizon and the lights of Oban twinkled down below.

She sensed him ascend the stairs, though she didn't look. Whispers of clothing rustled behind her.

"Ah...may I join you, m'lady?" he asked in a deep, lilting brogue, one no woman would ever tire of hearing.

Henri took a sip of wine before she faced him. Good Lord, he was an Adonis standing totally naked, his white skin lightly freckled and sculpted by years of toning his muscles into a precise fighting machine. Licking her lips, her gaze meandered to his cock— long, thick, aroused.

Licking her lips, she gestured to the table. "As you can see, the party's set for two."

"Perfect." He stepped into the tub and cringed a bit when his injured thigh dipped below the water line, but he didn't utter a word of complaint. "Now I reckon this is the kind of relaxation the doctor was talking about."

"That might be a stretch, but I'll go with it." She picked up a pair of chopsticks. "Sustenance first." Plucking a bite of chow mein, she held it to his mouth. He let her feed him, watching her with smoldering eyes as he chewed.

"Who knew a Scottish spy could make eating look so sexy?"

He reached for a pair of chopsticks and fed her as well. "No' half as sexy as you, Eagle Eyes."

Henri smiled inside as they ate. The first time he'd used the moniker, she hadn't been enthused, but it had grown on her. More due to the fact that Mike used it with respect in his voice. Respect and fondness. No one had ever shown her the love she'd felt from Mike. Though he hadn't spoken the words, he cared. He showed it in the way he protected her when they were held at the ruins, the way anger flashed through his eyes when Fadli had struck her. The love in his swollen eyes when he came to consciousness in their cell, and the way he tried to take point when they were sure to meet with enemy fire.

He even listened to her from time to time.

Picking up his glass, he slowly brought it to his lips and took a long drink. "What are you thinking about?"

"You." She smiled. "Know what? Aside from being a badass spy and former SAS officer, I don't know much about you."

"No' so much to tell." He turned on the Jacuzzi bubbles and reclined with the chow mein.

She licked her lips, considering how to approach the question that had been needling at her. Mike had a lot of artwork on the walls, but no pictures of himself or his family. It was as if he didn't care to be surrounded by memories of the past. After all, Mike was thirty-five.

May as well have out with it. "Have you ever been married?"

He looked up and stopped mid-chew. "Huh?"

"Marriage? Have you ever been married before?"

His Adam's apple bobbed with his gulp. "Me? Not a chance. Too busy chasing—"

"Bad guys," she finished, reaching for an egg roll and taking a bite. She should have known he'd deflect with a "too busy" remark. "Soooo...what about girlfriends? Anyone stick?" Henri wasn't sure if she wanted to know the answer.

But Mike shook his head. "None who could take the hours."

"Yeah, it was like that in the Army as well. Guys would deploy for three to six months, then come home and find no one there—so to speak."

"I ken how that is all too well."

"So, you've been burned before?"

He took Henri's half-eaten eggroll and shoved it in his mouth. "Last girlfriend dumped me for a Spanish hotel mogul—a gazillionaire."

"A gold digger?"

"Aye, but that woman never would have considered picking up a shovel and working a gold mine.

She was the type who wore stilettos and diamonds and wouldn't be caught dead in anything less than a five-star restaurant."

"Ah." Henri nodded. "A princess."

"I'd classify her no higher than a parasite."

"Ooo, she stung you bad, huh?"

He shrugged. "Better she showed her hand early on, afore I did something stupid."

"You don't seem like the type who'd tolerate a diva." Tapping her finger to her chin, she gave him a long look. "She must have been stunning."

A bit of color spread across Mike's cheeks. "Thought she was at the time. But she's nowhere near as bonny as you, Eagle Eyes." He cracked open a fortune cookie and pulled out the slip of paper. "*Enjoy each moment, for it is the last time you'll see it.*"

"I have to say I agree with that."

"Me as well." He handed her a cookie. "Your turn."

She bit it in two then read her slip. "*Your present plans will succeed.*"

Running his tongue along his top lip, he regarded her with a cockeyed grin. "How's it going so far?"

Picking up the bottle, she topped up their glasses. "Right on schedule. Cheers."

"*Slàinte.*" He took a sip then brushed his lips across hers.

"*Slàinte?*"

"It's Gaelic for cheers."

"You speak Gaelic?"

"A few words."

"See? There's so much I don't know about you."

He slid his arm around her shoulders and pulled her beside him so they both looked out over the view. "I'm no' all that complicated, lass."

"I think you're very complicated."

When his fingers brushed over her wound, she hissed.

"It's still a wee bit tender, aye?"

"I don't know." She shrugged. "Jeez, your gunshot wound was so much more serious than mine, I'd sound like a baby if I complained."

"This wee bullet hole?" He slapped his hand through the air. "I've had worse."

"Like what?"

"Shrapnel in the arse. Have you not noticed the jagged white scar on my right buttock—it forms a zed?" He raised the offending body part out of the water and pointed. "Couldn't sit for a fortnight."

She chuckled. "That little thing? I thought you were tougher than that." Henri pointed her toe and lifted her leg. "A Soviet rimless bottlenecked bullet. Four-inch graze. Afghanistan."

He waggled his brows. "I read about that one in your file. But I can top it." He held up the inside of his left arm. "Knife. Fighting Hamas. Gaza."

She thrust out her thumb. It was a small scar, but it had hurt like a bitch. "Icepick. Bootcamp piss up— had to pull the weapon out myself."

He blew a raspberry. "That's nothin'." He turned up his left palm and pointed to a scar that looked like a J. "Fish hook. Age nine. Oban Bay. Just a wee laddie and I yanked the damned thing out, barbs and all."

"Nine?"

"Aye." He shook his finger. "And I didn't cry, mind you."

She raised her glass. "Not one tear?"

"Not me."

"Then I salute you, soldier."

"Cheers." Winking with a satisfied grin, he took a drink.

"Not *Slàinte*?"

"All right. Let's go with *Slàinte*."

She poured more wine. "Know why I like you?"

He snorted. "Because of my fiery red locks?"

"No...In fact I was prejudiced against redheaded men until I met you."

"Prejudiced?"

"I thought they all lacked the toughness gene."

"But I changed your mind?" That damned grin turned cocky.

"Yeah—but I think you're the exception."

He gave her a kiss and stared at her, his eyes filled with mischief. "So then, if it's not my hair, what is it you like about me?"

"You're a sheepdog."

A furrow formed between his eyebrows. "A dog?"

"Come on, you've heard the term before—sheepdogs run into battle when everyone else is running away." She raked her gaze down his torso, admiring the copper curls on his chest. The smoothness of his alabaster skin, and the sculpted muscle beneath. "Sheepdog," she said, emphasizing the dog as if it were the coolest thing on the planet.

"Do you ken what I like about you?"

She shook her head.

"Everything." Again, he slid his arm across her shoulders and inclining his lips to her ear, he whispered, "This is a moment I never want to end."

"Then let's enjoy the hell out of it."

Soothed by warm jets of water, staring across the bay, sipping their wine. It was comfortable being with Mike, eating delicious food, drinking good wine, soaking, relaxing. They were so similar deep down, yet born worlds apart. Henri enjoyed being with him, even being quiet with him like she was with Grandfather. A certain, unexplainable ease thrummed through her as they sat together, just being.

She sighed. Contentment. That's what she felt. It had been far too many years since she'd been content. If she ever really had been.

When their glasses were empty, Mike set them on the table. He cocked his head to the side and cupped her cheek with his palm. "What are you thinking now, lass?"

She couldn't look him in the eye. Heck, even her cheeks burned. "I, ah...I was thinking..." she bit her bottom lip. God, she didn't want to ruin the moment.

Mike lifted the chin with the crook of his finger. "What?"

"It's silly."

"Nothing you say is ever silly." He kissed her lips softly. "Tell me."

She let out a breath, then looked him in the eye. "I was thinking how perfect it is—right now."

His grin could have lit up the Oban skyline. "Know what?"

Henri shook her head.

"I was thinking that very same thing."

He grinned and pulled her toward his lap but Henri held up her palm. "What about your leg?"

"Och, I'm feeling no pain." Reaching around, he rubbed warm water up and down her back, then pulled her closer. "Especially when you're in my arms."

"Well then..." She slid her hands over his shoulders and slowly lowered her head. As their lips neared, delicious anticipation and the slow burn of desire curled through her. With a rush of euphoric effervescence, they connected in a kiss. A kiss charged with so much electricity, they were joined by surreal and hypnotic forces while primitive instincts thrummed through their blood.

The arousal between them had simmered on a low boil since she'd invited him upstairs. But in two seconds, their passion went from smoldering to scorching hot. Barely able to breathe, she slid her hands over his solid muscles, down his rippling six-pack while she rocked back and forth along his cock.

She glanced over her shoulder. "The bed isn't far."

He chuckled, a seductively low rumble that made goosebumps rise across her skin. "I like the way you think."

Standing, he gave her another eyeful of his magnificence. Warm water slid down his chest, making it glisten. He reached for her hand and pulled her up as if he intended to carry her to the bed. She stepped out of the bath and swirled a finger around his coppery chest hair. "One thing at a time, Scottie-boy." Her eyelashes fluttered as she gestured to his thigh. "You're not lifting me until that gunshot wound heals."

He gave her the evil eye as she grasped his fingers and pulled him to the bed. When the back of her knees hit the soft mattress, he nudged her down. "Aye? So are you the boss of me now?"

"I am."

"I like that," he chuckled. "But I will still rearrange your priorities, lass. You'd best slide back because I aim to taste you."

She licked her top lip and obeyed, while the heat between her legs turned into a raging fire.

Sliding onto his hands and knees, Mike followed her with a wicked grin. "Open."

Henri managed to nod as he pressed between her thighs. Warm breath caressed her before his tongue swept over her clitoris. She sucked in a sharp inhale.

Her hips arched. Even if she'd wanted to, she couldn't help but move her ass in concert with his magical mouth kissing and sucking her clit. "Oh God." Her thighs started to shudder as Mike slid a finger inside. In and out he worked in a steady rhythm while his tongue relentlessly made love to her.

On the brink of losing it, Henri closed her eyes, spreading her legs wider. The image of his naked body consumed her mind. Her every muscle tensed as if she were about to explode. Her breathing sped. She bucked harder. Then it happened, and she cried out and grabbed his hair. Sweet release racked her body and sent her into a maelstrom of pulsing shudders.

Letting her revel in the afterglow, Mike threaded his fingers through her pubic hair, still kissing her gently. When she came back to Earth, he slid up and nuzzled into her neck while rubbing his cock along her wetness. "It turns me on to see you shatter," he growled.

She let out a sultry chuckle. "Know what's better?"

"What?"

"When we shatter together."

"Perfect..."

"But not yet." This time Henri wanted control. Careful to roll away from his injured leg, she used a karate move to shift to the top.

Mike raised his head. "What—?"

"Lie still," she said, kissing his lips then trailing kisses to his neck. Lower she went, swirling her tongue around each nipple, taking her time. Careful to draw out the torture, she kissed him all the way down to his abs. But she wasn't going in for the kill yet. It was difficult to avoid his cock as she continued lower, licking between his thighs, teasing his balls all the while ushering him to the brink of madness. When her fingers finally took possession of his erection, a deep, feral groan erupted from his throat. Slowly, Henri slid her mouth over him and swirled her tongue up and down his length. She stroked and suckled his spiciness— pure male, infused with a hint of salt. She teased him with strokes of her hand combined with quick licks of her tongue.

Until he reached down and pulled her over his body. "I want you so badly I'll explode if you keep doing that."

"But I want you to..."

"Together, remember?" He brushed a finger over her lips. "Are you ready to take me?"

Yeah, all she needed to do was gaze into those crystal blues and she was ready to come again. Henri kneeled across him, her breath ragged. Mike grasped her shoulders and stared for a moment, his gaze raking up and down her body as if memorizing every curve. "Perfection." He cupped her breasts and suckled each nipple. She thrust her hips forward, unable to quell the yearning as it mounted low in her belly. Rubbing herself along his cock, she made him slick with her moisture.

"I want you," she whispered. Never in her life had she been so incredibly hot, so deeply in love, so connected with another human being. Mike ran his hands up her spine and lifted her slightly. He shifted his cock between her legs and slid in just a little bit. Henri threw her head back as the light friction threatened to take her over the top.

Her lower half on fire, her breasts swelling with desire, she eased herself over him. "Take me."

Totally hard, unbelievably buff, Mike pulled out as he rolled Henri to her back, kissing her like she'd never been kissed. His tongue explored her mouth, demanding more. His lips trailed down to her neck and she cried out when he again took her nipples into his mouth. Down her body his kisses fluttered, her back arched and she reached for him when he stopped at her belly button. With a husky chuckle, he continued to lower—drawing out the ecstasy *and* the agony.

"Mike," she managed to moan. "I need you."

"Now, lass?"

"Yes. Now!"

He eyes grew even darker, his breathing as ragged as hers. He reached between them and grasped himself, until he entered her again. Instinctively, she rose to accept him. Her breath caught when he slipped in further as her inner walls gripped and milked him.

"My God." He shuddered over her, moving his lips to hers, kissing, swirling his tongue. Sex had always been mind-blowing with Mike but, tonight, they were on a completely different level, as if their souls connected.

He drew it out, making languid thrusts as her thighs clamped around him—wanting, demanding more of him. She grabbed his butt and pulled him deeper, moaning with pure pleasure.

Her fingers sunk into the thick muscles on his ass as he allowed her to control the tempo. Every nerve in her body electrified, her breathing faster. Her body became weightless while her need to push harder rose with Mike's urgent thrusts. All at once, a primordial cry erupted from the depths of his soul. Henri's passion soared to new heights while his release pulsed into her. And then she shattered. Reaching her peak, her body soared into rippling spasms of glorious release.

Drenched in sweat, Mike dropped over her, taking

his weight onto his elbows. "God woman, you are enough to drive a man to madness."

Henri ran her fingers through his hair, staring into those crystal blues and adoring everything about him. "That was amazing."

"Mind blowing." Mike chuckled. "And the best thing? We can do it again and again—as often as you'd like."

35

As Mike's leg healed, he enjoyed his holiday more and more. In fact, he never wanted it to end. After slipping to town to do a bit of shopping, he decided it was time to take the next step with Henri. No, it wasn't too soon. The timing was perfect. And for the first time in his life, he actually couldn't imagine being with anyone else. He didn't even want to look at anyone else. *Unheard of.* Who knew he'd been waiting all his life for an American sniper to win his heart?

He found her reading in the solarium. "Hiya." He dangled his keys. "The day's too bonny not to take a drive."

She set the book aside. "Oool! I've been wanting to drive that fancy car of yours."

Mike's gut squeezed. He'd never allowed anyone to drive the 911. "Perhaps after we travel deeper into the Highlands."

"Okay. Where are you taking me?"

"Out and about." He led her to the garage and pulled the cover off his red Porsche.

Henri whistled as she ran her fingers over the sleek lines. "She's a beauty."

"My pride and joy." He opened the door for her. "At least until I met you."

She hesitated for a moment, a pinch to her brow expressing unease. She bit her bottom lip as if hundreds bad memories suddenly flooded into her head. Mike almost regretted his words until she blessed him with a radiant smile. "Do you mean that?"

"Every word."

After he slid into the driver's seat, the car rumbled to life. Mike loved the deep purr of the motor and the way the tires hugged the curves of the road. He drove out of town up past Connel and along the A85 to Loch Awe. Just before they passed over the River Orchy, Henri pointed. "Look, it's a castle."

"Kilchurn Castle, built by the Campbells of Glenorchy."

"It's beautiful."

"It is, and in ruins like so many medieval castles in Scotland." He drove past the visitors turn, because that's not where he was heading. At least not today. A bit further down the road, he took a turn, then drove along a dirt road until he came to a stop at a cottage hidden deep in the wood.

"Where are we?" Henri asked.

"Me mum's place."

"Mother? You've never talked about your mom."

"I figured it was time you met her." He shut off the motor. "I'm warning you, she's a bit forgetful, but kind-hearted."

"Does she know we're coming to pay a visit?"

"Nay." He dashed around and opened Henri's door. "Come. She'll love you."

Eagle Eyes didn't look convinced. "If you say so." She ran her fingers down her braid. "But you should have told me where we were going. I would have brushed out my hair or something."

"Good idea." He pulled the elastic from the end of her braid and unraveled the yard of shiny, black locks. Running his fingers through it, he turned her hair into a silken mane. "There. Now you're ready."

"Okay." She didn't sound convinced but, nonetheless, she was stunning.

Mike pulled her toward the door and gave a knock. Just as he expected, as Mum opened it, an astonished grin spread across her face. "Michael! What a pleasant surprise."

He gave his mother a hug and made the introductions.

"Henrietta, now that's a name you dunna hear much anymore." Mum gestured inside the quaint cottage where Mike had grown up with his younger brother, James. "Come in and I'll make a pot of tea."

"And shortbread?" he asked.

"Of course." Mum led Henri to the settee. "I'm surprised Michael isna as big as the house. He adores my shortbread. Always has."

"I can't wait to taste it."

"How's the roof holding up?" Mike asked, sitting beside Henri.

"Good." She put the kettle on to boil. "How is the fishing up north, Michael? It must be good because I haven't seen you in weeks." It had been over six months.

"We're having a record year." He gave Henri a wink.

The lass mouthed, "*Fishing?*"

"You ken. I'm a commercial fisherman up in Iceland." Mike must have forgotten to tell Henri his alias job—the thing friends and family thought he did for a living. "You heard anything from James?"

"Who?" Mum asked.

It tore him up inside to see his mother so forgetful. In her prime, she'd been so sociable, a strong family matriarch. He cleared his throat and batted away the memories. "Your son. Two years younger than me."

"Oh, that James. Mm hmm." She moved back into the sitting room with a plate of shortbread that looked store bought. "And who is your friend, Michael?"

"I didna say? This is Henrietta Anderson."

Mum looked rapt. "Henrietta, now that's a name you dunna hear overmuch."

Henri gave Mike a look before she regarded Mum with a warm smile. "That's right, it is an unusual name. Can I help you pour the tea?"

A bewildered look spread across Mum's face. "Tea?"

Mike gestured to the kitchen. "That would be lovely, thanks." He waited until Henri moved to the hob before he took his mother's hands between his palms. "Is Mrs. Crabtree still coming around twice a day?"

"Och that woman practically lives here."

"But she takes good care of you."

Mum pursed her lips. "I suppose."

"You're looking bonny." Changing the subject, he squeezed his mother's hands and smiled.

"Thank you."

The afternoon proceeded as smoothly as possible. Henri was gracious, and as soon as she'd realized Mum was more than a little forgetful, she jumped in and helped with everything. They enjoyed a pleasant cup of tea with shortbread and then bid her goodbye.

Neither one said a word as Mike drove the car up

through the A82 to the picturesque Falls of Glencoe where they stopped for a walk. He held her hand as they climbed the slope to his favorite lookout where he could see through the majestic mountains clear down to Loch Leven.

"It's beautiful up here," said Henri, stopping to pan her gaze across the grandeur of the Coe—majestic mountains, trickling burns and lush summer grasses peeking through purple heather. "So green."

He slid his arm over her shoulder and pulled her close. "Aye. I feel like I'm on top of the world every time I traverse these hills."

"Your mother is sweet."

He was wondering when Henri would say something. Mike had taken her to the cottage because he wanted her to know his deepest secrets—things he didn't mention to anyone. "She has a form of early-onset Alzheimer's. It's horrible to watch."

"I'm sorry. It's an awful disease."

He nodded then took Henri's hand and pressed it over his heart. "I've never taken a lass to see Mum afore."

"No?"

He shook his head. "I havena ever been in love with someone enough to do it. You ken? To let anyone meet my Mum—to see the way she is now."

"Because you're embarrassed?"

"No' so much that, but it's personal. No one else's business." He squeezed her fingers. "It's family stuff."

Henri's breath caught. "But you don't mind that I know?"

"I *wanted* you to know."

"I'm glad. You already know my family is pretty messed up—I mean, I don't even have a mother to introduce you to."

"True." He pulled her into his arms. Closing his eyes, his heart swelled. Finally, he'd found his soul mate. "What I'm trying to say is I love you. I love you so much, I want you to ken everything about me, the good and the bad."

"You love me?" She gasped. "You...you do?"

"I do. I've never felt about anyone the way I feel about you. It's as if I've finally found someone hewn of the same cloth, and I never want to let go."

"You mean that?"

"With all my heart, love."

She sighed, her chocolaty eyes moist, her grin happier than he'd ever seen. "I can't believe it. All my life I've been a misfit—no one has ever accepted me without wanting me to change into something I'm not. I mean...You *really* love me?"

"Aye, and I'll say it again and again, 'cause I never want you to feel like a misfit again. You are perfect just the way you are."

A tear slipped from her eye. "No one has ever showed me love the way you have. Not one soul. Not ever. Jesus, Mike, I love you, b-but I'm afraid."

"Of what?"

"I-I don't know how to love somebody. What if I don't love you enough? What if I fail?"

"Huh? You gave me the confidence to jump off a two-hundred-foot cliff. I never would have lived through that if it weren't for your love. You know how to love more than you think. You have shown how much you care about me ten times over."

She smiled. "I do care for you."

"You're the strongest woman I've ever met." He slipped his hand into his pocket and wrapped his fingers around the velvet box containing the ring he'd purchased that day. "I ken we dunna have much time afore we have to go back to ICE, but before we do I need to ask one thing." He dropped to one knee and took her left hand in his palm, his mouth growing dry. Hell, he was nervous, but through it all, his conviction was rock solid. "Henrietta Soaring-Eagle Anderson, will you marry me?"

Her mouth hung open and she stood motionless. She didn't even blink.

"Henri?" He held up the ring.

"Yes? I mean, *yes*! Absolutely." Another tear slipped from her eye as she held in a combination of laughter and crying while letting him slip the diamond solitaire over her finger. The breeze picked up her wild mane of gorgeous black hair, making her look like the goddess of the eagles. "Oh my, *oh my*. I can't believe it. I never thought..."

"Believe it, lass." Standing, he pulled her into his embrace. "You ken, you have more passion in your trigger finger than most women have in their whole bodies."

She chuckled. "Only you would think of that analogy and that's why I love you so much."

"Now we need to break the news to Garth."

Wiping away the tears, she gave him an excited cringe. "Do we have to?"

"Aye, lass. And better sooner than later."

She reached in his pocket and pulled out his keys, giving him a wicked grin. "All right, but not before you let me drive the Porsche."

36

For the second time in her life, Henri fell in love. Right after she got behind the wheel of Mike's Porsche 911. It took her all of two seconds to get used to the steering wheel on the right side of the car and shifting with her left hand. Now, nothing would stop her. She sped around the narrow, twisting Highland roads like she'd been born there.

They drove past dark blue lochs and the ruins of ancient castles, through forests, and over rugged, barren hills.

Nothing could take away the euphoria bubbling inside. She'd taken on ICE and Fadli and, in the process, had won Mike Rose.

Never in her life had she dreamed she'd marry anyone, let alone a big redheaded Scot. A man who believed in her, who treated her as an equal, who would lay down his life for her.

Just as she hit the straightaway and punched the gas, Mike's phone rang. It was Garth's ringtone, the one she didn't want to hear right now. A rock sank to the pit of her stomach as she downshifted and slowed the car.

Mike reached for his phone and gave her a look. "He couldna give us a few more days, could he?"

"I swear that man has ESP." She pulled over into a restaurant parking lot.

"Hey, boss. What's up? The bad guys canna live without me?" Mike pressed the speaker icon.

"Bad guys never sleep, unlike you. Has your leg healed yet?"

Henri figured there was no time like the present to announce herself. "I think he needs another week of bedrest, sir."

"Anderson?" The CO's voice shot up. "I thought you were going back to Utah for a few weeks."

She looked at Mike while the interior of the car filled with a pregnant pause.

"Aw, hell." Garth barked. "Don't tell me you two are a damned couple. I've already had to bend the rules with Rodgers and Hamilton."

Mike blew a raspberry. "I wouldna say we're damned."

"Jesus Christ. Everyone in the outfit's going to hook up. Come on, Rose, not you, too. Do you have any idea how much it costs to train a new asset?"

Henri leaned forward. "Who said anything about leaving?"

"Sorry, sir. Love canna be helped." He gave Henri a wink. "Besides, if you bent the rules for Rodgers, you have no choice but to do the same for me. I've been with ICE eight times longer than either of those rookies."

"Jesus strike me dead. Don't think this changes anything," the old man barked. "I expect to see you at ICE in one week's time and if I need Anderson in Syria and Rose in Mexico, that's how it's going to be."

Henri laughed. Mike, too. "Yes, sir," they said in unison.

Mike pushed the end-call icon. "That was easier than I thought it would be."

"Me too, but when you think of it, what would Garth do without his best assets?" She reached over and threaded her fingers through his. "We're married to the job, may as well be married to each other."

"See?" He smiled—the cheeky, lopsided grin that made him so endearing. "That's why we make such a perfect match, Eagle Eyes."

EPILOGUE

With only a week to plan a wedding, Mike booked a honeymoon suite at the Bellagio in Las Vegas. Not a gambler, he chose Sin City for two reasons. First, it took twenty-nine days to get a marriage license in Scotland and they couldn't wait that long. But the second reason had his palms sweating. He'd ordered coffee and pastries and paced the suite, looking at his watch every five seconds.

Where the bloody hell is he?

Henri came out of the bathroom, dressed in yoga pants and a t-shirt that read, "badass sharpshooter". Probably not the best choice for the morning's meeting, but it would do. She'd found the shirt in the Vegas airport of all places. But she looked like a million quid with her hair partially dry and brushing her hips. Her gaze immediately homed on the coffee table. "Oh, good. You ordered breakfast."

He stopped pacing and almost told her to wait, but she'd already picked up the coffee pot.

"Just a minute," she said, a furrow formed between her eyebrows. "Why are there thee cups?"

A bead of sweat trickled from his brow. Good God,

put him in a hellhole fighting terrorists and his nerves were like stone, but this? "I—"

The suite's doorbell rang.

Mike gulped. *This was a bad idea.*

Henri set the pot down and picked up her cup. "You going to get that?"

"Yeah." *Just do it. If she really loves me, she'll forgive me...hopefully, by tomorrow.*

He opened the door to a man in his late fifties—blond hair streaked with gray, blue eyes. But even with the ethnic differences, there was a familial resemblance. Mike thrust out his hand. "Thank you for coming, sir."

"Thank you for inviting me." Jarrod Anderson gave a firm handshake and looked beyond Mike's shoulder. "Is she here?"

"Aye, but she doesna ken you are."

"Understood."

Before they left Scotland, Mike invited Henri's father to the wedding. What shocked him? Anderson not only RSVP'd, he'd also cried on the phone. The man was elated.

Standing aside, he gestured for Anderson to enter. "Ah, sweetheart. There's someone to see you."

Seated on the couch, Henri's jaw dropped. The cup fell from her fingers. Hot coffee splashed in her lap, but she didn't seem to notice. Her eyes grew wide and filled with hate and pain. "What the hell are *you* doing here?" she sniped, instantly on red alert.

Anderson held out his hands. "I—"

"I invited him," Mike said, moving forward and taking a seat beside Henri.

Her eyes shifted his way. "You *what*? Why?"

Mike shrugged, trying to ease the hostile tension in the air. "I was surprised he wanted to come."

Anderson slid into an armchair with a nervous smile. "Once I found out where you were, an army wouldn't have been able to keep me away."

"Are you serious?" Henri crossed her arms. "You abandoned me!"

Anderson looked to Mike. "I made a promise to her mother."

Henri's spine jolted to rigid. "You abandoned her, too."

The man shook his head. "That's where you're mistaken."

Henri slammed her fists into the couch and stood. "This is ridiculous."

"I know it was wrong," Anderson explained. "I was young and stupid. Your mother and I had been dating for a couple of months when she got pregnant with you. I stayed for the birth. I even offered to marry her."

"Wait." Henri held out her palms. "You weren't married?"

"No." Anderson bit the corner of his mouth. "And she didn't accept my proposal."

Henri looked bewildered. "Why?"

"I don't know. I wasn't a Paiute...I didn't want to stay in Saint George." His shoulders fell. "I guess she thought we weren't compatible."

Anger and disbelief filled Henri's eyes. "So, you just left, and decided to never see me again?"

Mike picked up Henri's cup and poured the coffee, though no one touched it.

Anderson heaved a sigh—the man couldn't have imagined this meeting would be easy. "Things were different back then. Your mother and I argued—a lot. I don't even remember about what, but she asked me to leave—told me she never wanted to see me again. She said you would be better off without me."

Henri clapped a hand over her mouth. "Mama told me that, too. I was better off without my *deadbeat* dad."

"Deadbeat?" Anderson asked.

"That's what she said. She told me not to bother contacting you. You rejected me because..." Running her hands down her face, Henri stopped and gasped.

"Why?" Mike asked.

She held out her arms. "I-I'm not like him. I'm a *half-breed*."

"No." Anderson stood. "You are my daughter. In the flesh. Look at you! You are *stunning*. You are a woman I could only be proud to call my child."

Henri stared, the battle raging inside her reflected in her stance. "But you left me. You had a choice."

"I know." Anderson cringed. "And I'm not proud of what I did. I owe you an apology. *More* than an apology. I only wish I could change the past. But know this: No matter what you thought of me or what you may think of me now, I love you. If you need anything. Anything at all. I am here for you."

"Even with your new family?"

"Yes."

"Where are they?" She planted her fists on her hips. "Hiding in California?"

He gestured toward the door. "They're here. They want to meet you."

"Please." Henri held up a palm. "I can't handle this right now."

Anderson shot a doubtful glance at Mike. "Perhaps I should leave."

"You should," she said.

"But I'm not leaving you." Her father squared his shoulders. "I'm just walking out of the suite to give you some breathing room." He again shifted his gaze to

Mike. "I hope you will join us for dinner as we discussed."

"We'll be there."

"We will?" Henri asked.

Mike led Anderson to the door. "If not, I'll give you a ring."

Again, the older man offered his hand. "I cannot thank you enough for this opportunity to see my daughter." A tear streamed from his eye and then he was gone.

Mike's jaw clenched as he bit back his own tears. But now he had to turn and face the dragon.

Henri stood against the wall, clutching her arms across her chest and looking shell shocked. "Why did you do it?"

"Because he's your dad. The only one you'll ever have."

"But he hurt my mother." She hid her face in her hands. "And he abandoned us."

"According to him, he was asked to leave."

"I'm so confused." She looked up. "And you! I can't believe you brought him up here the day before our wedding. Why would you do that to me?" The expression on her face was so filled with pain, Mike wished she'd just hit him. He could take a good jab across the jaw before he could deal with years of suppressed emotional turmoil.

"I knew it was a risk, but now you know. What if you'd gone your whole life without hearing his side?"

She dropped her hands. "God damn you. Maybe I don't want to hear his side."

That made as much sense as a floating rock. "Perhaps I was wrong. I'm sorry. If you choose, you never have to see him again."

"No, I don't."

"It's settled, then." Mike pulled his phone out of his pocket.

"Nothing's settled!"

IT DIDN'T TAKE LONG for Henri to compose herself. She was nothing if not resilient. Last night, she and Mike had an awkward, but interesting dinner with her family including her father, stepmother and half-sister and brother. They were so different than she'd imagined, so normal. No, she hadn't forgiven her father yet, but she was open to listening to him. And he did manage to convince her he wanted to be a part of her life now.

Strange, but she liked that.

Better yet, today was her big day. Mike had spared no expense and hired a wedding consultant to help Henri find a dress, take her to the salon and choose flowers. For the first time in her life, she didn't bother looking at price tags and just let everything happen around her.

Now, she stood in front of the mirror. Never one for fancy dresses, Henri had chosen a short, ivory dress with simple lines that flattered her figure. It had feminine lace—far more girly than anything she'd ever worn. Over her crown, the hairdresser had used a braid with an ivory ribbon laced through and left a cascade of soft curls in the back.

"You are stunning," said Aunt Chenoa from the chair. She looked to the consultant. "She could have been a model, but she put on a pair of fatigues and joined the Army instead."

Henri chuckled. "You'd better take pictures because it's the last time you'll see me dressed like this."

"It's time to go," said the lady, picking up Henri's single red rose.

"Are you ready?" Henri asked as her aunt set down her cup.

"The question is, are *you* ready?"

"It's now or never." She took the rose. Yes, she could have ordered a bouquet with a dozen roses, but she liked the simplicity of the single flower.

They made their way to the Terrazza Di Sogno, a terrace overlooking the Bellagio fountain. As Henri stepped outside, she caught a glimpse of Mike gazing out over the water. He wore a kilt of red and blue, and black waist-length jacket. Broad shouldered, tapered waist, powerful hips, and masculine calves. Her knees wobbled a little. Rose filled out the Scottish formal dress like her imaginings of a great laird—a man proud, commanding, and gorgeous. When her heels clicked the tiles, he turned. A grin as wide as the Grand Canyon spread across his face.

Stepping forward with a slight limp, he held out his gloved hand. "Thanks for coming, Eagle Eyes."

"I wouldn't miss it for the world, Lionheart." She arched a brow. "You look pretty tasty in a skirt."

"It's a kilt."

"I know."

He raised her hand to his lips. "And you are more stunning than any woman on Earth. Your hair looks like black satin."

The celebrant cleared his throat. "Are we ready?"

Henri looked at the small crowd—Aunt Chenoa and Martin. Her father, stepmother and two half-siblings. But to her surprise, Logan Rodgers and Olivia Hamilton were there as well.

"How did they get leave?" Henri whispered.

"Garth doesna know. They're flying back to Pakistan in the morning."

She smiled at them and mouthed, "Thank you."

Olivia nodded and waved while Logan smiled. Goodness, they made a cute couple.

"Let us begin," said the celebrant.

Henri stood, holding hands with Mike and looking into his crystal-blue eyes while they took their vows. Everything was so perfect. It was like floating in a surreal fantasy. Never in her life did she dream of marrying a Scottish spy, a man who routinely chased down terrorists and stopped them from anarchy. He was a man who would fight for right with everything he had and, when he was beaten, he would get back up and fight some more. He was a hero and he was hers.

I will love him until I take my last breath.

NEXT IN THE SERIES...

If you enjoyed Body Shot, the next in the ICE Series will be Mach One, where the Australian pilot, Luke Fox, is sent into Mexico to infiltrate an untouchable drug cartel. What he doesn't know is the American woman who gets him inside has been trapped by the villain's talons most of her life. Releasing on January 2nd, 2018:

MACH ONE

AMY JARECKI

NATIONAL BESTSELLING AUTHOR

MACH ONE ~ CHAPTER ONE

Luke made no audible sound, carefully rolling each step across the balls of his feet as he crept toward the building, the butt of his M4 rifle secured against his shoulder. His finger twitched on the trigger. Every breath roared in his ears like the thunder of a giant waterfall. Still, not a soul could hear his controlled inhalations. And no one but Luke could detect the air slowly expelling from his lungs. A bead of sweat trickled down his temple and pooled against the gun, making the rifle slip on his cheek. His finger twitched again as he blinked and tightened his grip. He was too close to the target to err.

He slid his foot forward, his gaze shifting rapidly. One misplaced step and this whole gig could explode. He'd counted each enemy combatant as he'd taken them out. Six down, and one bastard was still out there. Waiting.

God, he loved this, living on adrenaline and caffeine. A thrill-seeking-junkie, he'd joined NATO three years ago for this very thing. But it wasn't until he was recruited by the elite International Clandestine Enterprise that he'd found home. *ICE*.

The hair on the back of Luke's neck stood on end.

Reflexes took over as he crouched before taking another step.

Crack!

A shot blasted from ten o'clock, smacking into the wall above his head. He dropped and rolled, swinging his weapon toward the shooter. Closing his finger on the trigger, he fired off a repeating round, blinking the sweat out of his eyes as he searched for the perp through his NV goggles. He homed on a flicker of movement. Relentlessly, he fired until the dark outline of the enemy gunman dropped.

Seven down, suckas. Springing to his feet, Luke sprinted toward Building One. At last, he'd won—taken the biscuit.

The lights in the paintball court flashed on, blinding and bright.

"Fox, you're needed in the sit room ASAP," Garth Moore's voice reverberated across the room, splattered with red and blue paint.

Luke shifted his goggles to his forehead and flipped on the safety of his M4 paintball rifle. The weapon might only shoot paint, but it still hurt. "I won, fair and square, mates. Told you I could take the lot of you wankers." He looked to the American, Aaron Crosby, lumbering to his feet and swathed in blue paint.

"You ass. How did you know I had you in my sights?"

Luke tapped his helmet while the other six gathered around. He'd ducked because of a gut warning. He always did. "Sixth sense. Every pilot has to develop one, else he'll end up taking a nose-dive at Mach one on a three-second suicide mission."

"Yeah right." Crosby gestured toward the exit with his thumb. "The boss sounded serious."

"I hope he is." Luke headed for the door. "I've endured enough training to last a bloody lifetime."

Luke tried not to grin as he sped toward the sit room. An Aussie ex-RAAF pilot, he'd been training at ICE for four months. Hell, he'd been baptized by fire when he ended up the pilot of a mission that took out one of the top brass of ISIS and foiled their plot to get their hands on a nuke. He'd proved himself in the field and, though training had been necessary and fun, he was ready to get back out there. It killed him to watch the ops go down on the monitors in Command. He needed to be in the thick of it. Luke wasn't just a pilot and, with his training at ICE, there wasn't any job out there he couldn't tackle—not a scumbag he couldn't take down—not a mob of terrorists he couldn't stop.

Did he have an overly inflated ego? Probably. That happened when a man spent too much time acing simulated operations and left his teammates covered in blue paint. But he wasn't a novice. He'd earned his stripes in the trenches just like everyone else.

"Fox, you're late," Garth barked as Luke pushed through the doors of the inner sanctum—the situation room stood as a secured glass fortress in the center of the Command Center, Command for short. A place where top secret news was relayed and plans to combat evil were carefully laid.

Luke gave the CO a lopsided grin. "Sorry, sir." Garth Moore was an ex-Marine, turned mega-spy. He had cropped gray hair and eyes of steel, and controlled the operations of assets all over the globe in the most clandestine operation on the planet. ICE wasn't only secret, known only to presidents and prime ministers of NATO countries, ICE was remote, located in an underground World War II bunker, converted into an elite, high-tech training and monitoring facility. Forty-five meters below the surface of inner Iceland, not even a nuclear holocaust could take it out.

But ICE existed to ensure such holocausts never happened.

"We have a situation," Garth said, his expression growing dark, serious. His look alone said this was the real deal.

Bring it on. "Yeah? And you need an ace?" Luke couldn't help but grin.

"I need a pilot—someone who won't crack, no matter what. Would that be you?"

"Yes, sir."

"Yes sir? Isn't that a bit cavalier given you haven't heard where I'm sending you?"

"I'm ready for a challenge, sir."

"That's what all the rookies say."

"I'm no rook." After glancing to the blank monitors, Luke narrowed his gaze and leaned forward. "So…What's up?"

~ End of Excerpt to MACH ONE

ALSO BY AMY JARECKI

The King's Outlaws
Highland Warlord
Highland Raider
Highland Beast

Highland Defender
The Valiant Highlander
The Fearless Highlander
The Highlander's Iron Will

Highland Force:
Captured by the Pirate Laird
The Highland Henchman
Beauty and the Barbarian
Return of the Highland Laird

Guardian of Scotland
Rise of a Legend
In the Kingdom's Name
The Time Traveler's Destiny

Highland Dynasty
Knight in Highland Armor
A Highland Knight's Desire
A Highland Knight to Remember
Highland Knight of Rapture

Highland Knight of Dreams

Devilish Dukes
The Duke's Fallen Angel
The Duke's Untamed Desire

ICE
Hunt for Evil
Body Shot
Mach One

Celtic Fire
Rescued by the Celtic Warrior
Deceived by the Celtic Spy

Lords of the Highlands series:
The Highland Duke
The Highland Commander
The Highland Guardian
The Highland Chieftain
The Highland Renegade
The Highland Earl
The Highland Rogue
The Highland Laird

The Chihuahua Affair
Virtue: A Cruise Dancer Romance
Boy Man Chief
Time Warriors